# Land Use and Its Patterns in the United States

By F. J. Marschner, Collaborator, Farm Economics
Research Division, Agricultural Research Service

Agriculture Handbook No. 153
UNITED STATES DEPARTMENT OF AGRICULTURE

## Preface

The purpose of the study reported here was to contribute to a more mature understanding of the patterns of rural land uses in the United States. The underlying physical factors are described, and their influence is explained in relation to major historical and still evolving institutional determinants of agricultural development and land use. The varied and unequal impacts of industrialization and of the continuing technological revolution within agriculture are emphasized.

This report also demonstrates a methodology for research in land use that is applicable wherever men are concerned with improving the levels of human life through the development of agriculture. Students of agriculture everywhere, and in particular American students and professional agricultural workers, will find the report helpful in broadening their understanding of agricultural land problems. Students and professional workers in agricultural geography will be interested in the general methodological approach used and also in the graphic analysis and description.

A pioneering feature of the report is the use of aerial photographs of 168 local areas with descriptive legends. This part of the report will interest many technical and professional students of agriculture and geography.

In the preparation of the report, valuable cooperation was received from the Food and Agriculture Organization of the United Nations. The concern of this organization with improving the standards of human life through the development and improvement of agriculture in areas where the present level of agricultural production is low led to its interest in research methodology in land utilization in the United States as presented here.

# Contents

# Contents—Continued

**Washington, D. C.**                                                 **Issued April 1959**

For sale by the Superintendent of Documents, U. S. Government Printing Office, Washington, D. C.

# Land Use and Its Patterns in the United States

## Summary

At the beginning of the 20th century, the internal development of the United States took a new turning on the road to progress. Advances were made in rapid succession in the different fields of human endeavor, so much so that no universal yardstick can be applied to measure all the incidental consequences. Both human and material resources were involved. All aspects of man's life were affected. But when land use for primary production is the particular field of inquiry, the application of scientific knowledge and technical skills account largely for the many innovations and improvements.

The marked improvement in the use and productivity of the land necessarily had its repercussion in the lives of the people. When a trend toward declining returns is arrested and within a few years becomes a trend toward abundance, economic and social problems are associated with the change. The reaction to such changes is not confined necessarily to users of the land; their effects are felt by the entire Nation. Even the national boundaries do not represent the ultimate limits of the reaction; these changes affect the man–land relationship the world over to such an extent that a reorientation in the outlook for the future is required.

In the United States, we must recognize, therefore, two distinct periods with opposite trends in the productivity of the land. In one, the productivity of the land declined, sometimes to the point of making it useless for further cropping; in the other, depletion was halted and the productivity of the land improved. Before we inquire into the circumstances that provided the directive forces and helped in the reversion of the trend, a brief review of the events that led up to it is necessary.

The first period is roughly coextensive with the period of settlement, which came to a close at the beginning of the 20th century. Agencies that issued titles to land on which settlers located had no definite information as to the productivity of the land, nor were the settlers able to determine it objectively. All that could serve as a guide was a subjective appraisal of the land's quality, which to the dismay of the settlers, was frequently discouraging. Agriculture was the first industry that supported the settlers, and it was pursued without any particular care for the land. This was generally true of farmers who cultivated their own land, but it was even more the case with the many tenants who had no stake in the land. Abundance of land was the all-pervading concept that dominated the thoughts and activities of the people. Under these conditions, land use was exploitive, and as a consequence, it was frequently accompanied by diminishing returns.

Toward the end of the settlement period and more particularly during the last half of the 19th century, the large-scale application of scientific and technical principles in the manufacturing industries began to affect the national economy. Transportation and communication facilities had not only opened the country locally but had connected the East with the West and the North with the South. Mechanized industrial production had made a running start, which soon produced chain reactions. It not only increased production but also diversified the means of production by developing new sources of energy. The internal combustion engine made its debut at that time. It revolutionized transportation and was soon applied to farm operations.

In this respect, American farmers were in a better position to take advantage of mechanized farm operations than their Old World cousins. As a rule, European farmers had control over fewer acres than American farmers. Consequently, they enlarged their scope of operations proportionately. Even now, in the division of

European estates, approximately 40 acres are considered to be sufficient for a family-operated farm. Practically the same idea was embodied in the American slogan of "40 acres and a mule," which originated with the freedmen. Settlers, however, usually acquired a much larger acreage. According to the Census of 1900, in none of the States that form the eastern humid half of the country was the average size of farm less than 80 acres. In the drier Western States, which include the tier of States from North Dakota south to Texas, farms averaged from 200 to more than 1,000 acres, except in Idaho. Farmers in America therefore, were comparatively well supplied with land on which to use mechanical equipment. This was particularly the case in the Great Plains, where most of the small grains are grown.

Although technology transformed farm operations, science played a major role in increasing the effectiveness of farm labor and the productivity of the land.

Near the turn of the 19th century, a beginning was made in the study and survey of the soils of the country to obtain more reliable information as to how they could be used to produce crops. Their physical characteristics and chemical composition were studied. As a result, their use adaptability, and their adequacy or deficiency so far as plant nutrients were concerned became better known and served as a guide to the use of fertilizers, the conservation and management of the soils, and better adjustment of land use to the potentiality of the land itself.

To obtain a factual background of the manifest climatic divergencies in the different parts of the country, the Weather Bureau established many cooperative stations to record and report the daily readings of the instruments. With the accumulated records over the years, characteristics of local climatic regional variations, and to some extent the hazards of weather, could be determined. Thus, agriculture was able to adjust its enterprises and operations to conform to some extent to the vagaries of weather.

On the economic side, farm-management studies were undertaken throughout the country to help farmers organize their operations more efficiently. This was done especially with a view to improving farm incomes by taking the cost–returns ratio into account, and by adjusting farm enterprises to the advantages and shortcomings of the physical and economic environments in which they were carried on.

The work of county agents and experiment stations had a similar orientation. County agents were appointed for most counties so that farmers could avail themselves of their advice and counsel when special problems arose. The office of the county agent served also as intermediary in the introduction of advances made in agricultural production.

These are some of the more conspicuous landmarks established along the road of progress before World War I. When, therefore, the war emergencies called for increased production, the mechanism for doing the job was available and farmers responded with alacrity.

Progress in this direction did not end with the end of World War I. Although there was a temporary economic slackening, new improvements in industrial and agricultural production occurred. New machines appeared; higher yielding crop varieties were introduced; conservation and management of the soil received greater attention; conversion of feed into food became more efficient; new methods of food preservation and marketing were devised and established; and new wood-using processes provided the foundation for new industries. These and other innovations have affected agriculture and forestry in particular and the country as a whole in general.

Internal development of the country is linked inevitably with the use of the land. This has been true since the first settlers arrived from Europe four centuries ago. The transition from primitive conditions to a highly industrialized civilization was accomplished in a shorter space of time here than in other parts of the world. Moreover, the conversion of the country has been so effective that little land is left that does not bear the imprint of cultural features. This should not be construed as meaning that there is no room or need for further improvement. Actually, our land and water resources are not fully developed. Increase in population alone will require perennial adjustments and improvements in the use of both land and water to accommodate the needs of the people.

Expansions and contractions in the use of the land for primary production must be expected and accepted as part of the growing pains of the Nation. In addition, problems were inherited from the past. Not all the damage inflicted on the land during the exploitive period has been repaired. Of even longer standing is the unfinished business of boundary determination left by the colonies and the States that succeeded them. Uncertain boundaries of administrative divisions and land-ownership units, which stem from the methods of issuing titles that were prevalent in the colonies and the States, are still a fruitful source of contention. These problems, which are connected with civic order and national growth, have awakened interest in ownership and use of the land. To provide a better insight and causal understanding of these problems is the purpose of the study reported here.

# The Background

Strains and stresses in the man–land relationship make up one of the issues the world faces today. When examined from a realistic viewpoint, many of the impediments that arise are found to be centered largely in the difficulty of keeping the functional relationship between two factors of a different order in proper balance. Land is relatively static in both quantity and natural characteristics, whereas population is dynamic in both its action and its reaction on the use of land. The density or sparsity of population, its rate of growth, and shifts in the social groupings of the population are variables so far as time and place are concerned. Each has a marked reaction on the use of the land. To these must be added the influence exerted by an advanced economy and improvements in standards of living. As a higher standard of living usually means a greater demand for more diversified and improved products of the land and for proportionately larger acreages on which to produce them, use of a fixed acreage of land requires continuous adjustment to meet the changing needs of the population.

Changing the use of the land to meet the needs of the population is identified with the progress of civilization. Since ancient times, use of land has been intensified step by step to increase production. Primitive tribal society used the land mainly as a hunting and gathering ground. The products of the chase and the edible fruits and plants provided by the natural vegetation satisfied the needs of the population. Later, with the domestication of animals, nomadic herdsmen used the land as open range.

With the planting of crops, a new era was ushered in. It marked the beginning of more intensive use of the land and in turn changed the habitual way of living of the people. Crop planting was the initial step in the direction of development and use of the land for agriculture. Although the patches of land planted were shifted from time to time, people began to attend to fields and domestic animals from a fixed place of residence. Thus permanent settlement as the preferred mode of living was initiated.

In most parts of the world, increasing the production of food, feed, and fiber to provide for the needs of a larger population was not a particularly stringent problem in these early stages of civilization. With increased experience, agricultural practices became more efficient, and this in itself increased production. The standards of living were not so exacting that they could not be satisfied readily by moving to new land, which was abundant. Even though it was not located in the same region, it could be reached and settled through migration or, as was frequently done, acquired through conquest. In arid regions, irrigation was applied early to obtain a reliable supply of food and feed from agricultural production. These, in short, were the chief methods used to adjust the man–land relationship from ancient to modern times.

## New Ways of Adjusting Man–Land Relationship Needed

When the present world situation is used as the background of reference for this discussion, it becomes clear that some of the former ways of adjusting the man–land relationship are no longer realistic. All land is now partitioned and under the jurisdiction of one country or another. Some land is still not fully occupied or developed and could easily support more people. But, in most instances, the free movement of people, aside from travel for business and pleasure, is restricted to the confines of their own countries. Paradoxical as it may sound, this is at a time when modern transportation facilities have made man more mobile than ever before. For the most part, any improvement in the man–land relationship to promote the common welfare of the people must first be sought within individual countries.

That the maladjustment in the man–land relationship is now felt more acutely in some parts of a country, or in some parts of the world, as compared with other parts, usually cannot be attributed to a single cause. The combination of fixed and variable factors in each instance must be recognized and studied in its natural setting if the problems contained therein are to be analyzed and solutions found. Natural conditions and wealth differ from region to region, and the distribution of population does not always conform to the distribution of natural resources. In addition, each country or region has its own customs and institutions that govern the actions of the people and, in some instances, control the use of the land. Under these circumstances, it cannot be expected, nor is it possible, that people everywhere can attain a uniformly high level of living from use of the land.

Land use and level of living are related, but neither the one nor the other in itself is a reliable indicator of the potentiality of the land to support the population. Frequently, land use represents only one segment of the regional economy. So far as the level of living is concerned, land use may be secondary to other industries. From the land use standpoint, we have areas of both overproduction and underproduction in relation to local needs. In a country in which the agrarian economy has largely given way to industry and commerce, and where the greater part of the population resides in urban concentrations, surplus production in some areas is essential to balance the deficiencies of other areas. Actually, as a result of the spreading of cosmopolitan tastes and habits, few corners on the globe have retained a mode of living in which everything needed is furnished by the natural environment of the people.

## Adjustment to Physical Conditions

Because of the disparate distribution of natural conditions, resources, and people, the use of land has acquired the characteristics of a commercial enterprise. Many crops are grown entirely as cash crops. Frequently, they are grown for export as well as for domestic consumption or industrial use. This is true also of forest products and the products of the range. With the entrance of land use into the the commercial production field, it became more sensitive to the factors that influence prices and cost of production. Soils, climate, water supply, economic conditions, labor efficiency, increased yields per areal unit, improved quality of products, location of production areas with reference to markets, processing methods, storage and shipping facilities for products, and market demand, are all aspects of the land use complex, which in the more advanced countries receive added recognition and attention.

Food and an adequate diet, the most obvious and in places the most pressing physical needs of man, are singled out at times as the desired goal of land use in improving the level of living of the people. A proper diet is an essential element of human well-being, but in itself it is hardly sufficient to raise the level of living in backward countries and regions. In these countries and regions, more than land use must be taken into account. Raising the productive capacity of the land is conditioned first on an increase in the productive capacity of the people. Workers on the land must be able to produce more than they need for themselves. An advancement of the whole economy is needed to raise the level of living.

## Technology and Land Use

With the introduction of mechanized operations in production of food and fiber, the manpower requirements for land use declined. Many persons released from work on the land are now free to follow other gainful occupations. Land use itself is now an industry. Whether we approach the question of standard of living from the viewpoint of land use or of industry as a whole, therefore, we are likely to reach the same conclusion. Production and organization of all branches of industry are so closely interwoven that they must be considered together when improvement in the level of living is the aim. Translated into terms of action, this means that all natural resources must be developed to serve the economy of an area.

How the economics and production techniques of land use have benefited from association with industry is evident from the results obtained. In commercial agriculture, the input–output ratio necessarily receives considerable attention. The knowledge gained from special research and investigations in the physical, biological, social, technical, and economic fields readily finds application in competitive commercial enterprises. Therefore, wherever the results of research in these fields are applied to land use, as a rule, man, land, domestic animals, and plants produce more efficiently than was true a decade or so ago. Much has been done to advance human well-being by applying constructive knowledge and skills to use of land. In addition to these benefits, these accomplishments furnish evidence that progress can be made. They show the way in which it can be achieved, how some of the obstacles to better use of the land can be surmounted, and how production can be increased on a fixed area of land.

Although in recent years science and technology have established an all-time record of accomplishment, they have not succeeded in removing all obstacles to more intensive use of the land. Higher productive uses are excluded on much of the land area mainly because of unfavorable natural conditions. But between the most favorable setting for cultural use of the land and extreme instances in which all major uses are precluded are many intermediate classes with a diversity of complexes, to which use must be adjusted according to physical capability and economic feasibility. Land classes that range from the highest use capability to those with no productive use qualifications are found in the United States.

Within the approximately 3 million square miles of continental United States, physical conditions vary considerably from region to region, sometimes even from locality to locality. This was only imperfectly known at the time of settlement. In selecting sites for settlement, the pioneers relied mainly on their own resourcefulness and judgment, and they did not always locate on adequately productive land. Adjustment of settlement and land use to the physical conditions and the need for the products of the land has been going on since the first settlers arrived.

The United States, which is a comparatively young country, grew rapidly and is still growing. The chief period of internal growth was confined to the last 100 years or so. The population grew from 23 million persons in

1850 to 165 million in 1955. Hand in hand with the growth in population came development of the country's resources. During the latter part of the period especially, industrialization left its mark on countryside and people.

Growth and changes in the old order necessarily affected not only the use of the land but the economic and social status of much of the population as well. The proportion of urban to rural population changed. In 1850, as reported by the census, the urban segment of the 23 million people of the United States was 15 percent. In 1955, more than 64 percent of the 165 million people were living in cities. This movement means that more land is needed for residential and industrial purposes. With 107 million people concentrated in urban areas, the land requirements for outdoor recreation, travel, transportation, and communications have multiplied. Today, lands needed for urban

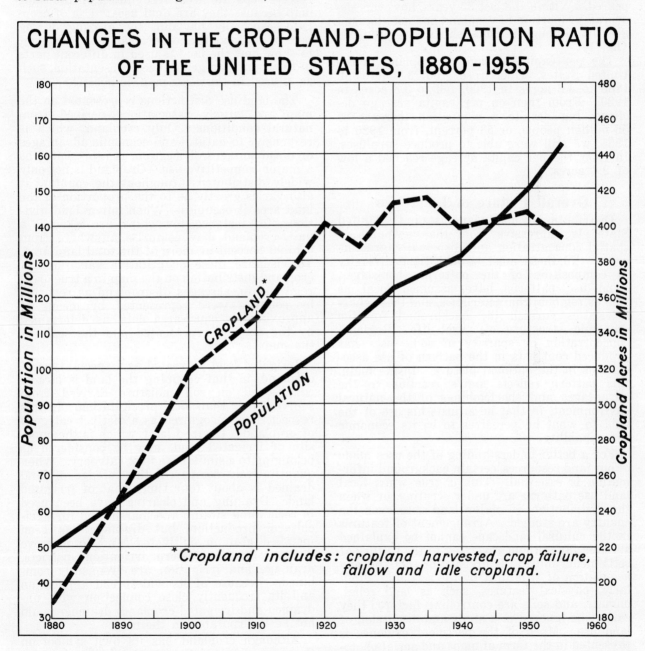

## CHANGES IN THE CROPLAND-POPULATION RATIO OF THE UNITED STATES, 1880-1955

*Cropland includes: cropland harvested, crop failure, fallow and idle cropland.*

U. S. DEPARTMENT OF AGRICULTURE      NEG. 58(5)-2486 AGRICULTURAL RESEARCH SERVICE

FIGURE 1.—This chart shows changes in the relationship between population and cropland from 1880 to 1955. Both population and acreage of cropland increased steadily until 1920. After 1920, only population continued to increase. Increase in population, expansion of industries, and scientific and technological advances in crop production brought about shifts in distribution of cropland and affected the man–land relationship.

settlements, rights-of-way for roads and rail-roads, airports, parks, and related uses in the aggregate approximate the area of the State of Wyoming (165).[1]

Land use expanded with the westward movement of settlement. Expansion in acreage of cropland in this direction kept pace with settlement, but the acreage of cropland continued to increase for about three decades after 1890, when the western frontier had almost disappeared. Within the last 35 years, however, the overall proportion of cropland has not changed greatly, although regional shifts have occurred (fig. 1).

The per capita acreage of cropland in the United States, which rose from 3.8 acres in 1880 to 4.2 acres in 1900, fell to 3.8 acres in 1920. From then on per capita acreage declined, but despite a population increase of 56 million people, or 53 percent, from 1920 to 1955, we still were able to produce surpluses. In 1955, the per capita acreage reached a low of 2.4 acres.

## Overall Picture of Land Use

Distribution of major land uses in the United States is impressive from the viewpoint of spatial concentration and dispersal characteristics. To these must be added the diversity in composition of the patterns themselves. Land use patterns have assumed local as well as regional characteristics, and these characteristics furnish the background for the economic structure of rural life. Regional concentration or sparsity of some uses has produced contrasts in the pattern of use associations in the national picture. In the main, this pattern reflects man's reaction to the advantages and shortcomings of the natural environment, in that he adjusts his use of the land to what he perceives to be its economic use capability.

For a better understanding of the uses made of our land resources, certain background information is essential. This is true when local land use patterns are under scrutiny, or when the distribution of major land uses over the country are studied. Arrangement of features in the cultural landscape cannot be explained successfully without reverting to the history of settlement, and to the division of the land and acquisition of title to it by the settlers. Similarly, physical features, such as land relief, climate, and soils are controlling factors; they cannot be ignored in a study and discussion of land use. Much of the pertinent evidence is presented in the form of maps and aerial photographs to record the spatial arrangement and distribution of features.

[1] Italic numbers in parentheses refer to Literature Cited, p. 273.

Most of these maps are included in the text, but to preserve clarity of expression in the overall picture, the color map, Major Land Uses in the United States (pocket), is necessary. Even so, the distinctions must be confined to major uses expressed in significant combinations.

Such major uses as the use of forest or woodland for grazing or recreation cannot receive separate areal recognition on the same map because they are dual uses. Use of cropland, especially hayland, for grazing during part of the year is another example. However, to show how the land is used in different parts of the country, a generalized presentation, such as is used in the color map, is necessary.

The land use distinctions represented on the map are largely associations derived from natural conditions. Only cropland, which is responsive to natural and economic advantages or disadvantages of location, is represented as a major competitive use. Cropland is not only widely distributed throughout the country; it also varies greatly as to the proportion of the land area it occupies. When minor land divisions, for instance, townships, are taken as a unit, cropland may comprise anywhere from 0 to 90 percent or more of the total land area. To visualize these quantitative variations of cropland distribution on the map in a true areal relationship, acreages of cropland as reported by counties were represented by means of approximately equal-area dots, as determined by the acreage represented and the scale of the map.

Irrigated land is treated as a special type of cropland, in that cropping the land is largely conditioned on soil moisture derived from sources other than local precipitation. In this respect, it is recognized as a distinct category of cropland. Drained land, which is the opposite of irrigated land, may be considered as belonging to a similar land use category. When quantitatively compared, the acreage of land drained is about four times that of irrigated land. Draining and clearing have been used in reclaiming swamp and marsh land for agricultural production, but drainage has been installed also on cultivated land to improve yields. In the western irrigation districts, drainage and irrigation are frequently combined. Because of its widespread application and its frequently close connection with undrained and irrigated cropland, drainage could not be incorporated in the map.

Although cropland has its own symbol on the map, its associations with other major uses are preserved. In the humid eastern section of the United States, where all three major uses are competitive, crop, forest, and pasture lands are interspersed. As may be observed, cropland is rather sparsely scattered in many places in the Eastern States.

This can be taken as illustrating distribution only; it cannot safely be interpreted as meaning underdevelopment in all instances. Cropland is more concentrated in the Central Plains, and in the originally forested plains of western Ohio, Indiana, southern Michigan and Wisconsin, the Bluegrass Basin, the Pennyroyal of Kentucky, and some other areas. But the main concentration is found on the treeless prairies and plains of the Central States. An exception is the Coastal Prairie of Texas, which has remained largely grazing ground for cattle. In the West, aside from the Columbia Plateau, where dry grain farming is prevalent, cropland is concentrated in the valleys and basins, and is frequently supported by irrigation.

In contrast to cropland, of which the bulk is confined to the eastern two-thirds of the United States, most of the grazing land is found in the western third of the country. Grazing land used here as an overall classification term includes a great range in variables of plant associations and carrying capacity. Because of these distinctions, two terms are in common use, and to a certain extent, they have acquired a regional preference. In the East, with its more diversified land use patterns, pasture is the more common term, and in the semiarid and arid range country of the West, grazing is the well-established designation. Between these two preferential use areas, however, there is no distinct dividing line. The most pronounced distinction between pasture and grazing is found in carrying capacity. In the East, farm pasture usually has a high carrying capacity; on the Western range, it is very low. Gradations occur, of course; on the Western range, grazing is associated with type of vegetative cover. The lowest grazing capacity is connected with the desert shrub type on which up to 18 acres may be needed to support a cow for a month. Less than an acre of humid pasture may be required. Subhumid and semiarid grassland, open pasture, and forest and woodland grazed are intermediate grazing types. Regionally, they are associated to some extent with seasonal grazing use.

Desert as mapped is land that for several reasons has no productive use. Desert land may be barren rocky ground; barren saline playas, like the Black Desert in Nevada or the Great Salt Lake Desert in Utah; or, as in the Mojave Desert, land that produces some forage plants but cannot be grazed for lack of stock water.

Swamps and marshes are natural land types. Both types consist of waterlogged land but the swamps are wooded and the marshes are chiefly open grasslands. Land use in these areas is somewhat incidental. The swamps may furnish special kinds of lumber from water-loving trees. In favorable seasons, swamps and marshes may provide some grazing, but both are favored areas of wildlife, and if not protected, they frequently become seasonal hunting grounds. Hunting and trapping of muskrats as it is done in the coastal marshes of Louisiana constitutes a rewarding occupation.

Forest and woodland grazed are areas devoted almost entirely to silviculture. Settlements with acreages of cropland too small to be segregated on the map are included in only a few instances. These solid forest areas occupy chiefly mountains and rough land, or land with poor soil. Many of them are included in National and State Forests and Parks. The most extensive solid area of commercial forest in private ownership is found in northern Maine.

Alpine meadows are confined to mountaintops above the timberline. Some of these areas may be grazed briefly in summer, but many of them are only rock outcrop with little or no vegetation. Consequently, they are of little economic significance.

The information needed for delimitation of the areas recognized on the map was derived from many sources. When available, aerial photography was relied on primarily to supply the distributional facts. Most of the country east of the Rockies is covered by aerial photography. But as the difference in scale between the aerial photographs and the United States map is considerable, the contents of the photographic images could not be generalized directly down to the scale of the final map. To do this, State maps of the United States Geological Survey on a scale of 1:1,000,000 served as an intermediary on which the land use patterns were developed from the aerial photographs. Soil, topographic, and geologic maps provided additional reference material. A set of manuscript maps showing land use in the States east of the Rockies resulted from this procedure. These maps provided the principal source for the areal delimitation of the land use features in this part of the country. For the Western States, aerial photography was used also, but less coherent coverage exists for these States than for those in the East. Moreover, the West has land use distinctions that must be determined from other sources.

Whether or not desert shrubland or forest and woodland is grazed is not identifiable on aerial photographs, except where barren ground indicates desert conditions. Actually, the boundary between desert and desert shrubland grazed is often indefinite and oscillating. During winters with some snow cover, sheep can be grazed farther out in the desert than is possible when springs and wells must be relied upon to provide the stockwater. In the delimitation of land use areas in the western part of the United States, material provided by the Bureau of Land Management and the Geological Survey of the United States Department of the Interior, the Forest Service and the Soil Conservation Service of the United States Department of Agriculture, and State publications that had a bearing on land use were consulted and utilized. Forest and woodland grazed is a distinction based mainly on the records of the Forest Service.

As a generalized graphic presentation of land use, the map shows the variations in land use that exist in the United States. From region to region, differences may be noted in the intensity with which the land is used, and in the composition of major land use associations. In most places, variations of this kind denote changes in physical conditions. The land use patterns delimited on the map indicate that there are great regional differences in the contributions land can make to the Nation.

# Settlement, Division, and Use of Land

In its broadest sense, land utilization may be defined as the use of land by man. The cultural landscape and the multiple combinations in the land use pattern are his work. A number of elements, however, may be discerned in the spatial order of these land use patterns. Some of the organizational features that appear in the design are those devised by individual users. Others are inherent characteristics of settlement by ethnic groups or of the institutionalized system of administrative land divisions. Differences of this kind are particularly noticeable when the areas of colonial settlement are compared with those of later development. (Compare, for instance, plates 32 and 38 or plates 143 and 144. All of them differ from those usually found in the Old World.) The historical factor, therefore, has much to do with land use. If we are to understand the layout of the patterns of land use, this factor must be considered.

In the United States, land use has gone through several stages that do not necessarily correspond to or coincide in all phases with those recognized in other parts of the world. Land use and civilization are closely related. A chapter on prehistoric land use would probably be concerned mainly with the hunting and collecting activities of primitive man. From these more indirect uses of the land, cultural uses gradually developed. At first, these cultural uses amounted only to common use of the land by the members of tribal society but from this use several types of ownership evolved. In some places, they were freeholds; in others, feudal tenure with entailed rights and obligations evolved; or a mixture of both were found. The transition from tribal use to individual ownership is missing in the history of land use in the United States. As a possible exception, the division of the land in Indian Reservations and the transfer of title to individuals could be cited. But this process did not evolve among the Indians themselves. There are also instances in which settlers at first used all or part of their land in common and then divided it among themselves. In so doing, they followed a custom they had brought with them from Europe.

## Pre-Columbian Era

### The Hunting and Foraging Period

The pre-Columbian history of land use in what is now continental United States probably differs very little from the early cultures of the Old World. From what we know now, these primitive American cultures appear on the time scale much earlier than was at first suspected. Stone artifacts found in interglacial deposits indicate that man was on this continent during the latter part of the Pleistocene Epoch. The actual age of these early American cultures is as yet a matter of conjecture. According to one source, however, they date back from 40,000 to 60,000 years (48, p. 534). More recently, by bringing other evidence to bear on the question, these estimates were extended to more than double the time during which the American continent may be considered as having been inhabited (19). More definite dates of site occupation, which were obtained from organic remains with the radiocarbon technique (160), have been established for a number of places, and new ones are added occasionally. So far, the oldest dates obtained in this way indicate that man was in the Americas thousands of years before the dawn of the Christian era. Only a few examples can be cited.

An archeological site on the alluvial terrace of the Trinity River near Lewisville in Denton County, Tex., probably yielded the oldest direct evidence of man's presence in America. This site, which consists of ancient hearths nearly 20 feet below the surface of the terrace, contained the bones of many food animals, fresh water clams, and snail shells, in addition to a flint spear point and charcoal. Radiocarbon tests on the charcoal indicated that it was more than 37,000 years old. A hearth near Las Vegas, Nev., was found to be some 23,000 years old, and a hearth on Santa Rosa Island about 30,000 years ago (106, 13).

Charcoal and bone from a fireplace 6 to 7 feet below the accumulations on the floor of Graham

Cave, Montgomery County, Mo., registered an age of nearly 10,000 years (27). Charcoal remains from a rock shelter on the Illinois side of the Mississippi River, about 40 miles south of St. Louis, registered an age of nearly 11,000 years (104). A similar age was determined for the occupation level of Allen Site on the Republican River Terrace (30). Evidence of early man's presence on the Pacific mainland is provided by "Several pairs of woven rope sandals found in Fort Rock Cave, covered by the Newberry Eruption in Oregon," which were made about 9,000 years ago (4).

The latest discovery of a site occupied by prehistoric man is reported from Alabama. Excavations in Russell Cave near Bridgeport, in the northeast corner of Alabama, of successive layers of 14-foot deposits encountered at the bottom a hearth, the remains of which indicated that it had been occupied 8,000 years ago (105). None of these prehistoric remains suggests that land was used in these early periods in any way except as a hunting and foraging ground. Indications that man had started to raise crops appear about 5,000 to 6,000 years later.

## Beginning of Crop-Growing Era

In the exploration of Bat Cave, Catron County, N. Mex., in 1948, 766 well-preserved corncobs were found in the successive strata of accumulated refuse (85). The corncobs in the lower layer, however, provided insufficient material for radiocarbon dating, but extrapolation from the other layers indicates that the corn is from 3,000 to 3,500 years old, which corresponds to about 1,500 to 1,000 B. C. (4). Charcoal samples from an undisturbed area in this cave, with which the culture of corn may be correlatable, go back to about 5,000 B. C. (79). These discoveries indicate that at that time the land was used for crops. This may postdate the beginning of agriculture by a lengthy span of time. The discoveries also record the progress made in improving corn as an agricultural crop.

The remains of corn in these caves are significant in other respects. Caves and cave dwellings are rather numerous in the arid Southwest. As corn is a cultivated crop, the implications are that to a considerable extent these cavedwellers must have been farmers, and this in a region in which today the natural conditions are not particularly suited to production of corn, except under irrigation. If the climate has not changed in the meantime, the cavedwellers had to grow their corn on favorable spots in the moist bottoms of arroyos, or they had to divert water from the rivers for irrigation. Indications are that they did both.

Centuries later, the Indians on the Atlantic slope of the continent grew corn, beans, melons, tobacco, and other crops. Special cultural methods of growing corn, the chief crop, had been devised, and these were transmitted to the European settlers. With some tribes, agriculture was more or less a community enterprise. Instances are reported in which Indian fields contained several hundred acres (31, p. 20). But the Indians were also skillful hunters, and game was plentiful. The number of Indians was comparatively small in proportion to the territory they occupied. Their needs were elementary and a desultory type of farming served to supplement the provisions acquired through the chase. Hunting, fishing, and gathering of wild fruits furnished most of their food. Land use by the Indians was not exacting or exhausting for either land or people. It did not change profoundly the natural environment in which the Indians lived, although some changes in plant cover occurred as a result of burning and other activities. Pioneer settlers sometimes found openings in the forest, mainly near streams, which were abandoned sites of Indian villages or meadows produced by burning the forest. It has been estimated that less than 2 percent of all land in Pennsylvania was cleared of forest growth in this way before the settlers arrived (47, pp. 2, 34).

Apparently, the migratory movement of the Indians in the eastern forest zone of America was confined largely to tribal territories or hunting grounds. To a considerable extent, it was seasonal. Families congregated in movable camps and villages, at least for some parts of the year. Even the primitive type of agriculture practiced by the Indians required some attention. Protracted hunting expeditions had to wait for the cooler seasons. But neither hunting nor agriculture was restricted to individual tracts, for land ownership was unknown to the Indians.

Tribal hunting districts, however, were well established and recognized by the Indians. When traders from the East were admitted to the Indian country on the western waters of the Appalachians, a Board of Commissioners, in agreement with the Indian chiefs, allotted one trader to a hunting district. Beaver, deer, and fur skins were the chief articles the Indians had to offer for barter (142, p. 34).

Hunting districts or grounds were therefore the spatial limits of tribal authority vested in the Indian chiefs. Evidently there were boundaries to define the districts. That these boundaries were not always definite may be inferred from the friction among neighboring tribes. There were instances, however, in which boundaries were defined by markers. When d'Iberville and his party ascended the

Mississippi River in 1699, they noticed on the first bluffs a large red pole about 30 feet high, decorated with bear and fish heads. They learned that the pole represented a marker to divide the hunting grounds of the Bayougoula Indians from those of the Houmas. Among the Indians, the pole was known as the Istrouma, or Red Pole, which the French translated into Baton Rouge. Thus, the approximate site of the pole is marked, and the French rendition of the name is preserved in the name of the capital of Louisiana (*96, p. 17*).

Farther west on the prairies and plains, most of the Indians were nomads, who used land only as an open hunting ground. The grassland was the natural range of the buffalo, which roamed over the open country in immense herds. As game animals, buffaloes were easy to hunt, and before the white man arrived on the scene, their reproductive capacity more than satisfied the needs of the Indians. The chroniclers of Coronado's expedition (1540-42) reported that the Indians "in the country where the cows are" did not plant corn. These writers noted also that the migratory habits of the Indians were conditioned by the erratic, and no doubt to some extent seasonal, movement of the buffaloes. Several tribes, however, had villages on the Missouri and Platte Rivers and also grew some crops (*102, pp. 603, 622, 870*).

# Colonial Period

## The Spanish Grants

A more effective use of the land on the Atlantic coast began with the arrival of European colonists, who brought with them their more advanced knowledge of agricultural skills, their seeds and implements, and, in addition, their concepts of property rights and individual land ownership safeguarded by legal provisions. Their immediate task was to establish themselves on the land and to improve it so that it would yield a living for themselves and their families. In so doing, they opened a new chapter in the history of land utilization in America.

Settlement started in Florida in the second half of the 16th century. Farther north it did not get underway until a century later. One of the first acts of the colonists usually was to locate on the land and acquire title to it, although the method of acquiring title and the acreage an individual could claim were not uniform among the colonial powers.

The Spanish crown, applying the law of the Indies to Florida, granted land in peonias and caballerias, that is, the grants were proportionate to the rank of the individual. A peon or laborer received a lot for a house, enough land to grow a crop, and pasture and woodland for a given number of livestock; a caballero received a larger lot and 5 times the acreage of arable and pasture land received by a peon. When, in 1763, Spain ceded Florida to Great Britain, the British Government gave those who preferred to emigrate 18 months in which to dispose of their land holdings. Aside from city lots, nothing remains of these old Spanish land grants. Some Spanish grants from this early period have survived in what is now Colorado, New Mexico, Arizona, and California, or the part of the West that was originally penetrated and settled to some extent by the Spaniards.

Land grants in Florida that were recognized by the United States date from the British occupation, 1763 to 1783, and from the second Spanish occupation from 1783 until Florida was ceded to the United States in 1819 (*141*).

Spain made no formal purchases of land from the Indians. In the English and Dutch colonies, settlement proceeded along different lines. The Indians' right to occupancy of the land was a collective right that was usually recognized; it was extinguished only through purchase from the Indians by the Colonial Government or the settlers.

## Settlement by Northern Europeans

Differences in conception of what the Indians' rights were to land, possession of which was claimed by European powers upon discovery, provided a distinctive approach to settlement of the land. Equally distinct were the policies and practices pursued in the colonies of conveying ownership rights of unoccupied land to private parties. Large grants to proprietary governors and trading companies which, in addition to established colonies, functioned under the provisions of their own charters, enabled each to adopt its own policy for disposal of the land. These policies usually followed established European patterns (*60, p. 39*).

In New England, tracts of land were at first granted to individuals, but after 1629 more definite rules of settlement were adopted to "avoid all contentions twixt the adventurers." Community settlements prevailed, but before a plantation or community could be organized, permission had to be obtained from the General Court. Grants of land in common for settlement were made to commoners, or proprietors, as they were called, as the responsible parties of the community. The boundaries of the grants were laid out. The land was divided and allotted to settlers according to rules adopted by the settlers themselves, which differed from the policy used with towns. Lots were not uniform in size. They varied with the personal worth of individual settlers. As a rule, not all the land within the townships was alienated at the same time. Land that was not assigned to the original settlers was used and held in common and parcelled out later when the need arose. Evidently, this was the prevailing procedure, although it was not always strictly followed. After 1725, sales of land became more general, and leading settlers were able to obtain grants of land on which they did not settle but from which they expected the economic benefits of development (*120, pp. 55-56; 69, p. 26*).

Land division and allotment in the township settlements were controlled by the community, which comprised an area usually not more than 6 to 7 miles square, and frequently much less. This type of land alienation produced continuity of land ownership without overlapping claims or interspersed gores of "no man's land." The system was not so rigid in its aims or applications as to produce geometric uniformity in the size and shape of lots, but its influence was felt when the system of land division adopted for the public domain was shaped (*37*).

The Dutch along the Hudson River had more than one form of land tenure. At first, the West India Company, as the colonizing agency, promoted a seignorial type of settlement, which consisted of large estates owned by the "Patroons." Patroons divided their lands into farms, erected farm buildings, and provided implements and livestock for the settlers. The settlers were tenants. Besides paying rent, they had also to render certain service to the patroon. After the exclusive privilege of the West India Company to deed the land was revoked in 1638, this was changed. A Dutch colonist with 5 family members over 15 years old could then claim 200 acres. Later, under Stuyvesant, settlement in villages was encouraged. Agricultural land surrounding the villages was laid out. With this land frequently went pasture rights in the village commons.

A different arrangement in land division was introduced by the Huguenots, who settled in the Valley of the Wallkill, where they founded what is now New Paltz. These settlers had bought from the Indians a tract of land of about 36,000 acres, title to which was confirmed by the Governor in 1677. The agricultural land was subdivided by the settlers into rectangular lots, but some of the land near the village and some of the more distant woodland was left in commons, and for a time it was used in common. These rectangular divisions of the land are still in evidence (*39*). As a type of land division, this was the forerunner of a similar system used later in the western territories.

## Indiscriminate Settlement

Another form of settlement, which is sometimes referred to as the indiscriminate type of settlement, took place in the mid-Atlantic and southern colonies. Here there was no preconceived method of allocating the land. Settlement in these colonies started on the lands most accessible from the ocean. These lands lay along the shores of estuaries and the banks of larger streams. Plantation owners of the southern Coastal Plains usually acquired large estates in these locations, as did the gentry for their manors in the central colonies. The policy of the proprietary governors of these colonies as to the acquisition of large estates, however, was not uniform. For instance, proportionately there are more manors in Maryland and Virginia than in Pennsylvania and Delaware. Large tracts of land were also sold to speculators who resold it to the settlers at a profit.

William Penn, as the proprietor of Pennsylvania and Delaware, was the largest landowner in the New World. Of necessity, he was at the same time Governor and sales promoter of his domain. Land acquired in his colony was deeded in his name. In 1682, soon after his arrival in the colony, he established a land office, which was charged with the sale of land. According to his instructions, the land was to be laid out in squares for community settlement. His commissioners, however, found it easier to accommodate individual buyers without adhering to a rigid system of land division. Except for Philadelphia, the streets of which were laid out by Penn himself, and Germantown, the system of rectangular land division was not generally applied in colonial Pennsylvania.

The land office functioned for a while, but as time went on, it could not prevent immigrants from moving westward and settling without legal sanction in whatever spot on vacant land they selected. William Penn's death almost caused the land office to suspend operations from 1718 to 1731. During this period, more squatters than legitimate settlers entered the back country. They established their claims and rights to land ownership through occupancy. Some futile attempts were made to dislodge them but after 1750, they were recognized by the proprietors. More land was sold when the office resumed proper operations, but the Revolution ended the disposal of proprietary land (*47, pp. 1-32*).

Although systematic land division had been proposed for Carolina and Georgia, preemption of land in the southern colonies proceeded with no attempt at conventionalized allocation of sites. Colonists entered the higher grounds from the east by following the waters or divides upstream. Others, who came from the north, followed the buffalo trails, which in turn became roads. The Piedmont and the Appalachian Valley received settlers in this way. Each settler selected his homesite, which was usually near a stream and far enough from his nearest

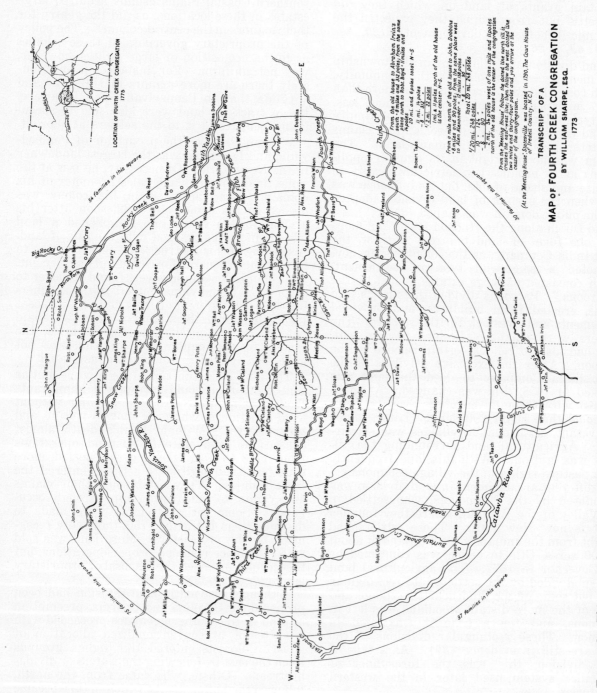

FIGURE 2.—This map shows how settlement and local government organization developed in the Carolina Piedmont. It illustrates the centrality principle of organization of settlement. The concentric circles drawn around the determined center of the community are spaced a mile apart. (Made available through the courtesy of Mr. Hugh H. Wooten.)

12

neighbor so that he would not encroach on his neighbor's claim.

In obtaining title to the land, the purchaser received from the Colonial government a warrant of survey for a stated acreage on prevailing terms. The warrant did not specify location; it could be applied to any vacant, unappropriated public land in the colony. A boundary survey of the selected land had to be made and presented, with the warrant of survey, to the land office. If no valid protest was registered within a certain time, the land office then issued a patent to the land. The boundaries on these land plats represented chiefly compass lines run by inexperienced surveyors. The line description started and ended at the same point. These so called "metes and bounds" surveys of the colonial period were not accurate. Conflicting claims resulting from this type of survey provide a continuing source of litigation (69, p. 23).

Group settlement developed in places to permit mutual protection and collective counsel and action. Frequently, more than one branch of a family were represented in a group. Thus group coherence was strengthened by ties of kinship. Later, when local administrative units were organized, these groups or congregations served as nuclei for units. The formation and location of such a group settlement is recorded in figure 2. This unique document was made by William Sharpe, an early settler in the Piedmont of North Carolina, who was a member of the Fourth Creek congregation. It illustrates the grouping of the pioneer settlers; their names reveal to some extent their family connections. It is also the first example found in America of the application of the centrality principle in organizing a community. From this community, Iredell County evolved. Statesville, its county seat, is located where the old meetinghouse formerly stood.

## Appalachians, the Colonial Frontier of Settlement

Settlement in these colonies was restricted to the eastern slope of the mountains by Royal Proclamation, but as the proclamation was ambiguously worded, it was not taken seriously by either the people or the colonial officials. Indian traders, hunters, explorers, and adventurers entered the "country upon the western waters" very early, but after 1774, settlers arrived in bands and located claims on the land. Among the settlers were holders of military and treasury warrants.

The restraining attitude of England toward the movement of colonists westward across the Appalachians was not shared by other European powers with colonies in America. Spanish explorers, missionaries, and settlers coming from Mexico had entered the Southwest in the latter part of the 18th century, where they established missions and settlements and received grants of land in scattered spots; others moved eastward into Texas where they established some colonies. Even earlier, Spanish explorers and adventurers used Florida as a starting point from which to push northward and westward in their quest of the treasure cities. The best known of these expeditions, of course, is that of De Soto, who advanced through what is now Georgia and the Carolinas into the Tennessee Valley, and from there to the Mississippi. Although these Spanish adventurers claimed for Spain the lands over which they had traveled, the Spanish Government made no effort to settle and develop the country.

## Settlement Extended to Western Waters

More than a century later, the French, who had settled on the St. Lawrence River, sent out expeditions to explore the West. They wanted especially to discover the transcontinental waterway which the Indians had told them existed. They explored the Great Lakes region and the upper waters of the Mississippi, which Marquette descended in 1673 to the confluence of the Arkansas. It was left to LaSalle to explore the Mississippi River to the Gulf. In 1683, in the name of King Louis XIV, he took possession of the Mississippi River basin for France, naming it Louisiana. French settlements grew up slowly near the mouth of the river. The trading posts established earlier in the Great Lakes country became colonies to which others were added along the river and the lakes. But French settlements were still widely scattered when, in 1803, Louisiana was bought by the United States from Napoleon for $15,000,000.

The Spanish and French chapters in the history of the United States have left enduring impressions on land and people. The Spanish and French names of settlements and natural features are their legacy; as are their patterns of land ownership and land use. With the accession of the land by the United States, valid land titles were accepted as issued by the former governments, although as a rule, they do not extend over large compact areas. In the public-domain divisions of the land that followed, they stand out as islands having their own land divisions, of which the long-lot division is characteristic of all French settlements (pls. 1 and 137). In themselves, the long-lot divisions would be sufficient to identify French settlements even though the name has been changed. An example is a town on Lake Erie in Michigan; it was originally called Frenchtown but was renamed Monroe in 1815.

After the colonies attained their independence and the colonists assumed the responsibilities of government, the land question was one of the first to need attention. The trans-Appalachian country west of Virginia to the Ohio and the Mississippi was claimed by Virginia. Within this vast stretch of country, even though settlers had established themselves and claims had been laid out, there was no legal authority to issue valid titles to land nor could conflicting claims be adjudicated. To remedy this situation, the Virginia Assembly created the land courts in 1779. The western country was divided into 4 districts. For each district, 4 commissioners were appointed who acted as, and performed the duties of, an ambulating land court. The records of the land court for Kentucky County, which was almost coextensive with the present State of Kentucky, show that the term of the court was 10 months. Meetings were held in forts, churches, and meetinghouses; they were required to be advertised 20 days ahead. The first session was held on October 13, 1779; the last on April 26, 1780. Within this space of about 6 months, which included time for travel in a "hard winter," 8 sessions, lasting in all 79 days, were held in different parts of the county.

The claims adjudicated by the commissioners during this time totaled more than 1,400, of which 1,328, comprising in all 1,334,050 acres, were allowed and for which certificates were issued. These preemption claims were granted as a result of settlement, for which 400 acres' each were allowed. For improvement, 1,000 additional acres were granted, making 1,400 in all. In addition, other claims based on military warrants, treasury warrants, and other surveys were located. Altogether, nearly 3.5 million acres, or more than an eighth of the area of the State of Kentucky, were claimed in 1779 under some form of preemption (159). The commissioners could not go to individual settlers and verify the boundaries of their claims. Adjudication of an average of 17 claims a day precluded such a procedure.

The land in what is now Tennessee was at first attached to North Carolina. When North Carolina ceded the western territory to Congress in 1784, and to the Federal Government in 1790, it did so with the provision that all land entries and military reservations made under the authority of North Carolina would remain valid. Therefore when Tennessee finally emerged as a State in 1796, it inherited a complexity of land claims and settlement schemes. Much land had been deeded in large tracts to influential men and land companies; North Carolina retained the military reservations and the right to additional land to compensate soldiers of the Revolution in case the

reservations could not accommodate the claims; Congress had some land reservations, which were relinquished in 1823. Finally, Indians still occupied some of the land and their claims were not extinguished (1). As may be surmised, the landownership divisions that evolved from these tangled claims are usually irregular. Except for Indian lands, which were acquired and divided later, regularity in lines is confined to certain localities.

## Defects of Colonial Land Surveys

With the advancement of settlement came also a broadening of the preemption policy. Sales and grants were extended to include the headright system. Essentially, the headright system provided that the head of a family could claim a certain acreage for himself and, in addition, a stated acreage for each member of his family; servants were sometimes included. The headright system was in operation in all the seaboard colonies, but its vogue was greatest in the South Atlantic colonies (60, pp. 194-236).

All these methods of obtaining title to land were loosely administered. In colonies in which the indiscriminate method of settlement was used, the land surveys were seldom verified in the field, and conflicting claims to land through overlapping were not unusual. Deeds to vacant lands were issued rather freely, although some colonies were more liberal than others in this regard. This policy did not change at once when the colonies attained statehood. Georgia, in which the headright system was predominantly applied, furnishes an outstanding example.

Only a belt along the ocean that extended inland between the Savannah and the Alta-maha-Oconee Rivers was occupied during the colonial period. The counties established within this belt are usually referred to as headright counties in contrast to land-lot counties, which were settled later. In the headright counties, land was granted according to the size of the settler's family but the grant could not exceed 1,000 acres. The granting of land with little restraint in these counties resulted in conflicting claims. After a check of these colonial grants, the Surveyor-General of Georgia on June 17, 1839, furnished the State Legislature with a statement in which he showed that "the twenty-four counties existing in 1796 contained actually 8,717,960 acres of land, whereas the maps and records in the Surveyor-General's office show that in these counties there had been granted 29,097,866 acres" (83, p. 57). The report leaves little room for doubt that there were weaknesses in the method of acquiring title to land.

These brief notes on the prevailing customs and procedures of acquiring land titles during the colonial period represent examples selected to illustrate the different ways in which the settlers occupied the land and acquired ownership of it. All of them fit into the general picture of the times. There was a superabundance of vacant land that had little more than a nominal value. No fixed policy of, or administrative machinery for, settlement existed in the colonies to guide the settlers or to regulate allocation of land.

Land titles could be obtained rather easily. Anyone who was willing to settle in the wilderness and improve the land could obtain a warrant for so many acres, select the land, have it recorded, usually without having the boundaries verified in the field, and pay quit-rent. In some instances, even this formality was ignored. Many settlers claimed the land on which they had located, by virtue of occupancy and the improvements they had made. In other instances, individuals and land companies obtained extensive tracts for speculative purposes. They sold the land, not infrequently the same land, to different settlers. Insecurity of title, administrative difficulties, and legal problems resulted. Boundary litigations were frequent. When the public lands question was debated in the House of Representatives of the First Congress in Philadelphia, December 27, 1790, Elias Boudinot from New Jersey said (*133*), "more money had been spent at law, in disputes arising from that mode of settlement, in New Jersey than would have been necessary to purchase all the land of the State."

# Rectangular Land Division System of the Public Domain

## The Ordinance of 1785

The shortcomings of indiscriminate settlement were therefore known to the founding fathers, who were confronted with a formidable land question. A proposal that the original States cede their western land to Congress was made as early as 1778, 4 years before the provisional treaty of peace was signed. When in the intervening years, the States ceded the territory north of the Ohio and west to the Mississippi to Congress, a system of alienating public land that would avoid the trouble inherent in indiscriminate settlement became a necessity. A Congressional Committee of five, with Thomas Jefferson as chairman, was charged with the task of preparing a survey ordinance that would divide the public lands preparatory to settlement and development. A draft of the ordinance (*34, p. 178*) was reported from the Committee on May 7, 1784. "This ordinance required the public land to be divided into 'hundreds' of ten geographical miles square, and those again to be subdivided into lots of one mile square each, to be numbered from 1 to 100, commencing in the northwestern

corner and counting from west to east and from east to west continuously; . . ." The ordinance was tabled for a year. Then, after debate and amendment, it was passed by Congress on May 20, 1785. In the amendment, the original 10-mile-square "hundreds" of the rectangular-land-division system were reduced to 6-mile-square townships.

Surveying began in the same year in Ohio, where the Ohio River crosses the Pennsylvania State boundary. From this point, a line was run westward which served as the northern limit of the "First Seven Ranges" that were to be laid out. As a result of difficulties in the field, the original provision of true alinement of the division lines in an east–west and north–south direction was disregarded, and compass bearings were used instead. Only the exteriors of the townships were laid out in the field at first. The subdivisions were drawn in on the plats; in the field, they were added later. Ohio provided the proving ground of the rectangular system of land division. Tract by tract, as the land was ceded by the Indians through purchase, it was divided into townships 6 miles square, and subdivided into sections, although this was not always strictly in conformity with the system. In Symmes Purchase between the Miamis, the land was divided into sections and townships, but the townships were numbered from west to east instead of north to south. Only in the survey of the last tract in northwestern Ohio was the system applied in its final form.

## The Ordinance Modified

The western boundary of Ohio had been surveyed in 1817; it was used as the controlling or principal meridian for northwestern Ohio. From the principal meridian, a parallel or base line was run to the east, thus dividing northwestern Ohio into two tracts in which the ranges and townships were numbered and identified as located NE or SE with reference to the principal meridian and base line (*110, p. 233*). In a rectangular coordinate system, the initial point, or the point of origin as it is now called, is the starting point of the surveys from which the principal meridian and the base line are run true to astronomical bearing north–south and east–west. These lines control the system.

Indiana was the first State in which all the divisions of public land, except the wedge-shaped portion of Congress lands along the Ohio boundary, were controlled by one principal meridian and one base-line parallel. The land surveys of the remaining parts of the Northwest Territory, of Mississippi, Alabama, and Florida in the South, the land that was ceded to the United States in 1803 in the Louisiana Purchase, and the later accessions

# RECTANGULAR COORDINATED LAND DIVISION SYSTEM

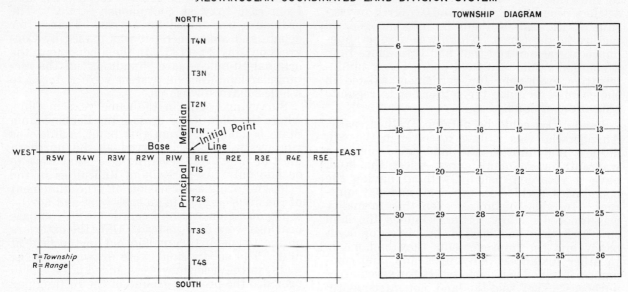

**TOWNSHIP DIAGRAM**

U.S. DEPARTMENT OF AGRICULTURE

NEG. 58(5)-2487 AGRICULTURAL RESEARCH SERVICE

FIGURE 3.—The 6-mile-square township as shown here was the standard unit of land division named in the Land Ordinance of 1785 for the Northwest Territory. It remains the standard unit for accessions to the public domain. But the intersection of lines may depart from the right angle, and acreages of sections vary. Identification of townships and ranges and numbering of mile-square subdivisions were not always consistent.

of territories across the Rockies to the Pacific Coast, are controlled by these systems of coordinates. But as these land divisions were marked on the ground before the land was settled, these survey districts, to which the individual systems of coordination apply and for which they provide the legal identification of the land divisions, usually are not identified with States. Some of them embrace several States. The smallest applied to about 12 survey townships. A survey township comprises 36 square miles, each of which is numbered as indicated in figure 3.

In the "Seven Ranges" on the Ohio, where the land-division surveys started, and in the district "Between the Miamis," the numeration of townships and ranges, as well as that of sections, does not conform to the system as it developed later. The land-division system, with its rectangular coordinated township identification and numbering of sections as indicated in figure 3, reached its final stage in Indiana. From then on, no further modifications were introduced. All federal land surveys west and south of Ohio were executed in harmony with the principle of the system, although no uniform standard of accuracy was obtained.

The rectangular system of land division as used by the General Land Office is confined to the public domain belonging to the Federal Government. Because of this, the States that originated from the public domain are often referred to as the public-domain States.

## Comparison with Roman System

The rectangular coordinated land-division system used in the United States is essentially the same as the one used by the Romans in their colonies more than 2,000 years ago. Size of unit squares, confinement of rectangular coordination to the area of a colony, and terminology are the chief differences. To the Romans, the centuria of 200 jugera (125 acres) was the coordination unit. In the United States, the coordination unit is the township of 36 square miles (23,000 acres). What is now called the initial point or point of origin of the system was called the *Umbilicus* by the Romans. The axis of ordinates, now known as the principal meridian, was called by the Romans *Cardo Maximus,* and the axis of abscissas, which we call the base line, was known to the Romans as the *Decumanus Maximus* (*78*).

One advantage of the rectangular land-division system is that the exact location of a subdivision tract can be described with a few symbols. For instance, the only 160-acre tract of land in the United States that can be identified as the SW Quarter, Sec. 35, T. 11 N, R. 5 E, of the second principal meridian is the quarter-section that forms the southwest corner of Shelby County, Ind.

The extensive and varied uses of the rectangular land-division system in the United States are largely responsible for the interest manifested in the history of the system. A good many papers have been written on the

16

subject, some with the intention of giving credit to the inventor of the system. So far, apparently, none has appeared in which the whole range of development of the system from its origin to its present application has received the attention it deserves. As an institution, it had an important part in the evolution of scientific principles and their application in civilization. In this instance, the evolution of rectangular coordination, as we know it, is tied directly to the rectangular land-division system and consequently is not the invention of one individual.

An adequate treatment of the history of the rectangular land-division system—its origin, evolution, and transmission—would be beyond the scope of this publication. Briefly, however, a rectangular land-division system was used in China more than 3,000 years ago, and some centuries later one was used by the Romans. Evidently, it is the latter that we have inherited. For purposes of colonization, the Romans divided the land into squares by means of an institutionalized rectangular coordinated system. Each square was called a centuria, and land so divided was referred to by the agrimensori as agro centuriatio—land divided into hundreds. The squares of the land divisions of some of the colonies founded by the Romans in the Po Valley in the second century B. C., notably those near Padua, Cesena, and Lugo, are to a considerable extent still in use today (78).

The origin of our rectangular land-division system provided for some time a fertile field of conjectural writing. No statement of its ancestry accompanied its introduction. The connection between the Roman system and ours may be perceived, however, if we remember that in 1784, Thomas Jefferson called these divisions in his draft of the survey ordinance "hundreds," the Latin centuriae. The deduction based on the etymological relationship of the two terms receives additional support from the fact that by that time Latin texts describing the system were fairly accessible to students. By the middle of the 18th century, 20 printed editions of extant parts or whole texts, written by the Roman land surveyors, were issued in different cities of Europe (11). This was at a time when new lands in America were being opened up and settled, thus providing opportunities for its application. Systems of this kind were actually propounded by William Penn for Pennsylvania, John Locke for Carolina, and Robert Montgomery for Georgia, and all these proposals were made in Europe.

For the national system, evidence pointing in the same direction was recently uncovered through intensive study of historical records. According to these findings, Dr. Hugh Williamson, who had studied at Utrecht and was the spokesman of the congressional delegation from North Carolina, had suggested the application of rectangular land division to Jefferson. Although this important discovery may not constitute absolute proof of the Roman connection with our system, it clears up an old and moot question as to Jefferson's source of information (97).

## Rectangular Land Divisions of Non-Federal or Reserved Public Lands

Many of the older States—the 13 original States, Maine, Kentucky, Tennessee, and Texas —had considerable acreages of unsettled and unappropriated land when they joined the Union. To avoid the confusion created by indiscriminate settlement, the national example was followed and the remaining land was divided into rectangular tracts or lots. Ohio, which is usually considered a public domain State, also has some diverse rectangular divisions. Except possibly for one or two small areas, however, the rectangular land divisions laid out by the State governments themselves or by land companies or Federal agencies did not conform entirely to the system used by the General Land Office.

### The Northern States

Although these lands were divided into rectangular tracts, the organization of the system differed between districts. In some instances, the divisions are similar to those of the national system. The lands of the Ohio Company were divided into 6-mile-square townships, but irregular lots are not infrequently found in the subdivisions. The lands included in the Connecticut Western Reserve and the United States Military Districts in Ohio were laid out into 5-mile-square townships, quartered, and then subdivided into mainly rectangular tracts but without the regularity of the General Land Office system (110).

The unoccupied land in northwestern Pennsylvania was used largely to compensate the soldiers of the Pennsylvania line in the Revolution. For this purpose, the land was divided into rectangular parcels of specified sizes, and the parcels were numbered to be assigned by lottery (28).

In New York, large acreages of the western lands were still unoccupied and in dispute between Massachusetts and New York at the end of the Revolution. Commissioners from these States, who met at Hartford, Conn., on December 16, 1786, succeeded in reconciling the claims. It was agreed that New York would retain jurisdiction over the territory while the rights to preemption of the land remained with Massachusetts. Payments on large tracts of land sold by Massachusetts were later defaulted, so that much of the land reverted to Massachusetts. Eventually, Robert Morris, a signer of the Declaration of Independence, obtained title to most of the land through purchase deeds from Massachusetts. He then employed surveyors to lay out the land into half-mile-square lots and arrange them in ranges and towns. Morris sold the land to persons in New York who acted as trustees of Amsterdam merchants, usually referred to as the Holland Land Company, who in turn sold the land to individual settlers (8, 43). Only a part of the State-owned land was subdivided by the Surveyor General of the State.

In Maine, rectangular land divisions were used while Maine was still a district of Massachusetts. A few ranges were laid out in the south-central part of Maine, and the 50 townships in the eastern part were surveyed and disposed of by Massachusetts by lottery from 1786 to 1788 (98, p. 44).

During the colonial period, settlement in Maine was largely confined to the southern part, although some French pioneers had settled in the bend of the St. John River in the north. Much of the land was unoccupied when, in 1820, Maine was admitted to the Union. Although in the process, Maine as a sovereign State obtained jurisdictional authority in its domain, it did not get complete preemption rights over all public lands in the State. For half of the unappropriated public land, or somewhat more than 8 million acres, title remained vested in the Bay State. Massachusetts offered to sell the land to Maine for $188,922, or about 4 cents an acre, but Maine thought the price too high and declined the offer.

From then on, both States had land for sale in Maine, but in order to segregate the land assigned to Massachusetts from the land belonging to Maine, it had to be surveyed. Accordingly, the land was laid out in ranges and townships chiefly 6 miles square, but no uniform system was used. For many of the townships, only the exteriors were surveyed. Lands were then classified as timber, settling, or waste lands. Each State had a land agent who supervised the sale of the lands. After 1832, the two land agents acted jointly in sales of land until about 1854, when Maine acquired from Massachusetts the remaining share of more than a million acres. Much of the land was alienated in large tracts by lumber operators; some was retained by the State; but most of it has remained forest land. It constitutes one of the principal forest regions in eastern United States (162, pp. 48-65; 156, pp. 5-13).

## The Southern States

In Tennessee and Kentucky, most of the land was settled indiscriminately, but even after both territories had become States (Kentucky in 1792, Tennessee in 1796), tracts of land were occupied by Indians. All land located between the Tennessee and Mississippi Rivers and north of the present Alabama-Tennessee line was still Indian land. This tract was bought from the Chickasaw Indians by the Federal Government in 1818. Andrew Jackson and Governor Shelby of Kentucky negotiated the purchase as Government agents, and even now this part of Tennessee and Kentucky is sometimes referred to as the Jackson Purchase. The tract was divided into ranges and townships governed by principal meridians and base lines. One of these coordination systems is confined to Kentucky's part of the purchase, in which most of the townships are also subdivided into sections as in the national system. But a good many parcels scattered throughout the area do not form part of the system, especially in the northern part of the tract.

In Tennessee, the purchase area was divided into two belts. Each has a principal meridian and the southern boundary functioned as the base line to govern the layout of ranges and 6-mile-square sections, as the townships are here called. Although parcels of land are mainly rectangular and are oriented with the exterior of the sections, they are irregular and are not derived from a uniform subdivision of the sections. In southeastern Tennessee, the area still held by the Cherokees when Tennessee acquired statehood was later laid out into ranges and 6-mile-square townships, divided into mile-square lots. Two systems were used. In one, the ranges are oriented north to south; in the other they are alined with the trend of the mountains in a northeast to southwest direction (24, 157, 137).

Georgia's colonial charter included the back country to the Mississippi River. The land that extended beyond the present western boundary was ceded to the United States in 1802, and included in the national public domain. Only about 23 percent of the present State of Georgia was settled at the turn of the 18th century. The rest was still occupied by Indians. From 1802 to 1835, in a number of treaties, the Indians ceded the rights of occupancy, and the lands were opened for settlement. In doing this, the old headright system was displaced by the lottery system. As a result of this change, the land had to be surveyed and divided into lots before a title could be issued. This was done on the rectangular principle. Land districts were established by the original counties and were subdivided into lots; districts and lots were numbered. Although these lots were squares, they were not uniform in size; they varied with the supposed value of the land. In the Cherokee Gold Districts, along the foothills of the mountains, the lots comprised only 40 acres. In other districts, they were squares of 160, 202.5, 250, or, the largest, 490 acres.

Although these are the cited acreages, the squares frequently departed from them by a few acres more or less. The surveying was not precise and was done in a comparatively short time, between 1804 and 1832 (*83, 56*).

## Texas

Texas differs in historical background, methods of settlement, and systems of land division, from the States on the Atlantic coast. Changes in its government were rather frequent during the first half of the last century. Texas was part of the Spanish province until 1821 when Mexico gained its independence. After that, Texas formed part of the State of Coahuila and Texas, as a State of the Mexican Federal Republic. At the successful conclusion of the revolution in 1836, Texas became an independent republic, which was admitted into the Union in 1845.

Only a few settlers entered Texas under the Spanish regime. Greater efforts to attract settlers were made during the Mexican and independent periods. Empresarios contracted with the government to colonize assigned areas in the eastern and southern parts of the State. The colonists they brought in were mainly Americans and Germans. When Texas entered the Union, the treaty agreement specified that Texas remain responsible for the public debt incurred by the late republic but retain the public lands that belonged to the former government. However, a large share of its western land claim was sold to the Federal Government in 1850 and thus became part of the national public domain.

Millions of acres of public lands remained at the disposal of the Texas legislature; they were used freely for the development of the State. Land was donated to railway companies, internal-improvement companies, and soldiers and their families. Large acreages were granted to educational institutions. The erection of the capitol building was paid for in public lands, and land scrip was sold by the Republic and the State. But the land had to be surveyed before title could be conveyed to these organizations and the people. Usually, this was done in blocks, which were subdivided into mile-square sections. The sections were numbered for identification (*82*).

Land ownership maps show that not all the blocks and their subdivisions have a north-south to east-west orientation of boundary lines. Nor is there any sharp line of separation between the land divided into squares and the irregular divisions. Tracts with irregular divisions are scattered among the blocks of regular divisions, while inversely, tracts of regular rectangular divisions are found in the area of the older settlement. This arrangement of land divisions over much of the older settlement area in Texas showed more order than is found in some areas of indiscriminate settlement in the East (*119*).

## Other Areas

In addition to the areas divided by the States into rectangular divisions, a few tracts of diverse origin were subdivided in this way. Two of these tracts are in Florida—one in Wakulla County and the other in Gadsden County. They are part of the extensive Forbes' Purchase. In the rest of this purchase, the land-office system was expanded. Two more such tracts are found in Indiana—the Vincennes and Clark's Grants made to soldiers of the Revolution. Another is the Beaufort district on the coast of South Carolina, which was divided into land parcels by means of the rectangular coordinate method during the War Between the States for the United States Direct Tax Commission for the District of South Carolina (*163, pp. 41-42*).[2]

The largest numbers of these rectangular division lines are oriented north-south and east-west. However, there are exceptions, some of which have been noted. To permit a more complete picture, it will be well to review the situation. In Maine, the lottery land in the southeastern part of the State, and the towns in the south-central part of the State, are all oriented in a northwest-southeast and northeast-southwest direction. This is true also of the two military grants in Indiana. One of the land-division systems in southeastern Tennessee received its orientation from the trend of the mountains. In Georgia, the land divisions between the Ocmulgee and Oconee Rivers derived their orientation from the trend of the rivers. The tract in Wakulla County, Fla., has its divisions oriented by the general direction of the coast, and the one in Gadsden County by the direction of the River Hurricane. Land blocks with boundary lines that deviate from the north-south and east-west orientation are found in a number of places in Texas, mainly scattered among the other blocks of rectangular division. In the national system, theoretically at least, all dividing lines are supposed to be in true north-south and east-west direction, except in eastern Ohio, where magnetic orientation was substituted for astronomical determination.

The land ownership patterns found in the United States are closely related to the period, and to the prevailing administrative provisions in the area when settlement took place.

Settlement by townships is confined to New England. Indiscriminate settlement, in which selected tracts were deeded to settlers by the grantees of the crown, the colonial government,

---

[2] A set of the plans of Beaufort District is on file in the National Archives, Washington, D. C.

# LAND DIVISION TYPES

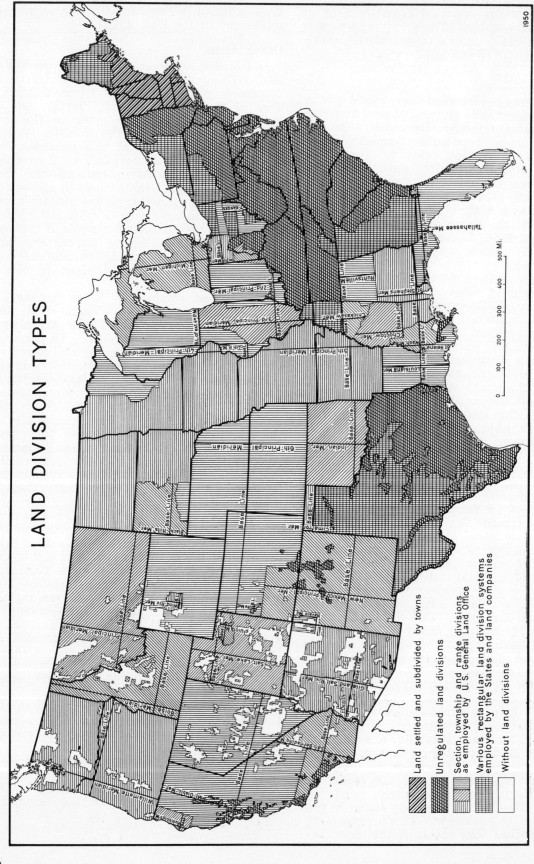

1950

Land settled and subdivided by towns

Unregulated land divisions

Section, township and range divisions as employed by U. S. General Land Office

Various rectangular land division systems employed by the States and land companies

Without land divisions

U. S. DEPARTMENT OF AGRICULTURE                    NEG. 58(5)-2488 AGRICULTURAL RESEARCH SERVICE

FIGURE 4.—The areal spread of the different land-division types is illustrated on the map. To distinguish control areas of particular meridians and base lines within the national rectangular division system, different directions of the same space ruling are applied.

land companies, or the newly formed States, is found in eastern United States. The French and Spanish settlements in Louisiana, Texas, the Southwestern States and some other scattered places, must be included in this category.

Divisions into rectangular sections, townships and ranges were applied in the Federal public domain; such land comprises approximately 69 percent of the total area of continental United States. The survey has not yet been completed. There still are some national parks and forests, or lands of low grazing capacity, in which township and section lines are gradually being added to close the open gaps and provide land divisions for management purposes. In addition, more than 9 percent of the total land area, mainly in the older States, has been divided by applying some other rectangular system of land division.

The areal distinctions in the application of land divisions are indicated in figure 4.

## Acquisition and Disposal of Public-Domain Lands

With the recognition of the United States as an autonomous country in 1782, the outlook of the people changed. Movement across the mountains and settlement on the "western waters" were encouraged. In fact, soldiers' claims to land compensations could be satisfied only beyond the western fringe of settlement. Most of the States on the Atlantic slope still had vacant land in the mountains, some of which was used as bounty land. The Trans-Appalachian States, which were created from the territories of Virginia and North Carolina, had prior commitments to accommodate the bounty claims of soldiers. Military land reserves also were set aside for that purpose. Soldier bounty warrants were recognized in locating on Federal public-domain lands.

Soldiers, however, were only a small fraction of the many people who started to move to new land across the mountains. Many settlers from the East joined the movement to the West. With the opening of the national public domain for settlement, the westward movement of pioneers gained momentum. The increasing number of immigrants from Europe who came to America to establish new homes added to it.

### The Northwest Territory

The northern section of the national public domain was at that time known as the Northwest Territory. It consisted of the treaty lands, which were bounded on the west by the Mississippi, on the south by the Ohio, and on the north by the Great Lakes. The Eastern States had conflicting claims to these lands as a result of inconsistencies in the colonial charters. These lands were ceded to the Federal Government. Ohio, Indiana, Illinois, Michigan, Wisconsin, and a part of Minnesota were organized from this territory. The southern section of the Federal public domain comprised Georgia's claim to the land as far west as the Mississippi, which also was ceded with a stipulated compensation to the Federal Government. It provided the major part of the land of what is now Alabama and Mississippi. These territories and the land belonging to the individual States —in all some 844,000 square miles—constituted the original 1783 treaty area of the United States, which had the Mississippi as its western boundary.

### Later Accessions

The western boundary, demarked by the Mississippi River, did not last long; however, in 1803, France sold the rest of the Mississippi Basin to the United States (this was the Louisiana Purchase), which slightly more than doubled the original land area of the Union. Within the half-century that followed, a number of other accessions occurred. These accessions included Florida, the Oregon Country, the Pacific Southwest, and Texas. They ended with the Gadsden Purchase from Mexico in 1853. They are summarized and their location and areal extent is illustrated in figure 5.

There were a number of settlements on land grants in Florida, Louisiana, New Mexico, and the Pacific Southwest, but the acreage acquired by these settlers was comparatively small. Parts of Texas had been settled and developed to some extent before it joined the Union, but in so doing, the State did not relinquish its claim to the vacant land. Only the land originally claimed but located outside the present border of Texas was acquired through purchase by the Federal Government and included in the public domain.

### Land Disposal

Settlement, development, and disposal of land in such a vast estate did not follow a preconceived plan or policy that could be applied consistently throughout the area. Actually, at the time of acquisition the western country was not sufficiently well-known to permit the evolving of a definite policy adapted to the many different natural conditions to be found there.

The general knowledge of the country was derived from the reports of parties from this and other countries who had started to explore the West from the Pacific or had made their way by land across the continent (35). Nor was there a modern antecedent to serve as an example and to provide the guiding experience for formulation of a settlement and development policy that would fit such a vast acreage of diverse virgin land. Under these circumstances, the initial policy—to dispose of the land

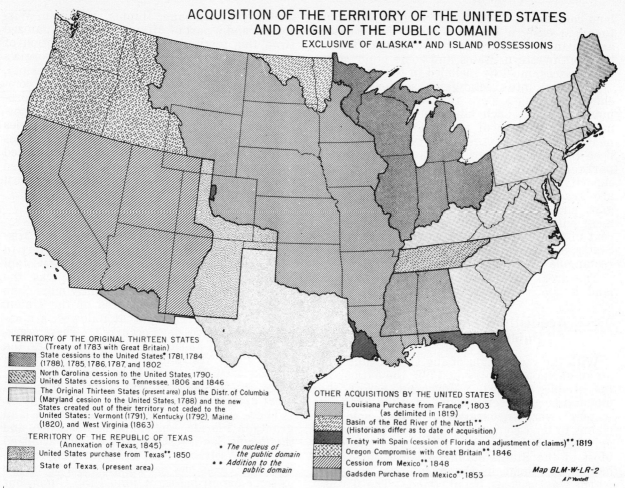

# ACQUISITION OF THE TERRITORY OF THE UNITED STATES AND ORIGIN OF THE PUBLIC DOMAIN

## EXCLUSIVE OF ALASKA** AND ISLAND POSSESSIONS

**TERRITORY OF THE ORIGINAL THIRTEEN STATES**
(Treaty of 1783 with Great Britain)

State cessions to the United States; 1781,1784 (1788), 1785,1786,1787, and 1802

North Carolina cession to the United States,1790; United States cessions to Tennessee, 1806 and 1846

The Original Thirteen States (present area) plus the Distr. of Columbia (Maryland cession to the United States, 1788) and the new States created out of their territory not ceded to the United States: Vermont (1791), Kentucky (1792), Maine (1820), and West Virginia (1863)

**TERRITORY OF THE REPUBLIC OF TEXAS**
(Annexation of Texas, 1845)

United States purchase from Texas**, 1850

State of Texas, (present area)

* The nucleus of the public domain
** Addition to the public domain

**OTHER ACQUISITIONS BY THE UNITED STATES**

Louisiana Purchase from France**, 1803 (as delimited in 1819)

Basin of the Red River of the North ** (Historians differ as to date of acquisition)

Treaty with Spain (cession of Florida and adjustment of claims)**, 1819

Oregon Compromise with Great Britain**, 1846

Cession from Mexico**, 1848

Gadsden Purchase from Mexico**, 1853

Map BLM-W-LR-2
A.P.Yonteff

FIGURE 5.—The land acquired by, and at the disposal of, the Federal Government during the first 70 years of its existence inclusive of the lands ceded and purchased from the States, is usually referred to as the public domain. It comprised 2¼ million square miles of land. Much of it was virgin land for which the tribal use rights of the Indians had not been extinguished.

for settlement and development through sale—received its orientation more from the depleted condition of the United States Treasury in the early days of the Nation than from any other consideration.

Although the expected revenue from the sale of the land did not materialize, the system remained in operation for a long time, but other systems and policies for disposal of the land were soon added to permit settlement and development of the country. The cash sale policy for revenue purposes was modified in 1800 by the credit system. It was modified still further in 1841, by the preemption law that permitted settlers to obtain patents to the land by complying with the prescribed length of residence on it, the cultivation requirements, and payment of the statutory minimum price for the land. Paying for the land they had to improve, however, was not popular with the settlers, and the free homestead law was enacted in 1862. Under

this act, a settler could locate and claim 160 acres of public land and receive a patent to it by complying with the requirements, which included the building of a house, living on the land for 5 years, and cultivating a certain acreage. In 1910, when homesteading reached the semiarid country, the original homestead act was amended by the Enlarged Homestead Act, which permitted settlers to file a claim and receive a patent to 360 acres of dry-farming land. In 1916, the acreage was again increased in the Stockraising Homestead Act, which allowed 640 acres of desert grazing land to be patented to a settler.

Somewhat different in aims and requirements was the Desert Land Act of 1877. Under this act, desert land capable of irrigation could be bought at the rate of $1.25 per acre by an entryman who could demonstrate that he was able to irrigate and cultivate the land. He was not required to live on it.

These are the principal laws that affected the settlers directly. The land alienated under these laws to homesteaders, through sale or grant, totaled approximately 285 million acres. This does not include military bounty land and private land claims, which add to 95 million acres. Title to an aggregate of 333 million acres was obtained largely by individuals under various laws and mainly through sales, which included preemption sales, scrip location, sales of townsites and lots, timber and stone land, timber-culture land, desert land for irrigation, and so on (*127, p. 63*).

## Land Grants

The public land-disposal policies of the Federal Government, however, were not confined to conveyance of land titles to individuals. To expedite and support the development of the country, considerable acreages were granted to the States, Territories, and railroad companies. Land was granted as a subsidy to public institutions, and as an assistance to public works. For the common schools in the Territories and States created from the public domain, 77 million acres were granted to the States. All States also received public-domain land totaling nearly 17 million acres, as a subvention to colleges and other schools; the school lands of the Eastern States were necessarily located in the Western States and Territories, as no public land was available in the East. Tracts of public-domain land comprising nearly 65 million acres also were granted to the States for the building of railroads, wagon roads, canals, river improvements, and other purposes. Finally, under the Swamp Land Act of 1849–50, the transferring of ownership of swamplands in the central and southern parts of the public domain to the States began. This act was later expanded to include swampland in the northern and western public-domain States. The nearly 65 million acres of land granted to the States under these acts had to be reclaimed for cultural use. When combined, the land grants to the States totaled approximately 224 million acres.

Grants of land were also made directly to the railroad companies. The lack of transportation facilities in these early days was a handicap to the development of the country. This was especially true for the West. Months were required for a train of covered wagons to cross the country. The situation was somewhat better in the East. Navigable rivers entered many parts of the country. To these were added a number of canals. However, large areas were without access to water transportation. Settlers had to depend on wagon transport over rough roads to reach markets. Transportation facilities were a prime necessity for the opening of the country. As an aid to construction of railroads, nearly 92 million acres of public-domain land were granted to the companies after 1850. This does not include the land granted that reverted to the Government. The distribution of this land is illustrated in figure 6.

Along the Illinois Central, the zone granted on each side of the road was 6 miles wide, whereas along the Central and Union Pacific Railroads, it was 20 miles wide. Along the Atlantic and Pacific, as well as the Northern Pacific, the zone extended for 40 miles on each side of the road. For many of the railroads, the zones were expanded considerably to provide additional acreage for selection of land in lieu of occupied tracts within the zone of the grant (*34, p. 949*). Much of the railroad land has been sold, but the transcontinental railroads still own a few million acres, which consist mainly of grazing land.

## The Remaining Public Domain

Taken together, title to more than a billion acres of the original Federal public domain has either passed into private ownership or has been granted to the States. This does not include the Indian reservations. When the Indians ceded their tribal rights to the land to the Federal Government, they were not left homeless. More than 57 million acres, most of which were part of the national public domain, were set aside as Indian reservations. A few small Indian reservations were established in the Eastern States also.

What remains of the national public domain is land that is either arid, rough, or mountainous. Little of it is suitable for homesteading and cultivation. The arid segment consists of large compact areas which for many years were used as free open range. Competitive grazing affected both the ranchers and the land itself. Through overstocking, the range became severely depleted. The most valuable forage plants of the range, mainly grasses, are the first to become scarce or to disappear from the plant cover altogether. This, in turn, greatly reduces the grazing capacity of the land (*136*). As a conservation measure and to bring order into use of the public domain as grazing land, the Taylor Act was passed in 1934 and amended in 1936. Under its provisions, the remaining unappropriated and unreserved public-domain land was withdrawn from homesteading and sale for purposes of classification, and the grazing land was organized into grazing districts. These districts comprise roughly 266 million acres, which include 95 million acres of non-Federal lands administered by agreement or through lease. Permits are required for grazing in these districts.

Conservation to preserve the use value of public lands that could not be homesteaded in

# FEDERAL LAND GRANTS FOR RAILROADS

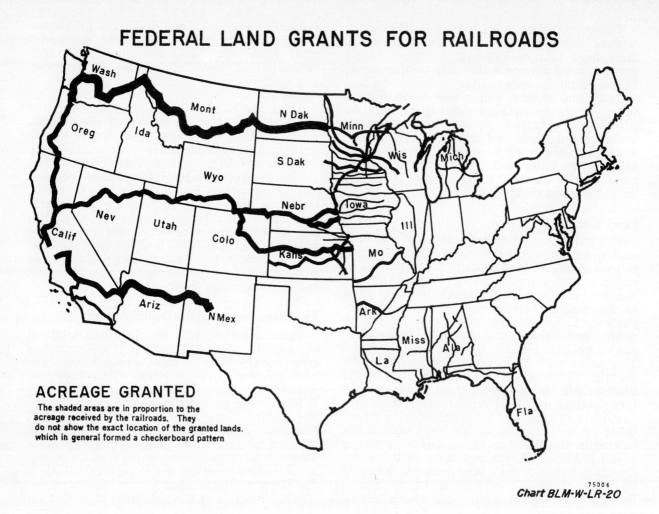

ACREAGE GRANTED

The shaded areas are in proportion to the
acreage received by the railroads. They
do not show the exact location of the granted lands.
which in general formed a checkerboard pattern

75006
Chart BLM-W-LR-20

FIGURE 6.—The public-domain land granted to the railroads included alternate sections in a zone from 6 to 40
miles wide on both sides of the road. As the land granted to the roads within these zones usually consisted
of the odd-numbered sections of townships, a checkerboard pattern of ownership was produced. Later, the
grants were reduced because the railroads did not meet all statutory requirements.

the interest of public welfare was not new.
Forest land in public ownership had been as
much abused as the open range. To bring these
forests under proper management, legislation
passed in 1891 authorized the setting aside of
public-domain forests as reserves. The authority was later expanded to acquire eastern forest
lands through purchase. Most of these Federal
forest lands are now included in the national
forests and serve multiple purposes. Production of timber on a sustained-yield basis is
frequently not the most important purpose. In
the West, the bulk of the forests are on
mountainous land, which receives the higher
precipitation and furnishes water for the arid
lowland. Protection of watersheds to prevent
erosion is therefore important. Summer grazing is regulated through permits to preserve
the grazing capacity and with it to protect the
functional value as watersheds. Recreation and

wildlife shelter are secondary uses. In round
figures, the Forest Service manages 161 million
acres of national forests, of which 140 million
were reserved from the public domain and the
rest is mainly purchased land. In addition,
nearly 48 million acres of national forests are
administered by other agencies.

## National Parks, Monuments, and Wildlife Sanctuaries

Conservation was the leading motive in the
establishment of national parks, monuments,
and wildlife sanctuaries. National parks were
set aside to preserve the scenic values of outstanding natural features for the enjoyment
of citizens and future generations. National
monuments are dedicated to the preservation of
areas having historic or scientific interest. The
preservation of the native fauna and flora of
these park and monument areas is essential

24

in maintaining the use values for which they were established. Some of the natural wonders of the world are represented in these reservations. The 4,000- to 5,000-foot chasm known as the Grand Canyon of the Colorado, Yellowstone Park with its geysers, canyons and waterfalls, the peaks, lakes and glaciers of the Rockies, the natural bridges of Utah, the 2,000- to 3,000-year-old Sequoia trees of the Sierra Nevada, the prehistoric ruins of Pueblo cities and cliff dwellings of the mesas (pl. 109), and many others are included. As they were conceived as recreational areas, the parks had to be developed in that direction and made accessible to the public. Roads to and within the parks had to be built and accommodations for visitors provided. More than 2 million people visit the nearly 14 million acres of park and monument reservations yearly.

Wildlife reservations are intended to protect and preserve the wildlife species of the country. Land utilized for these purposes usually has little value for other uses. In the eastern United States, it is chiefly swampland (pl. 156) and in the West, it is of low grazing value. Migratory bird refuges are frequently combined with reservoirs (pl. 88) and other

bodies of water, although in some instances, special water-control structures have been installed (pl. 85). In all, as of 1955, approximately 4 million acres were contained in these reservations.[3]

Very little of the Federal public domain is now unreserved and open for homesteading or for sale. Other types of Federal reserves have been set up for national defense, soil conservation, reclamation, mineral reservation, and other purposes. These reserves are administered by the different agencies of the Federal Government in accordance with the purpose for which they were established. More administrative difficulties are encountered in some regions than in others. These difficulties stem mainly from the complicated pattern of land ownership and administrative units that has evolved in the absence of a "well-planned land policy in keeping with the physical nature of the different regions" (29, p. 15). Any revenue derived from the use of public lands is shared

[3] The acreage figures that pertain to the national public domain and the Federal land reserves are based mainly on the latest publications of the Bureau of Land Management, Department of the Interior (127, 107, 108).

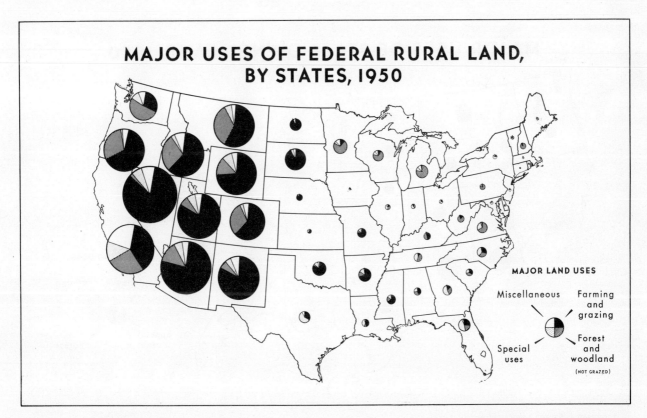

MAJOR USES OF FEDERAL RURAL LAND, BY STATES, 1950

MAJOR LAND USES

Miscellaneous — Farming and grazing

Special uses — Forest and woodland (NOT GRAZED)

U. S. DEPARTMENT OF AGRICULTURE

NEG. 58(5)-2496 AGRICULTURAL RESEARCH SERVICE

FIGURE 7.—The pie charts for each State represent the proportion of land in Federal ownership. When the country as a whole is considered, 23.5 percent of the land is administered by the Federal Government. The combination of the two major uses of this land—farming and grazing—may be misleading, as the cropland ratio is only about 1 percent, too small to be represented.

proportionately by the States and counties in which it is collected. The relative distribution of Federal-owned rural land by States, and its major uses are illustrated in figure 7.

Most of the federally administered land lies in the 11 Western States. The proportion is highest in Nevada, where 84 percent of the land has remained in Federal ownership. In the older Eastern States, where title to most of the land was at first transferred to private owners, the Federal Government bought the land. It is now mainly in national forests and parks.

## State-Owned Lands

Title to some public land is also vested in the States, and the land is administered by the States. The origin of State-owned land can be traced to several sources. When the colonies became States, they acquired title to the un-appropriated land within their boundaries, and some of this land has remained in their possession. In the public-domain States, large land grants were made to the States by the Federal Government to promote development of trans-portation and communication facilities and in support of schools and other institutions. The

swamplands in the public domain were deeded to the States for reclamation. Much of this land, particularly in the Western States, has remained in State ownership. In addition, a considerable acreage of privately owned land, mainly cutover land in the Lake States, has reverted to State ownership through tax fore-closure, and some of the land has been acquired through purchase for particular purposes. In 1950, the States owned a little more than 80 million acres (29, p. 50).

To some extent, the administration of State-owned lands is comparable to the national pattern, in which purpose of ownership and use capability of the land are the deciding factors. Accordingly, we find State forests, State parks, recreational areas, fish and game reserves, grazing areas, militia camps, and so on. Administrative problems occur in connection with State-owned lands as they do with Federal lands. They are mainly the result of widely scattered tracts. In the Western States, where State-owned land usually is identified with certain numbered sections in a survey township, the problem stems from the method of transferring public land to the States, and it is

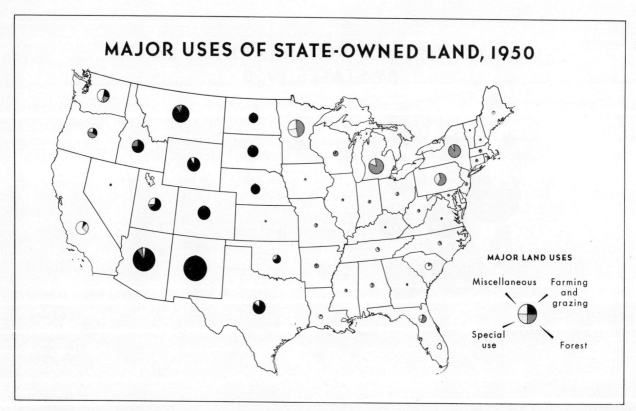

U. S. DEPARTMENT OF AGRICULTURE

NEG. 58(5)-2503 AGRICULTURAL RESEARCH SERVICE

FIGURE 8.—The acreage of State-owned land in this country is a fifth of the acreage federally owned. Pie charts show distribution by States. Public-domain States have the largest acreages. The importance of cropland is magnified because it is combined with grazing lands. Of the 80 million State-owned acres, 3 percent is used for crops, 55 percent for grazing, and 22 percent for forest-woodland. The rest is in other uses.

probably more troublesome here than in the East. As a rule, these sections are neither large enough nor located favorably enough in regard to water supply to provide an operational unit in themselves. They can be used only in conjunction with adjacent land. Distribution of acreage and major uses by States are represented in figure 8.

## Expansion of Settlement and Development in the United States

Geographic location played its part in the colonization and development of the United States from the beginning, and it is an important economic factor now. The large and sheltered harbors on both sides of the North Atlantic, and the somewhat shorter sailing distances between them than between South Atlantic ports were decisive in veering the stream of settlers from Europe in that direction. The rate of growth of the different colonies supports this conclusion.

### Early Settlements

The first settlement on the Atlantic coast, made in 1565 by the Spaniards at St. Augustine, Fla., was also the southernmost colony and the slowest to grow. The second, made by the London Company on the James River in Virginia in 1607, which was followed by other settlements on the shores and tributaries of Chesapeake Bay, expanded rather slowly. When the North Atlantic colonies were opened for settlement shortly thereafter, their growth was accelerated by the frequent sailings from Europe to these colonies. These ports functioned as a funnel through which the main stream of settlers from Europe entered America and from which they spread over the adjacent country. The population in these colonies increased rapidly, so that by the end of the 17th century the population and towns of the North Atlantic colonies were larger than those elsewhere on the Atlantic seaboard. Once this leading position was obtained, it was not relinquished by these colonies nor by the ensuing States. Nor have more recent developments changed the situation. The coastal belt between Boston and Baltimore has developed into the most densely populated area of its size in the country.

Comparable figures for equally spaced intervals of the colonial period are not readily available. No census was taken in the colonies. What we know now of the increase in the population of the colonies is the result of research and interpretation of material from many sources (52). The first census of population was taken in 1790, by the United States. It is only from then on that we can retrace the progress made from decade to decade in the settlement of the country.

### Westward Thrust

The attraction of the wide empty spaces in the Central Plains, the frequently not-so-favorable characteristics for arable use of the land on the eastern slopes of the Appalachians, and the ever-increasing population, provided a combination of factors that engendered the westward movement of the people. But not all sections of the older areas of settlement contributed to the movement to the same extent. Advancing the frontier of settlement westward was far from a uniform expansion movement, nor was it a well-organized and directed effort for the placement of people on the land. The pioneers usually chose the routes they followed and the land on which they settled. Exceptions were largely confined to the older States, where lotteries were sometimes used to decide land ownership.

The westward thrust of people was stronger in the North than in the South. In the northern sector, the movement received considerable impetus from the continuous stream of people arriving from Europe. Most of these immigrants arrived with the intention of joining the movement to the west in search of land on which they could establish new homes. Westward expansion of settlement can be taken, however, only as indicating a general direction. After the pioneers had crossed the mountain saddles, they usually followed the rivers and valleys and spread out in the basins and plains. Sometimes they left unsettled islands for late comers. The first settlers preferred river banks and adjacent uplands. The rivers provided transportation, and from the trees growing near them, even in the grassy plains, the settlers could build their homes and obtain the fuel they needed. The more fertile prairies of the plains were occupied by later arrivals.

In the deep South, the movement was inhibited for want of people. In 1790, Georgia was only partly settled along the eastern border. Here the frontier moved westward very slowly. The neighboring State to the west, Alabama, received its settlers from both north and south. For years, the largest unsettled island was the one along the Alabama–Georgia boundary. Thus some of the more desirable land in the Coastal Plain of Georgia was settled last. The land-division surveys in the districts west of the Flint River were finished in 1827, and the remaining land was disposed of by lottery in the same year. This procedure was followed also in the more hilly and mountainous districts of northern Georgia in 1832 (56).

Settlement gained momentum when the advance settlers reached the plains. By then, settlement and development of the newly acquired public domain had formed a realistic partnership in the minds of the people. Various activities preceded actual settlement. On the national public domain, and in most parts of the country where the rectangular land-division system was used, surveyors usually were there before the settlers. Hunters, Indian traders, herdsmen, members of military expeditions, and explorers, also acted as forerunners and advance guards of the settlers. Like the Indians, they relied for subsistence chiefly on the natural resources of the country. On the plains, the herds of buffalo provided meat for their use and skins and robes as articles of trade. Later, buffalo hunting became an organized commercial enterprise of both Indians and whites. Hunting for meat was degraded into slaughter, and the extensive herds that roamed the plains were soon reduced. As settlement advanced, the buffaloes retreated. Toward the end of the 19th century, when white men had taken possession of the plains, the buffalo, as a free roaming animal, had disappeared as a scenic landscape feature. All that is left of the species are a few individual animals in captivity on reservations. Without the existence of the buffalo, development of the Plains would have been slower (65).

Activities in furtherance of the country's development were also in evidence behind the frontier of settlement. The frontier, which was defined by the census as the population-density limit of 2 settlers to the square mile, was in its nature only a conceptional line. If we assume that the 2 persons belonged to the same homestead, and the preemption right was 160 acres, it would mean that only a fourth of the land was actually settled. With this as a premise, it is reasonably safe to conclude that for some time settlement behind the frontier was more active than settlement ahead of the frontier. Settlement, however, was only the initial step in development. Settlers who had located on the land could not remain isolated members of society. They were followed closely by churches and schools. Fast-growing cities and towns sprang up over the country. To bring and keep the people in contact with each other, and to make the resources and products of one part of the country available to others, improved transportation and communication facilities were essential. At first, these facilities were provided by the navigable rivers, wagon trails, and canals. Railroad construction started in the East, and in 1830, some lines were open to traffic. Forty years later, the first transcontinental railroad was in operation.

## Opening of the West

In the Southwest, some land grants and settlements had been made by Spain. But it was only after the West became United States Territory, in 1846 and 1848, that the cross-country movement of pioneers gained momentum and the economic development of the West began. The Mormons were among the first to found a colony in Utah in 1847. Shortly after that, the "Forty-niners" started their journeys across the mountains and basins to the Pacific Coast. The covered wagons in which they traveled, however, were slow and the way was hazardous. Travel to the West was greatly facilitated a few years later when, in 1869, the central transcontinental railroad was opened. It was soon followed by other trunklines. These railroads pierced the frontier and ran ahead of settlement. Travel facilities accelerated greatly the westward movement of people, although it was clear by then that the West could not be settled and developed as had the East or the Great Plains.

In pioneer reports from the West, the semiarid high plains and the country between the Rockies and the Sierra-Cascade Mountains were frequently cited as the Great American Desert. Precipitation on the high plains and in the basins was too low to permit arable use of the land, and the mountains and ranges were rugged. Water was scarce; in its early stages, settlement depended on a readily available supply of water for irrigation. Only in the Pacific Valleys, the Columbia Plateau, and on some benches and mesas at the foot of the Rockies is dryland farming possible. Most of the land in the West can be used only for open grazing. The grazing capacity of the range per areal unit was not high in its original state, and it has since been reduced considerably through overgrazing. Severe natural restrictions preclude homesteading of the land that now makes up most of the remaining public domain (136).

The westward movement of the frontier and occupation of the land during the first 100 years of existence of the United States was the prelude to its economic development. Except for some tardy areas, the frontier disappeared near the end of the 19th century, although this did not terminate the westward movement of people. Strong migratory currents from East to West, which again originated mainly in the Northern States, were reported in the early decades of the 20th century (117). Internal movements of people in response to areal changes in economic conditions are still in evidence. The progress of settlement made from 1790 to 1890 is illustrated in figure 9.

## Natural Environment Changed Through Settlement

The arrival of the settlers also marked the beginning of changes in the natural environment. Houses were built; woods were cleared; and sod was broken. How these activities were carried on depended on the individual who acquired the land and where the homestead was located. When the land was divided into rectangular sections or lots, these divisions usually

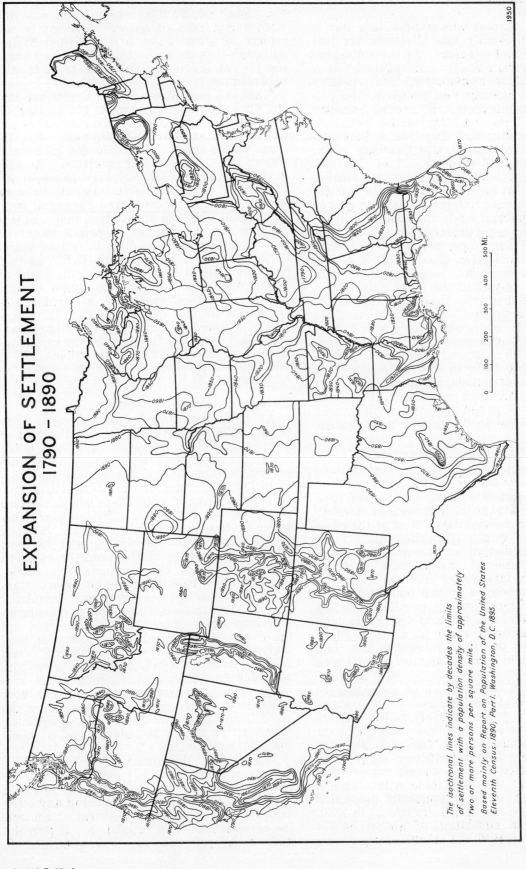

## EXPANSION OF SETTLEMENT
### 1790 – 1890

1950

*The isochronal lines indicate by decades the limits
of settlement with a population density of approximately
two or more persons per square mile.*

*Based mainly on Report on Population of the United States
Eleventh Census: 1890; Part I. Washington, D.C. 1895.*

0 100 200 300 400 500 Mi.

U. S. DEPARTMENT OF AGRICULTURE

NEG. 58 (5)-2489 AGRICULTURAL RESEARCH SERVICE

FIGURE 9.—The westward movement of the frontier from 1790 to 1890, when it came to an end, is shown on the map by means of isochronal lines. The frontier of settlement was not a terminal line, but a ragged fringe. The part of the Great Plains that is now Oklahoma was not opened to settlement until 1889. In the West, settlement was confined for many years to places where water was readily available.

9

471954 O–59–3

had more than one function in the development of the country.

The main purpose was to provide a way to describe and identify land divisions for title registrations and transfers. As these divisions were run systematically and regularly, they had much to do with shaping the landownership pattern. In defining real property, the rectangular divisions necessarily provided also the foundation of the land-tax roll for assessors. On public grazing and forest land, they provided the definitions of site locations in the administration and management of the land.

The rectangular divisions not only controlled land ownership; for a large part of the country they provided the grid from which the ground plan of the cultural landscape evolved. In the Central Plains in particular, where much of the land is used for crops, the roads on which farmsteads are located usually follow section lines. The farms on both sides contributed half of the rights-of-way of the roads (pls. 38, 51, 62). In agreement with the grid lines, internal farm divisions follow the same direction. This has produced a rectangular block design formed by the spatial arrangement of fields and pastures, in which scattered farmsteads provide the outstanding features of the landscape. A scattered type of settlement, in contrast to the village community type prevalent in other parts of this country and many parts of the world, is closely related to the land-division system.

## Development of Urban Communities

Rural settlement and cultural use of the land are not the only features of the landscape that reflect the original rectangular land-division system. The system also influenced development of urban communities. Most of the cities and towns that sprang up on sites on which the land had been divided into townships and sections have preserved the original divisions. The grid of the land survey provided the spatial order from which the ground plan of the city evolved. Additional streets, parallel to section lines, were fitted into the land-division system, and now constitute the city plan. Chicago, as an example of this type, is used to illustrate city development on a rectangular ground plan (fig. 10).

As may be noted, the map of the developed city is confined to the Loop District of Chicago. Notwithstanding this limitation, the concentration of houses, streets, railroads and their terminals, canals, harbor facilities, and the solidly built-up business district suggest the size of the city. The accomplishment of a development of this magnitude within such a short space of time is necessarily associated with the growth rate of the city itself. In 1850, Chicago had a population of almost 30,000 inhabitants. In 1950, the urbanized population

of Greater Chicago within Cook County alone was close to 4,500,000 people. Because of this phenomenal rate of growth Chicago is not typical of other cities in the United States. Although it is unique in this respect, nevertheless the city is symptomatic of the trend toward urbanization in the United States.

Although most cities whose streets are laid out on a rectangular pattern are located on what was formerly the public domain, they are not confined exclusively to the public domain. Some of the eastern cities founded in colonial times have the same characteristics. As previously mentioned, Philadelphia was one of the first cities in which the rectangular divisions were applied. Baltimore and Savannah were others. But in none of the cities that was laid out on the rectangular principle have the builders adhered as closely to the classic model as in the plan of Washington, D. C. In that city, the Capitol building marks the point of origin of the rectangular coordinate system. The axes intersect each other at right angles and divide the city into four parts. Identification of streets and numbering of buildings are controlled by it. In this respect, the capital no doubt furnished an example for other cities in which the numbering of buildings follows the same principle.

## Reactions to Land Divisions

An additional function of the rectangular land-division system takes us into the field of political geography. Over much of the country where rectangular divisions are in effect, the survey lines marked on the ground have furnished the boundary lines of political divisions. In some instances, even State boundaries are identified with the system. The boundaries between northwestern Ohio and Indiana, between South Dakota and Wyoming, and between Oklahoma and New Mexico, and the northern boundary of the Texas panhandle are examples of this kind. These lines were used most extensively, however, in delimiting and organizing the counties. In some States, county boundaries and boundaries of minor civil divisions are based almost exclusively on rectangular land divisions. This is not true in western Texas. Because counties in western Texas show considerable regularity as to size and are rectangular with uniform orientation, one may conclude that county boundaries also are derived from the land divisions. In this instance, however, the county boundaries and property lines do not coincide.

The use of the rectangular land-division system on such an extensive scale, and with the many functional applications it has found in the United States, has no parallel in any other country. To a considerable extent, it controls the movements of the population. It provides a frame of reference for orientation and, to this extent, it has become a part of American life. Americans are accustomed to the rectangular spatial order, but visitors from abroad are frequently impressed by it; they regard it as a distinctly American characteristic.

The system has both excellent qualities and shortcomings. Its greatest advantage when properly applied consists of the ease and certitude with which a tract of land can be defined and identified as to size and location in instruments of land ownership. It has also produced continuity in land ownership without overlapping claims or interspersed gores of no-man's land.

In regard to land use, especially when the land is used for crop production, it cannot be said that the rectangular land-division system is uniformly well adapted to all situations. On level and slightly rolling land, the system provides compact operating units that can readily be organized into separate fields. On strongly rolling and hilly grounds, this advantage is less apparent and there are disadvantages also. In order to conserve the soil, the farm plan should take into account the lay of the land. The steepest parts should be left in woods or pasture. The cultivated fields should be adjusted to the contour of the slopes and cultivated accordingly (pls. 48, 55, 57). In many places, this has not been done and severe damage from erosion has resulted.

From economic and social viewpoints, the scattered type of settlement produced by the division of the land into squares has certain inherent disadvantages. Economic disadvantages are mainly the result of the inevitable increase in mileage over which community service must be furnished to isolated farms. Mileage of roads, telephone and electric powerlines, mail delivery, and school bus service could have been reduced by using long-lot rather than square divisions for farms (*6*).

The mode of settlement and division of the land were the first historical events that left a lasting impression on the land and produced regional distinctions in land use patterns. Advances in technology and modification of social and economic conditions have also affected land use profoundly, particularly the distribution and extent of land needed for the higher uses. Changes in land use that have resulted from these innovations form a part of land use history. Changes of this kind have affected both urban and rural land requirements and land use patterns.

## Shifts in Land Use

Shifts in major rural land uses have occurred since the first settlement of the country, but only after the West was opened for occupation did they become of regional significance. Many settlers first chose sites that were poorly adapted to agriculture. Later, they moved to the Central Plains and western valleys. Within the area of early settlement, particularly in the northeastern mountains, the many abandoned farm sites have left their imprint on the present land use pattern. Much of the former cropland has reverted to woodland or is used only for pasture (pls. 3, 7). A somewhat similar movement has recently taken place in parts of the South, where considerable acreages of cropland have been abandoned. Dilapidated farmsteads and old fields furnish mute evidence of the change in the land use picture (pls. 129, 134).

Although in the East the acreage of cropland has been greatly reduced, an equally remarkable expansion occurred in the plains and valleys of the West, largely because of technological implementation and improved management of water. On the semiarid western plains, an operator could hardly have cultivated enough land with the old implements to produce an adequate economic return from small grains. Cultivation and harvesting with machines have eliminated this handicap to a large extent, although occasional crop failures must still be taken into account. Large fields are the rule in this part of the country (pls. 62, 63, 65, 74). In the arid or semiarid valleys of the West, application of water through irrigation has changed markedly the land use potentiality and with it the land use pattern (pls. 79, 82, 84, 88, 106, 107, 108, 124).

At times, changes in land use have been introduced without proper account taken of the use potentiality of the land, or of the actual or future needs of the people. Statistically, these changes are recorded as shifts in the relative acreages used as cropland, grazing land, and forest. For a long time, clearing forested land for agricultural use exceeded in extent the commercial cutting of forest for lumber. But the demand for lumber increased rapidly, and most of the eastern forest land was cut over faster than it was taken up by settlers. Actually, a large part of the forest land is physically unsuited to use as cropland. Nonetheless, our natural timber wealth has been depleted severely. A similar situation prevailed on the grazing lands of the West. Much of the western public domain can be used only for grazing. It was used in common for that purpose by competing herdsmen. In this instance, overgrazing reduced the carrying capacity of the range.

Exploitation of our land resources in crop, grazing, and forest land was characteristic of the early stages in national development. To some extent, it was unavoidable in the process of opening up the country and settling the people on the land. In time, however, warning signs of danger ahead appeared. The movement for conservation resulted. How conservation has been implemented to some extent through inclusion of land in reservations and districts was mentioned previously.

Inclusion of certain lands in reservations is an effective device of conservation, but it can be applied only to publicly owned land. It does not reach the land that is at the same time the most valuable and the most vulnerable to destruction—the cultivated land in farms. Conservation measures to protect the Nation and its farmers were ultimately extended to cultivated land. In the main, these measures are designed to combat erosion damage to the land and thus to conserve its productive capacity. Use of erosion-control measures is voluntary. Such preventive cultural practices as contour plowing, strip cropping, and terracing provide a characteristic distinction in the land use pattern that is usually associated with soil-conservation districts (pls. 18, 114, 126, 149, 163).

Changes in the land use pattern are not confined to rural uses. In more recent times, impressive changes have occurred in urban land uses, particularly on the urban fringes of the larger population centers. With the increase in population and its urbanization, cities are expanding rapidly. Rural and urban settlements, which in antiquity and the Middle Ages were separated by walls, are gradually merging. With modern transportation facilities, feasible commuting distances have increased enough to permit many people to live in the country and work in the city. As a result, in most places, no distinct line of separation exists. In the transition zone, urban and rural land uses are frequently interspersed (pl. 8). Expansion and improvement of roads and of air transportation have carried the urban influence far into rural areas. Frequently, urban elements in the form of nonfarm residences, factories, and landing fields are injected into the otherwise rural land use pattern.

These are the more important historical events and influences that are expressed in existing land use associations and patterns. Others that are not mentioned here may have produced equally pronounced distinctions. For instance, reclamation in its two major forms—irrigation and drainage—and mineral exploitation, which affects surface use, have their historical backgrounds. Usually, however, they are closely allied with other factors. They are discussed later in this report.

# Physical Conditions and Land Use

It is an old and tried dictum that land use capability for production of food, feed, and fiber is closely related to the prevailing physical conditions of the area. The distributional characteristics of major land uses in the United States demonstrate its truth. The higher uses are usually concentrated in areas in which natural conditions for cultural use of the land are most favorable. In other areas, physical limitations may be so severe as to exclude them altogether or make them possible only when human ingenuity can overcome the drawbacks.

Land relief, temperature, precipitation and water supply, soils, and natural vegetation, each contribute in varying degree toward shaping the natural environment, or the so-called biological complex, to which plant and animal life adjusts itself. That the natural environment is so complex is due not only to the many physical factors involved but to the fact that these factors are causatively related among themselves. In extensive areas, however, one or the other of these factors plays a dominant part and thus eliminates one or more major uses of land. Although these factors are related, they must be considered separately.

## Land Relief

The spatial arrangement of mountains and plains had its origin in distant geologic ages, which are usually expressed in millions of years. During these earlier geologic periods, the tectonic forces were more active; it was then that the volcanic activities and crustal movements produced the highlands from which rock weathering and solution, runoff, and erosion carved the mountain massifs, chains, and plateaus that flank the country in the East and West (fig. 11). In this respect, the alinement of our mountain systems is distinct from those of the rest of the world in that their trend is mainly in a north to south direction. Rainfall, natural vegetation, and certain soil characteristics derive their orientation largely from the physiographic background.

## Rock Formations Affect Land Use

Aside from the broader aspects of the influence of geology and physiography on the country as a whole, they are also of local significance. Landforms, which provide the background of the more localized activity of man, frequently show distinctions derived from the nature of the surface rocks, to which land use also had to be adjusted. Whether the surface rock is limestone, shale, sandstone, or one of the igneous or metamorphic rocks is reflected not only in terms of soil texture but often in surface configuration as well. In many places, abrupt changes in rock formations have caused

LAND RELIEF OF THE UNITED STATES

U. S. DEPARTMENT OF AGRICULTURE

NEG. 55(9)-749 AGRICULTURAL RESEARCH SERVICE

FIGURE 11.—In its major aspects of mountains and plains, plateaus and basins, land relief furnishes the key to an understanding of the spatial distribution of climatic phases, natural vegetation, soils, and tillable land. The mountain ranges on the east and the west and the extensive plains in the center of the country, where much of the cropland lies, provide the physiographic setting for the use of our land.

33

almost equally sharp changes in surface conditions, which are also recorded in the use of the land (pls. 27, 111, 159).

A contact line of different bedrock formations may also mark a change in the slope gradient of the surface configuration. In these instances, rock outcrop and slope are related, but slope is frequently a more effective agent than the underlying geologic formation, either in adding to or in detracting from the desirability of the land for arable use. Actually, slope may be the chief factor in determining the use capability of the land. In their extremes of occurrence, slope characteristics are frequently strong enough to preclude cropland use altogether, or at least until corrective measures have been applied. Drainage improvements may need to be installed on level land, and terracing and contouring may be required on strongly sloping land to prevent soil depletion through erosion. Frequently, on steeply sloping land the soil mantle is too thin and rocky for cultural use. All of these slope features are sometimes closely associated in the natural environment, and to a considerable extent, they determine the land use patterns. Some reaction of land use to slope conditions can be detected on most of the aerial photographs included. (See especially pls. 9, 10, 13, 15, 16, 23, 28, 29, 34, 35, 43, 44, 48, 53, 56, 90, 92, 106, 115, 123, 130, 131, 139, 141, 145, 146, 147, 148, 149, 158, 161, 164.)

Location of minerals is closely associated with the geologic background of an area, but only when they are known and exploited do these deposits affect the surface use of the land. This is true particularly when the deposits are near the surface and are mined in open-pit operations, as is done in strip coal mining or the mining of pumice in New Mexico and Oregon, and as was done in placer mining operations in California. Strip mining usually prevents further use of the land for cultivated crops (pl. 17). The total acreage affected by strip coal mining, as compared with the total acreage of cropland in the United States, is relatively small, but it increases at the rate of 10,000 to 15,000 acres each year. Because of its exploitive nature, strip mining frequently affects the economy of the community (149). Oil and gas fields and other mining operations, although not so destructive as strip mining, interfere with the use of the land for other purposes and reduce its productivity while they are in operation (pl. 14).

## Glaciation

The relation of preglacial geology to physiography has been explored and described by many authors (41, 44, 45, 80). The case is somewhat different for the Glacial or Pleistocene period, which comprises the events of an estimated million years, according to some geologists, and up to 2 million years according to others (48, p. 1; 64, p. 16). The forces that were active during this period, and that, so to speak, put the finishing touches on the major topographic features, have been the subject of intensive research and study only in comparatively recent years. The facts that have come to light are fascinating. But as a rule, the geomorphic features of the landscape whose origin can be traced back to the glacial period do not have the overall implications for land use capability that the mountains and plains have. In some regions, however, these features have not been negligible in shaping the conditions for cultural use of the land.

The glaciated area extends over much of the North American continent. Virtually all of Canada, but only about 700,000 square miles, or 24 percent, of the land area of continental United States, is included in the area. Obliteration and modification of old landforms and formation of new ones, however, are not confined to the glaciated area. Glaciation itself was the result of climatic changes that must have produced reactions over the entire earth, but which were most effective in a broad belt adjacent to the drift border, the periglacial zone. The repeated accumulation and recession of immense ice masses near the poles also caused an oscillation of the land and sea level with a corresponding advancing and retreating of the shorelines along the Atlantic and Gulf coasts. Quaternary marine deposits indicate the extent to which these lowlands were submerged at times. In the glaciated region, the periglacial zone and the submerged coastal belts are soil and topographic features attributed to glacial, wind, and water action during this period that either improved or reduced the use capability of the land. The extent to which the land was glaciated and the area that was submerged for a considerable time are shown in figure 12.

## The Glaciated Region

Modifications of the preglacial topography in the glaciated areas are due mainly to the action of the glaciers themselves. The abrasive and grinding force of these slowly moving ice masses, which were estimated to have had thicknesses in places of more than 2,000 feet, must have been enormous. This is evident from the rounded mountain slopes in New England, and the striae (grooves) engraved on the rocks. In the plains, the deposit of drift material, in the form of boulders, gravel, sand, and clay, obliterated the old topography in many places by filling in established drainage channels. Some of the main streams were obstructed and diverted so that they had to cut the new channels (pl. 74).

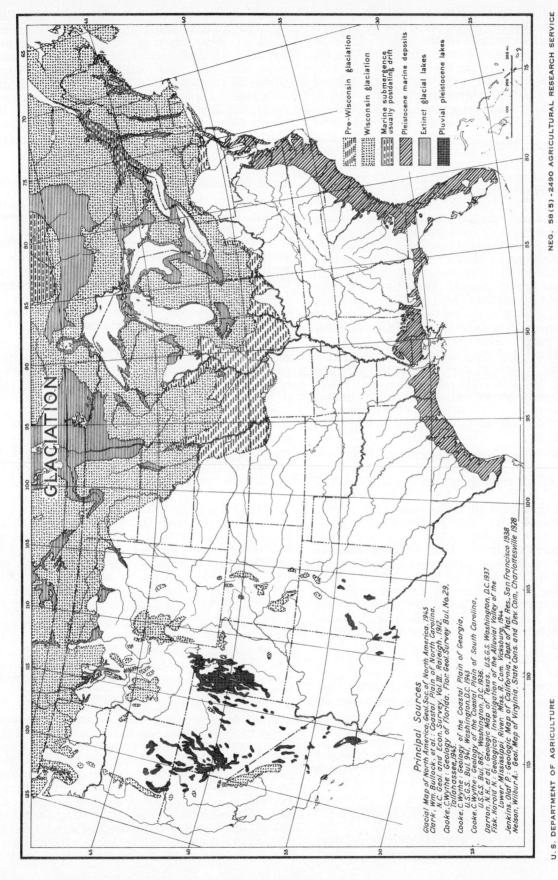

GLACIATION

Pre-Wisconsin glaciation

Wisconsin glaciation

Marine submergence
usually postdating drift

Pleistocene marine deposits

Extinct glacial lakes

Pluvial pleistocene lakes

Principal Sources

Glacial Map of North America, Geol.Soc.of North America, 1945.
Clark, Wm. Bullock, et al.: Coastal Plain of North Carolina,
N.C. Geol. and Econ. Survey, Vol.III, Raleigh, 1912.
Cooke, C.Wythe : Geology of Florida, Flor. Geol. Survey Bul. No.29,
Tallahassee,1945.
Cooke, C.Wythe: Geology of the Coastal Plain of Georgia,
U.S.G.S. Bul. 941, Washington, D.C. 1943
Cooke, C.Wythe: Geology of the Coastal Plain of South Carolina,
U.S.G.S. Bul. 867, Washington, D.C. 1936.
Darton, N.H., et al: Geologic Map of Texas, U.S.G.S. Washington, D.C. 1937
Fisk, Harold N: Geological Investigation of the Alluvial Valley of the
Lower Mississippi River, Miss. R. Com. Vicksburg, 1944
Jenkins, Olaf P.: Geologic Map of California, Dept. of Nat. Res. San Francisco 1938
Nelson, Wilbur A.: Geol. Map of Virginia, State Cons. and Dev. Com. Charlottesville 1928

U. S. DEPARTMENT OF AGRICULTURE

NEG. 58(5)-2490 AGRICULTURAL RESEARCH SERVICE

FIGURE 12.—Broadly speaking, the Ohio and Missouri Rivers are frequently considered as forming the southern limits of ice invasion. Outside the glacial limits extensive lakes, of which only small remnants remain, formed during pluvial periods. Pleistocene marine deposits along the Atlantic and Gulf coasts reveal that the sea level fluctuated considerably with the advancement and retreat of the ice sheets.

Accumulations of drift material, frequently of considerable thickness, were left by retreating glaciers over most of the glaciated plains. Where the extensive glacial lakes had formed, these deposits were partly reworked and lake deposits were added (pl. 40). As ground moraines and lake plains usually have smooth surfaces with inadequate drainage, large areas had to be drained. The larger part of the land improved by artificial drainage lies in the glaciated region (pls. 45, 54). But not all wet lands can be drained economically. Over much of the younger drift plains, the dissected stream-erosion type of topography has not yet developed. The surface is billowy and there are shallow depressions. On the open plains are areas with many such depressions, or kettleholes. These kettleholes resulted from the melting of imbedded ice blocks left by the retreating glaciers in the drift, or were produced as pools in shallow runoff channels made by the waters of the melting glaciers (pl. 71). In themselves, the kettleholes may not be large but because of their numbers, they reduce the cultivable acreage materially. Also, because of their irregular distribution, they are a serious obstacle to field operations. This again reduces the acreage available for cropping. In the Great Lakes forest region, where rainfall is fairly heavy, development of drainage was retarded because of glaciation, and many lakes and swamps are found there.

Glaciers also produced landforms that protrude above the general level of the country and thereby affect the use of the land. Terminal moraines in the form of low ridge belts are accumulations of drift and till along the convex edge of the glaciers. The surface configuration of these moraine belts consists of a random arrangement of knolls with more or less sharply defined depressions interspersed. Terminal moraines may be so rough that the land cannot be used for cultivated crops. In more moderate instances, only the scattered smoother portions can be so used (pl. 69). Eskers are curved, low, narrow ridges composed of stratified drift deposited by water within steeply walled channels or tunnels in the ice. More prevalent than eskers are drumlins, which are low, oval-shaped hillocks more or less densely arranged over broad fields. As a rule, drumlins are about 60 to 100 feet high and up to a mile or more long; they were shaped by the moving ice with the major axis in the direction of the flow. Slope and elevation in these areas usually are not sufficiently prominent to act as a detriment to use of the land for cultivated crops, but fields must be adjusted to the trend of the drumlins (pl. 47). In less developed areas, fields are scattered among the drumlins.

Outwash plains and glacial lakebeds are also associated with glaciation. Outwash plains and deltas consist of stratified sediments deposited by waters that issued from melting glaciers. Most of these deposits comprise the coarser particles of drift, which sometimes approach pure sand. In these instances, the land is not suited to cropping (pl. 49). Glacial lakebeds, as a rule, have heavier soils and smoother surfaces, and consequently a higher use value. In places along the beachlines of these lakes, cultivated fields are adjusted to the orientation of the beaches (pl. 70).

## Land Use Affected by Glaciation

Distinctive landforms and soils are the main surface features of the glaciated area that have affected land use to a considerable extent. In distribution and spatial arrangement, these two distinctions may be closely associated within restricted areas, or in extensive tracts one or the other may determine the land use capability. Land use necessarily shows man's reaction to these conditions and this has produced diversity and contrasts in land use patterns.

Immature relief and drainage development on late till and morainic deposits are the order over extensive areas. What the relief would be without glaciation can be perceived when the driftless area in southwestern Wisconsin is considered. The driftless area appears as an island in the glaciated region, although it was never entirely surrounded by ice. As the area was not glaciated, the old relief features that developed from sedimentary rock formations exposed to protracted erosion were not obliterated by till, nor was the process of erosion interrupted by ice. The tilted and dissected plain was preserved (pl. 48). In contrast to the old erosion surface, the proximate areas of late till and morainic deposits present a chaotic assortment of hillocks and depressions with no well-developed drainage system (pl. 46). In both instances, the land use pattern reflects adjustment to these features.

The soils of the glaciated region, perhaps more so than the landforms, have had both beneficial and restrictive influences on land use. The millions of acres of waterlogged and swampy lowland composed of large tracts and small depressions have an organic soil cover, mainly peat. In their natural state, these lands support some tree growth. Where the peat is deep, however, even the trees are stunted (pl. 50). Reclamation for agricultural use is feasible for some areas but not for others. Also prevalent over extensive areas are the rocky and stony soils that restrict land use to forestry, recreation, and support of wildlife (pls. 3, 5, 6, 41). Almost equally detrimental to agricultural use of the land are the extensive sandy plains already mentioned. At opposite extremes are the drift plains and glacial lakebeds on which some of our most productive soils developed (pls. 12, 40, 51, 37, 42, 45).

In the mechanical processes of grinding, mixing, sorting, transporting, and redeposing surface minerals, the action of ice and water during the glacial period produced a series of land characteristics that have affected the economic use potentiality of the land. The spatial arrangement of these features, however, is far from uniform. Large land areas were improved by these redistributional processes; the productive capacities of others were depleted or impaired. In the glaciated region, these dissimilarities in surface conditions, together with differences in climate, account for the diversity in the physical adaptability of the land to cultural uses. This diversity has found expression in regional and local land use patterns.

## The Periglacial Zone

Although ice and water brought about superficial changes in the glaciated area, no less important surface modifications were produced through the operation of climatic forces in the adjacent belt, which is usually referred to as the periglacial zone. The periglacial zone was defined by Zeuner in 1945 as "that zone surrounding an ice sheet, in which the cooling effect of the ice produced frost climate" (*101, p. 1467*). Temperature, however, was not the only climatic agent during the Pleistocene Epoch that affected conditions of life and changed the surface of the land outside the glaciated area. Air-mass movements caused by changes in temperature distribution, combined with pluvial and dry periods, were even more effective than temperature in shaping some of the surface features that condition land use today. Evidence of their activity during the Pleistocene Epoch can be found as far south as the Mexican border or the South Atlantic Coastal Plain. For our purpose, therefore, the whole of the United States outside the glaciated region is considered as located in the periglacial zone.

The periodic changes in temperature that accompanied the repeated advancing and retreating of the ice sheets had their counterpart in pluvial and dry periods attended by strong air-mass currents. Wind and water were the primary agents that modified soil and topographic features in the periglacial zone, while the floral and faunal associations adjusted themselves in response to periodic changes in temperature and moisture conditions. Only in terms of climatic changes can the occurrence and distribution of some of the surface features and fossil remains of plant and animal life be explained.

## Pluvial and Dry Periods

That pluvial periods alternated with drier periods is evident from the beachline records that reveal the geologic history of the intermountain lakes (*48, pp. 469–476*). Lakes Bonneville and Lahontan, the two great lake systems in the intermountain basin-and-range region, covered a number of adjacent basins during the pluvial periods of the Pleistocene Epoch. The high-water level of Lake Bonneville, on the eastern side of the intermountain region, was more than 1,000 feet above the present level of the Great Salt Lake. At that time, it covered an area of more than 19,780 square miles. At its highest stage, Lake Lahontan in western Nevada, which extended into some basins of Oregon and California, covered an area of 8,422 square miles and had a maximum depth of more than 500 feet. Pyramid, Winnemucca, and Walker Lakes are existing remnants of Lake Lahontan, and there were other Pleistocene lakes in the intermountain basins. In most instances, they are now playas; their shorelines provide mute evidence that at one time they were lakes.

These high beachlines indicate that precipitation was higher and evaporation lower than they are at present. The delta deposits covered by lake deposits and shorelines on intermediate levels support the conclusion that these variations occurred in cycles. In their present state, these old lakebeds have their own land use characteristics in that the lowest parts of the basins are practically desert. Longtime flooding of these closed basins and leaching of the soils and surface rocks of the easily soluble salts they contained concentrated the saline contents through evaporation at the bottom of the lakes. Because of the toxicity of these salts, most plant growth is eliminated from these now dry lake bottoms. The Black Rock Desert in Nevada and the Great Salt Lake Desert in Utah are the two largest and best known.

The pluvial periods also find expression in the stream-erosion topography of the periglacial zone. A marked distinction in topography occurs between the younger drift plains (pl. 36) and the unglaciated plains (pl. 35). In much of the younger drift plains, drainage is not fully developed. In the unglaciated plains, stream erosion has been active longer and has dissected the plains more thoroughly. The topography of the badlands in the Dakotas and Montana could hardly have resulted from the present low rainfall in these areas. It suggests that the origin of these lands is associated with the pluvial periods of the glacial epoch. Because of the dissected surface, much of the land in this region is not suited to arable use (pls. 68, 72).

Farther south, in Texas and New Mexico, "the surface features of the High Plains as well as the development or at least the extensive modification of the larger canyons, and the bounding escarpment are the result of quaternary erosion and deposition" (42, p. 435). The High Plains, especially the Llano Estacado, are not as incisively dissected by streams as is the country below the escarpment to the east. Only shallow draws that carry water intermittently have formed on the plateau. There is little runoff. Most of the precipitation that falls is absorbed by the soil and the sand dunes, or it is caught and retained in the many shallow depressions and playas that dot the surface. Subsidence or slumping in some of the older rocks beneath the smaller basins and deflation through wind action during arid stages, with solution as a contributory factor, explain the origin of these basins (pls. 119, 120).

## The Alluvial Valley of the Mississippi

Erosion induced by running water was not confined to uplands. The waters of the rivers, which were charged with the sands and gravels washed out upstream, were effective in their scouring actions. In places, they cut deep trenches. The canyon of the Canadian River, which divides the Texas High Plains, and other canyons farther north, such as the canyon of the Cimarron River, are of this type (pl. 113). A more voluminous job was done by the Mississippi River.

According to the latest investigations, the Alluvial Valley of the Lower Mississippi River contains the buried river system that was in operation at the late stage of glaciation (46). At a time when the water level of the gulf, as compared with the elevations of the land, was much lower than it is today, the Mississippi River excavated a valley that was a great deal deeper than the present valley. At the upper end, near Cairo, the main channel was approximately 100 feet above the present sea level, or about 200 feet below the present valley floor. Near the gulf coast, these channels were more than 350 feet below the present sea level, or about that much lower than they are now. The gradient of the 600 miles of the Lower Mississippi had therefore about 150 feet more descent than it has today. The river was straighter, and sediment could be carried farther and in greater volume. It has been estimated that at that time about 1,500 cubic miles of sediment were removed from the lower valley and transported by the river into the Gulf of Mexico. This figure does not include the sediment brought into the valley by tributary streams (46, p. 11).

With the melting of the ice sheets and the attendant rising of the gulf's water level, the streams that had excavated the valley began to fill it up again. Aggradation was accomplished in several ways. The master stream periodically flooded the valley and dropped its load of gravel, sand, and silt, while the tributaries built alluvial fans where they entered the flood plain. With construction of the flood plain went also modification of river channels. With the decrease in the slope of the valley, the Mississippi River developed meander loops, built natural levees, and shifted its channel frequently. It has not changed greatly since. "With its diversion through Thebes Gap the Mississippi River established for the first time a comparatively deep-water channel from the head of its alluvial valley to the Gulf of Mexico. From the standpoint of flood control and navigation, this channel is the best that has existed in the history of the alluvial valley" (46, p. 55).

The reconstruction of the Mississippi flood plain therefore is in the main glacial with surface deposits that consist of recent alluvium. In elevation, the present flood plain has not attained the old level. Some remnants of the old plain have elevations that place them above the flood level (pl. 133). In all, the Alluvial Valley of the Lower Mississippi comprises about 50,000 square miles, the delta included. This total consists of about 35,000 square miles of flood plains and about 15,000 square miles of old plain terraces in the northern and central part of the valley.

*Flood Control and Drainage.*—From the land use viewpoint, the structural history of the Alluvial Valley of the Lower Mississippi is significant in that it is reflected in the land use pattern. Ever since white men settled in these extensive flood plains, they have struggled to control the river. The soils of these plains are inherently productive, but in its natural state very little of the land could be used for crops with safety. Only the higher portions, which consisted of natural levees built up by the larger streams, were sufficiently well drained to permit cultivation, and even these were subject to occasional flooding when the river reached high-water stages (pls. 132, 135, 137, 140).

The Mississippi River still floods the valley periodically. These floods are not only damaging; they are sometimes disastrous. Local and State efforts to control them were formerly of little or no avail. Not until the Federal Government developed a comprehensive flood-control program, built levees, and set aside bypasses, was the threat of damaging floods materially reduced. Flood protection is the chief safety measure needed by the inhabitants, but it is not sufficient for a fuller development of the valley (61). A rather high annual precipitation, which increases from an average of 40 inches in the north to 60 inches in the south, keeps much of the lowland wet and swampy (pl. 135). Artificial drainage has been installed to some extent, but more can be done to expand the agricultural use of the land. The Alluvial Valley of the Lower Mississippi has undeveloped potentialities. Not all the land can be reclaimed for crop production, but the proportion used for the purpose is comparatively small. Of the 42,000 square miles, crops were harvested from only about 14,000 acres in 1954. Most of the reclaimed land lies at the upper end of the valley and in the Yazoo Delta.

## Wind Reactions

As a modifying agent of surface conditions in the periglacial zone, wind has either improved or reduced the use capability of large acreages. Pluvial periods during the Pleistocene Epoch alternated with periods of aridity, which were accompanied by heavy sand and dust storms. Evidence of these storms is found across the country. Aeolian rock sculpture and rock polish commonly occur in the arid region. They indicate that the winds of the Pleistocene Epoch were stronger and more prevalent than are winds today. This supposition is supported by the observations of investigators, who report that the rocks polished by these sandblasts are now losing their polish through exfoliation (66). The arrangement and location of sand dunes and the occurrence of loess shows that the predominant direction of these strong winds was from west to east.

Aeolian sorting, transport, and deposition of sand and silt (113) in the Pleistocene Epoch, and more recently, have affected extensive areas, particularly in the Columbia and Snake River Basins and the Central Plains. In all of these areas, agricultural use of the land is involved.

## The Columbia Basin

In the Columbia Basin, most of the uplands and plateaus are covered by a disjointed mantle of loess from a few to 250 feet thick, from which the soils developed. That the loess mantle of the Palouse country, as the loess-covered eastern plateaus of the Columbia are frequently called, is older than the last stage of glaciation is evident from the channeled scabland tracts that cross the westward sloping plateau. During the Wisconsin stage of glaciation, the escape waters of the glacier, which had advanced to the northern rim, ran across the plateau and washed out these braided channels through the loess down to bedrock (14). Much of the plateau was made useless for crops. Scabland can best be used for pasture. Similar loess deposits have accumulated on the high benches on the eastern side of the Snake River Basin. As in the Palouse country, they are used for production of small grains. The loess on the plateaus consists of the wind-

sorted-out silt from the lower parts of the basins. Sands and sandy soils are prevalent on the lower levels and silt is characteristic of the plateaus (pls. 90, 91, 92, 93).

A similar sorting action by winds occurred in the Great Plains, though on a larger scale. This, at least, is the explanation advanced for the existence of the extensive areas of sand and loess in this part of the country.

## Sand and Loess Deposits in Plains

The largest of the sand areas, known as the Sand Hills of Nebraska, occupies an area of about 18,000 square miles in north-central Nebraska, or about one-fourth the area of the State. The sandhills are arranged in dune-ridge formation, although not all of them are made up entirely of sand. Some of the larger ridges, especially, contain a hard core of tertiary material in places. Apparently the wind started to work on the tertiary deposits in the early stages of the Pleistocene Epoch. The sandhills probably started as blowouts and coalesced later. In the process the lighter materials—the silt and clay particles—were ripped out and transported eastward by the winds, at times for hundreds of miles, before they were deposited as loess (pl. 59). As the coarser sand grains could not travel far, they were left behind (pl. 66).

The Sand Hills of Nebraska, as well as the smaller sandhill areas south of the Platte River and those in eastern Colorado and other places, must be regarded, therefore, as source areas of the loess mantle that covers the land to the east. In addition, the Box Butte tableland west of the sandhills, the plains of Wyoming, and other parts of the Great Plains are still making noticeable contributions to these loess deposits. From an experimental 8 days' collection of dust in Lincoln, Nebr., following the duststorm of March 20 to 22, 1935, it was calculated that at that time the deposit was 4,800 pounds per acre (81, pp. 156–167; 158).

Loess deposits in the Central Plains reach a thickness of more than 200 feet in places. They cover extensive areas in eastern Nebraska, northern and western Kansas, practically the entire area of pre-Wisconsin glaciation, and bluffs, especially those on the east, along the Alluvial Valley of the Lower Mississippi. Because the loess deposits usually are deepest on the valley slopes near the main rivers, it has been thought that the alluvium of these valleys was the main source of the loess. But apparently this supposition is not supported by the findings of recent investigations, at least not for the Missouri and Upper Mississippi Valleys. To what extent the broad loess belt along the eastern side of the Alluvial Valley of the Lower Mississippi obtained its silt from the Great Plains or the alluvial valley is still undecided.

Considered from the viewpoint of land use, the action of the wind has changed the use capability of vast stretches of land. Most of the sandhill country in the Great Plains can be used only for grazing. The cropland found in these areas consists mainly of shallow depressions within the ridges, in which the soil is loamy and more retentive of moisture. Some cultivated crops are grown in these depressions. The main crop, however, is hay from native grasses, which grow luxuriantly in these moist places. The hay is used for winter feeding. As a rule, the soils that developed from loess are very productive, but they erode easily and must be cultivated with care. Because of this, the steeper slopes cannot be used for crops (pl. 139).

*The Llano Estacado.*—How wind action has affected land use in a more restricted area may be observed with reference to cultivated land on the Llano Estacado, the southern part of the Texas High Plains. That winds have helped to shape ground conditions may be deduced from the presence of sand dunes and their distributional arrangement.

The Llano Estacado is a tilted tableland. It rises from 3,000 feet along its southeastern escarpment to 5,000 feet at the northwestern promontory. (See figure 20.) Consequently, it is exposed to winds. It is defined by bounding escarpments, except at its southward extension, where it merges into the Edwards Plateau. The eastern escarpments are about twice as high as the western. Differences in elevation between the Pecos River Plains and the Llano Estacado marked by the escarpments are usually only about 100 to 200 feet, but they serve to control the movement of the drifting sands. Sandstorms that originate in the Pecos Valley have lodged the sands in dune formation at the foot of the escarpments, and only where the escarpment is broken have the sands drifted onto the tableland.

Two distinct traverse dune belts were formed in this way. The northern belt has an average width of less than 10 miles, but it is more than 100 miles long and traverses 4 predominantly agricultural counties. The southern dune belt traverses chiefly grazing land. It is not quite as wide as the northern belt and is only about 70 miles long. Traverse dune belts whose formation was controlled by gaps in the surface obstruction are unusual. The only other dune belt of this type in the United States is in Wyoming. This belt has its inception on the flats of the Big Sandy River in the Bridger Basin, crosses the Continental Divide north of the Leucite Hills, and thence enters the Red Desert. It is from 1 to 2 miles wide and about 50 miles long. But as it is located in open range country, this dune belt affects land use less than do the traverse dunes on the Llano Estacado.

On the Llano Estacado, sand dunes are not the only modification of surface conditions that can be attributed to wind action and that affect the use capability of the land. Larger tracts of land than the sand dunes cover either received a surface layer of light sand or were subjected to wind erosion and deprived of most of the topsoil. Because of this, most of the land in the more exposed counties next to the southwestern border of the tableland is suitable only for grazing. In Andrews, Karnes, and Yoakum Counties, Tex., and the eastern part of Lea County, N. Mex., the greater part of the land is covered by light sand. In Lea County, however, the tableland next to the Mescalero Escarpment has a shallow rocky soil. A similar situation prevails farther south over much of the land in Ector, Upton, Reagan and Glasscock Counties, where the soil either is shallow, gravelly and rocky, or has a heavy silty clay surface soil (*21*). Land used for crops in this broad range belt on the tableland is confined to scattered areas in which the soil is deep enough and retains enough moisture to permit its use for that purpose.

In the transition zone, from the range belt in the southwest to the agricultural section at the northern end of the Llano Estacado, a number of large playa basins show evidence of wind action. These basins are much larger than the many saucerlike depressions that dot the plateau. Saline lakes or playas that contain water during most of the year occupy the lowest parts of the basin floor. Subsidence may account for some of these basins, but the more directly observable evidence is deflation through wind action. The eastern sides of most of these playas contain dune ridges that parallel the shoreline. This is evidence that wind was at work (*42, p. 488*).

Not all of the observable ground features that are the characteristic result of wind action can be thought of entirely as finished products of the Pleistocene Epoch. We know that dramatic wind action did not cease with the retreat of the last glacier. But usually it is conceded that the strong winds that produced these modifying surface features occurred in cycles during the Pleistocene Epoch. Deductive evidence that during periods of relative aridity in that epoch, air currents were more powerful and persistent than they are today is provided by the playa dunes. These playa dunes have now entered a stage in which degradation through water erosion is more effective than the building-up process through aeolian deposition (pl. 120).

Although wind deposits and denudation on the Llano Estacado demonstrate the effect of wind on the use of the land for crops, equally large accumulations of sand are found in other parts of the West. In most instances, these sandhills and dunes occur in arid and semiarid country. Therefore, they are not controlling factors in cropland use. In some instances, these dunes are almost sterile of vegetation and thus exclude productive surface use. These sandhills are found in the valleys and plains of New Mexico, the San Luis Valley in Colorado (pl. 81), the Imperial Valley of California, and many other places. Aeolian accumulations of sand are found also in the more humid part of the country, particularly along streams and on the southeastern and eastern shores of Lake Michigan. As these last are in the glaciated region, they probably postdate glacial drift. All these inland deposits, however, have one characteristic in common; all are found on the eastern side of the valley or basin in which they occur. In this respect, loess and sand dunes furnish corroborative evidence that the strong winds that built up these deposits were predominantly westerly winds.

### The Coastal Belts of Pleistocene Marine Submergence

The lowland margins of the Coastal Plains along the South Atlantic and Gulf Coasts, although they may be considered as lying in the periglacial zone, have their own Pleistocene history, which differs markedly from that of the rest of the country. The difference in the geologic history between these lowland belts and the rest of the Coastal Plains consists of the repeated submergence by and emergence from the waters of the ocean during Pleistocene time. Low and high sea levels were the companion events of the respective glacial and interglacial stages. Vast quantities of water were locked up in the polar icecaps during the glacial stages and released when the glaciers melted and wasted away. At its highest stage, the sea flooded the land to an elevation of about 270 feet, and at its lower level, the shoreline receded on the Continental Shelf. Findings at the mouth of the Mississippi River indicate that the sea level was more than 350 feet lower than it is today. The extent to which crustal movements may have contributed to the oscillation of the ocean level is an open question.

Although we have no definite time scale to show the duration of glacial and interglacial stages, there are indications that the warmer intervals may have been the longer ones. Judging from the accumulations of marine deposits, they must certainly have lasted for thousands of years. The first submergence evidently was the highest; each succeeding one flooded a correspondingly smaller margin of the lowland. Evidence of the repeated flooding of the lowland is preserved in the marine deposits of clay, sand and gravel, and in the old beachlines

that separate the lowland terraces along the lower Coastal Plains (pl. 161).

Surface erosion is not very active on these terraces. Natural drainage channels have not been cut back far enough to dissect the interstream flats. Thus much of the land is inadequately drained. The best drainage usually is found in the interior belt and on rising ground next to the bottom lands of the larger creeks and rivers (pl. 168). Deficient drainage has impeded economic development over much of these coastal belts. One requisite for further economic development of these areas, therefore, is drainage improvement, although conditions are not the same everywhere. The eastern lowlands differ markedly from those west of the Mississippi, as is evident from the present stage of development. Aside from surface configuration, soils and climate have much to do with this distinction.

In the western section of the Gulf Coast lowland, much of the land that rises above the tidal marshes that fringe the coast is used for crops. The rice-growing area of Louisiana and Texas lies in this lowland belt. The central part of the Gulf Coast Prairie in Texas is used largely for grazing, although the soil is fertile and with proper drainage much of it could be used for crops.

Toward the southwest, soils and climate change. The soil becomes more sandy and some dunes appear (pl. 125). Rainfall decreases to the extent that irrigation is needed to grow crops on the better land. The acreage of cropland might be expanded within this part of the Coastal Belt, but improvements in drainage would be needed (pl. 127). Most of the lowland north of the Delta is in forest, but with improved drainage, more of this land could be used for crops.

On the Atlantic side, the Coastal belt, which was submerged during the Pleistocene Epoch, stretches from the southern tip of Florida to Sandy Hook, N. J., although the submerged area is not equally well defined everywhere.

The Middle Atlantic Coastal Plain from New Jersey south to North Carolina is deeply incised by estuaries that reach up to the Fall Line. Over most of the area, differences in elevation from divide to tidewater are sufficient to facilitate drainage and induce erosion. Back of the tidal marshes lie some areas in which improvement in drainage is necessary for cropland use, but on the whole drainage is not the problem that it is farther south. In this part of the Coastal Plain, geologists are not in full accord as to the upper limit of Pleistocene marine submergence (49). As presented on the map, it is a generalized interpretation of various sources.

*Pocosins and Bays.*—A different situation prevails in the South Atlantic belt from Virginia to Florida. The Dismal Swamp on the Virginia-North Carolina boundary in the north, and the Okefenokee Swamp on the Georgia-Florida boundary in the south (pl. 156) may be considered as significant terminals of this coastal belt. In this part of the country, where wet lands and swamps are outstanding characteristics, "swamp" is a general term for waterlogged land. Locally, especially in the Carolinas, these swamps and wet depressions are usually referred to as pocosins and bays.

Pocosin, as a generic name of wet land, is derived from the Indians and is usually translated as "dismal." The bays probably received their names from the bay trees and bushes that grow in these swampy depressions. For purposes of discussion, bays and pocosins must be considered as distinct entities, although in some instances they are interrelated. The chief distinction between the two lies in their distribution, size, and form. Bays consist of elliptic depressions of various sizes with or without sandy rims. They occur on the upper and lower parts of the submerged belts. Pocosins are the large irregular bodies of waterlogged land that occupy the interstream flats on the lower terraces.

From the beginning of settlement, these upland swamps and depressions have impeded extension of cultural use of the land. During the early stages of settlement, landowners tried to reclaim parts of these large swamps, mainly with negative results. The fact that similar projects have been proposed in more recent times is an indication that the nature of these swamps is not yet fully appreciated.

Of the two types of wet land, the bays are the more remarkable. Most of them have a symmetrical oval form, which is smooth in outline and sharp in definition. With exceptions, they have a fairly uniform northwest-southeast orientation. So far, these terrestrial surface features have been reported in no other part of the world (pls. 162 and 167).

In the Carolinas, these oval depressions number around 3,000. As they have a clustered distribution, in some localities they occupy much of the land. In the aggregate, pocosins comprise an even larger acreage than bays. In a few instances, however, bay formations have been engulfed by pocosins, and in these instances the two are merged. In connection with land use, bays and pocosins, as the major drawback to the development of the region, are of more than theoretical interest.

These depressions in the Coastal Plains of the Carolinas were reported by the early explorers, but it was only after aerial photography came into wider use that the elliptical shape of the bays was fully exposed. Aerial photography supplied the first documentary evidence of the characteristics of form that aroused interest from which studies of their origin were started. Studies having as their objective the genesis of these swampy areas are preponderantly centered on the oval bays. How widespread public and scientific interest in these unique surface features is may be judged from the many articles on the subject that have appeared. Meteoritic scars were the first suggested explanation of their origin. This was followed by several others, so that the origin of the Carolina Bays has become a controversial question. Not all the papers on the subject have been examined by this writer, and no review or appraisal of the different hypotheses advanced can be attempted here. But judging from what earlier and later papers had to say on the subject, apparently no attempt had been made so far to correlate the occurrence of bays with the geologic formations of the Coastal Plain or with the findings of related fields of inquiry. When this was done, it led inevitably to conclusions that differ from the ones currently propounded.

Distribution of bays usually is described as confined to the Coastal Plain and extending northward to the Virginia boundary and southward into Georgia. To obtain a more definite concept and picture of the distributional characteristics of the bays, the aerial index photographs were used as source material and their location was plotted on a small-scale map (fig. 13). Although the map shows only the larger bays, it discloses the distributional limits, the clustered concentrations in some places, and the open scattered occurrence in others. Both the limit of occurrence and the distributional pattern indicate that development of bays presupposed propitious ground conditions.

That ground conditions are involved is evident from the restricted distribution of bays. Bays are not casually scattered over the entire Coastal Plain; they are confined to the quaternary or marine deposits of the Pleistocene Epoch. Even within this belt, the clustered concentrations, or the widely scattered occurrence or absence, of bays indicate that not all sites were equally favorable to their development. In general, however, bays are more numerous in the upper half of the belt than in the lower half near the coast.

With occurrence of bays confined to the marine deposits of the Pleistocene Epoch, their inception is automatically restricted to the later stages of that period. This conclusion is supported by the findings of direct investigations. Moreover, the distributional characteristics indicate that more or less favorable sites existed for their development, although so far no field investigations have been undertaken to establish the relationship. In the absence of more specific information as to how the bays orig-

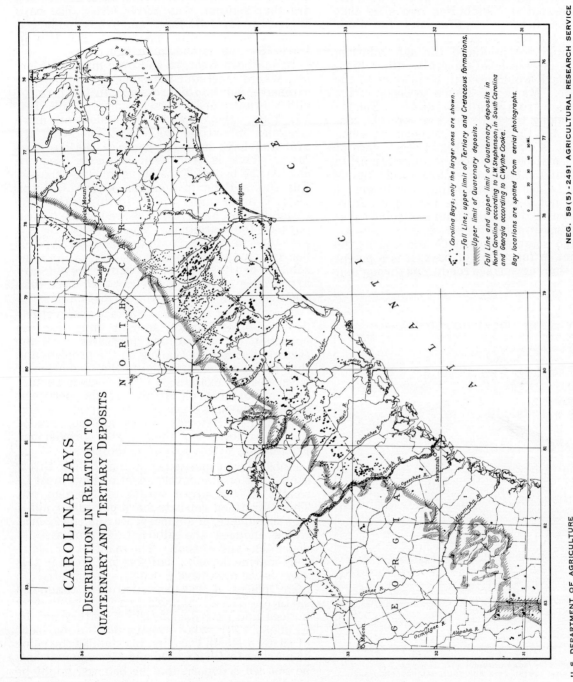

## CAROLINA BAYS
### DISTRIBUTION IN RELATION TO QUATERNARY AND TERTIARY DEPOSITS

*∵ Carolina Bays, only the larger ones are shown.*

*—— Fall Line; upper limit of Tertiary and Cretaceous formations.*

*- - - Upper limit of Quaternary deposits.*

*Fall Line and upper limit of Quaternary deposits in North Carolina according to L. W. Stephenson; in South Carolina and Georgia according to C. Wythe Cooke.*

*Bay locations are spotted from aerial photographs.*

NEG. 58(5)-2491 AGRICULTURAL RESEARCH SERVICE

U. S. DEPARTMENT OF AGRICULTURE

FIGURE 13.—The Carolina Bays consist of smoothly outlined, shallow, oval depressions, with major axes alined in the slope direction of the Coastal Plain. They are usually found on undrained interfluvial tracts. Not all of them could be represented on a map of such small scale. However, the clustered distribution pattern and the upper limit of occurrence may be seen. Bays are swampy, semiswampy, or lakes.

inated, the findings of geologists can be used only as a premise for the formulation of a working hypothesis in which subsurface conditions receive consideration.

Obviously, subsurface conditions cannot fully explain the formation of bays, but they hold the key to the spatial distribution and sites that have the structural requirements for their formation. If, for instance, bays are considered akin to sinkholes produced through solution, one of the more soluble minerals, either limestone or marl, would need to be present in the substratum. Marls are known to occur in the Coastal Plain from Virginia south into Florida and west along the gulf, but they are not continuous in the Carolinas. Consequently, when an attempt is made to correlate occurrence of bays with marlbeds, no consistent relationship can be found. Bays occur over and outside marlbeds, which indicates that formation of bays does not depend on the lithologic nature of the deposits; it also eliminates solution as the chief bay-producing process.

Although solution cannot be adduced as the chief agent in formation of bays, it is a potent factor in shaping surface conditions throughout extensive areas in the Coastal Plain. In the northern part, particularly in the Great Dover Swamp and White Oak and Lake Pocosins, where remnants of rims of exceptionally large bays are found, sometimes with eccentric smaller ones inside the larger ones, indications are that solution was active also. The bays evidently formed first and were enlarged through solution into pocosins. The bay in Dover Swamp is shown in figure 14.

In southern Georgia and over much of Florida, where marl and limestone formations are extensive, solution depressions, in the form of either swamps or lakes, are numerous (pls. 154, 157, 158). Usually these depressions are more irregular in outline than bays, but some are oval and have acquired some of the bay features. This is true even of those that are outside the belt of Pleistocene marine deposits. Big Dukes Pond in Jenkins County, Ga. (pl. 160), is an example (50). In this part of the Coastal Plain, however, bays are not the typical bays of the Carolinas. Therefore, there is a zone of transition from the solution type of depression and the area of real bays. As some solution depressions have acquired the outward appearance of bays, it is clear that more than one agent was active in the formation of bays.

*Development of Bays.*—Surface observations in themselves cannot account fully for the operation of bay-forming processes. All the factors that have a bearing on the problem and that may have contributed to the formation of bays must be examined. They include surface and subsurface conditions. If the pertinent factors known to exist in the area are correlated, new exterior forces are not needed for a satisfactory, though still provisional, explanation of the origin of the bays.

Subsurface conditions that may help to throw some light on the development of bays must be sought in the upper strata of the deposits. These stratified deposits mark periods of uplift and subsidence, of submergence and emergence, which induced the alternating processes of deposition and erosion. The mantle of Pleistocene marine deposits that was laid down in this way is comparatively thin. Apparently, in many places, it was deposited on a channeled surface. These channels were probably first noticed and described nearly a century ago by Emmons (40), who investigated the marlbeds of eastern North Carolina to establish the value of marl as fertilizer. During his examinations, he noticed a deposit that he believed might be used in certain instances as a soil amendment. These deposits were associated with the marl. He writes: "The circumstances attending its deposition were peculiar. It appears to have been deposited immediately after a period of denudation, as it rests not only upon the marl, but extends into, and fills deep channels which

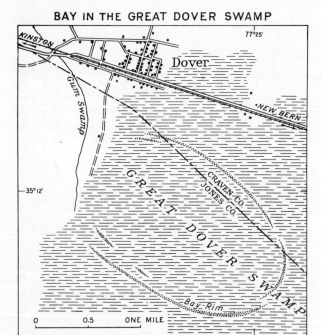

BAY IN THE GREAT DOVER SWAMP

U.S DEPARTMENT OF AGRICULTURE
NEG. 58(5)-2492 AGRICULTURAL RESEARCH SERVICE

FIGURE 14.—Bay rim remains are found at the western end of Great Dover Swamp in James County, N. C. The bay is about 2 miles long and more than a mile wide within the outer rim. Its position and elongated shape indicate that Dover Swamp with its bay developed over the preglacial channel of the Neuse River. The bay lies within the bend of the river and is oriented in line with the river above the bend.

had been cut out of the marl during the period alluded to. Hence, it appears to send down long tapering columns which extend sometimes to a point near the bottom of the bed. This formation, however, was formed from quiet waters, as there is no evidence of a rush or violent flow of waters, by the presence of larger rocks or even coarse pebbles." Since then other geologists have reported on these channels.

Channeling of the erosion contacts of the Tertiary with the overlying Quaternary deposits evidently was involved in the formation of bays in that it provided internal drainage channels where no surface drainage had developed. With some variations, these channels corresponded roughly to the slope of the plain, as do the major axes of the bays.

That development of bays had its inception during the later part of the Pleistocene Epoch was confirmed by the pollen investigation of Jerome Bog and Singletary Lake, both of which are in the cluster of bays that extends through Bladen County, N. C. Associations of pollen fossils in the successive levels of deposits provide a record of the adjustment of vegetation to changes in climate. The pine-fir-spruce level indicates the coldest stage; it is identified with the Wisconsin glaciation period. To supplement the pollen record, organic layers of Singletary Lake were used to determine age by means of the radiocarbon technique. It was found that the zone of maximum pollen concentration provided by the hemlock-beech-hickory-oak association, which is near the top of the sediments and indicates a moderate postglacial climate, had an approximate age of 10,000 years. The radiocarbon data indicate that the middle organic layers are more than 38,000 years old (15, 51, 103). But if a uniform rate of sedimentation is assumed, the lowest layers of bay sediments are estimated to be anywhere from 40,000 to 100,000 years old.

More important than changes in temperature during the Pleistocene Epoch in any attempt to explain the formation of bays were the changes in precipitation and wind velocity. Sufficient evidence has accumulated to indicate that mechanical rather than chemical processes were active in the surface layers, and that they were supplied primarily by the precipitation and winds of Pleistocene time.

Pluvial and dry periods have left incontestable marks of their occurrence, but there is no evidence to permit comparison of intensity with present conditions. Indirect evidence, derived mainly from biogeographical records, and the assumed reaction of the air-mass movement to the extension of northern ice sheets provide an idea of the amount of precipitation that fell during the later part of the Pleistocene Epoch. A map of North America, indicating the "Hypothetical mean annual rainfall at the maximum of the Wisconsin glaciation," in comparison with the present mean annual rainfall, has been worked out on this basis (33). As represented on this map, precipitation in the southern Coastal Plain was heavier during the Wisconsin glaciation than it is now. Even currently, this area receives a rather heavy precipitation (fig. 15). The annual average ranges from 45 to more than 50 inches, a good proportion of which falls in heavy downpours.

Frequent heavy drenching of nearly level or slightly undulating land, in which much of the moisture is absorbed by the soil, sets in motion the internal sorting action of the particles that comprise the soil. In the process of infiltration, the percolating water washes the finer particles of soil down from the upper levels, and they are precipitated in the lower levels. How effective this process is in dislodging the finer particles of soil may be judged from the results of an experiment conducted at the New Jersey Agricultural Experiment Station. The experiment extended throughout a year in which total precipitation at the station was recorded at 45 inches, about normal, but with a heavy concentration of rainfall in the early part of the growing season. From measured spot results of the experiment, it was calculated that of the finer particles of soil, more than 800 pounds per acre had been washed down from the upper plow-depth level into the subsoil, some of them to a depth of 20 to 30 inches. Consequently, the pores of the subsoil became clogged, internal drainage was impaired, and damage to the crop resulted (95, p. 13).

During the pluvial periods of the Pleistocene Epoch, where surface drainage was inadequate most of the water infiltrated the soil, but eluviation or leaching did not always stop at the subsoil level. Apparently over channeled contacts the downward moving water gravitated toward the subterranean drainage channels. Protracted washing dislodged the finer particles of the sediments and flushed them down into the underground channels. In time, this, combined in some instances with solution, reduced the overburden and brought about slumping over the underground outlets. The shallow depressions thus formed must have been filled with water repeatedly. The action of waves evidently helped both to smooth the shorelines of the bays and to build the rims. Sand left on the surface was exposed to the action of the wind during dry stages. Wind action no doubt accounts for the broad spoilrims on the eastern quadrant of some of the larger bays.

Evidently, the process of eluviation continued intermittently for some time. Gradually, it silted up the underground channels. The channel fillings discovered and described by Emmons (40) may have been of this type. The progressive clogging up of the pore spaces in the channels retarded the movement of water. The water was held in the depressions long enough so that the sediments brought in by wind and the percolating water had time to precipitate at the bottom. Accumulation of sediments in the bays was slow. In Singletary Lake, the rate of accumulation has been calculated at 1 inch for each 730 years. The shallow waters and wet bottoms of the depressions were favorable for establishment of the swampland vegetation that produced the accumulation of organic deposits, which are more or less prevalent in the bays.

For the time being, the genesis of the Carolina Bays can be presented only as an inference of the available evidence. But interior limits of bay occurrence, and their age, distributional characteristics, and orientation, all point toward the premise that the underlying geologic structure provided locally a favorable ground condition, and that the waters and winds of Pleistocene time were the forces that produced the bays. Not all the premises on which the conclusions are based can be verified. Others that might be verified have not yet been investigated as, for instance, the relationship of bays to subsurface channels. Until these points are cleared up, the conclusions reached remain hypothetical.

*Other Wet Lands.*—Wet lands, swamps, pocosins, and bays are the predominating physiographic features of the landscape in the lower Coastal Plains. Very little pocosin or swamp land has been reclaimed. Much of this land is not suitable for reclamation through drainage. The extensive peat deposits in these swamps would not provide a desirable soil for the usual types of farming. Consequently, these lands would be better left in forest to serve as wildlife refuges (pl. 156). A number of the smaller bays on higher ground, for which drainage did not involve elaborate engineering, have been reclaimed and the land is now used for crops (pl. 162). Aside from the comparatively small reclaimed areas in these parts of the Coastal Plain, cropland is closely adjusted to drainage. Usually, cropland is found in belts along the swampy bottoms of rivers and creeks, where drainage is better or can be improved through ditching (pl. 168), and along the old shorelines of Pleistocene time, which are usually a few feet higher than the surface of the interstream flats (pl. 161).

The bays and pocosins of the Carolinas, however, are not the only basins found in the Coastal Plain. Clustered or scattered shallow depressions occur on the Delmarva Peninsula, as far north as Townsend, Del., and over much of southern New Jersey. Although these basins are thought to be related to the Carolina Bays, they lack the most impressive characteristic of the bays, the prevailing elliptical shape with major axes oriented in a southeast–northwest direction. They have other characteristics in common. All the basins are associated with poorly drained land and consequently produce the same economic reaction. As a rule, they have retarded conversion of the land to primary production, and as they depend largely on interior drainage, they are instrumental in helping to recharge the ground water supply (*161, 100*).

The agricultural use potentiality of the land in the lower Coastal Plain is not necessarily restricted to the land now used for crops. A more diversified type of farming, featuring more livestock, might be introduced. Crop specialties for which the climate is favorable could be grown also. Growing of these specialties, however, usually requires heavy applications of fertilizer, as soil leaching is more active here than in other parts of the country. In either case, expansion of agriculture would need to include reclamation. Aside from the extensive swamps, a considerable acreage of wet land with fairly good soil would require clearing and community drainage for agricultural use. In most instances, the natural obstacles cannot be removed by individual effort. Because public aid would be required, the public at large would need a fuller understanding of these obstacles.

## Influence of Climate on Land Use

It is evident that climate controls the use of the land to a certain extent. Because of this, climate deserves more than casual recognition by those who use the land, especially those who live in transition zones where the hazards of weather are greatest. Precipitation, temperature, sunshine, and wind operate in conjunction and in varying degree affect the use capability of the land. Variations in climate and their spatial distribution are largely the result of differences in latitude, along with modifications produced by the arrangement of land and water bodies and the location of mountains and plains with reference to prevailing winds.

### Precipitation

In the lower and middle latitudes, the amount of precipitation permits or restricts the number of alternative major uses that can be made of the land. The three major land uses—crops, grazing, and forests—are possible as alternative uses with adequate precipitation during the growing season. With a decrease in precipitation, the number of alternative uses is reduced. Forest use is eliminated first, and finally only grazing remains. With increasing aridity, even grazing becomes impossible.

In the United States, the use capability of large areas is affected by insufficient precipitation. In general, precipitation decreases from east to west but no uniform precipitation re-

# AVERAGE ANNUAL PRECIPITATION

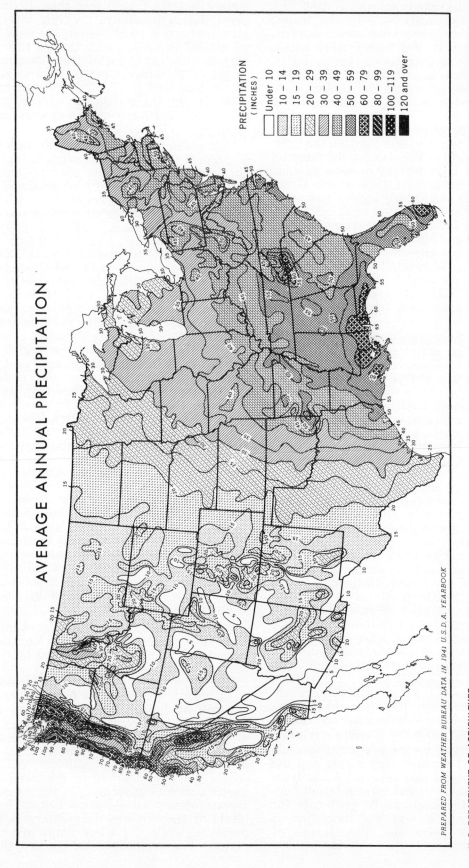

PRECIPITATION
( INCHES )

- Under 10
- 10 – 14
- 15 – 19
- 20 – 29
- 30 – 39
- 40 – 49
- 50 – 59
- 60 – 79
- 80 – 99
- 100 –119
- 120 and over

*PREPARED FROM WEATHER BUREAU DATA IN 1941 U.S.D.A. YEARBOOK*

U. S. DEPARTMENT OF AGRICULTURE        NEG. 58 (5) -2501 AGRICULTURAL RESEARCH SERVICE

FIGURE 15.—From this map, the overall distribution of precipitation can be visualized. Averages were derived from records that have varied widely over the years. They do not indicate what may be expected in any one year at any particular place. Distance from the ocean and arrangement of mountains and plains with reference to the prevailing direction of the wind affect the amount and distribution of precipitation.

quirement can be cited as constituting the lower limit to cropland use. In the South, which has a higher evaporation and transpiration ratio, more is needed than farther north. In this connection, average annual precipitation is frequently cited as indicating such limits. Admittedly, average annual precipitation is useful in illustrating general conditions, but it is not a reliable index of what may be expected, nor does it reflect the prevalent seasonal distribution of precipitation within a region throughout the year (fig. 15). The seasonal distribution of precipitation is important in some regions and for certain crops. In the semiarid Great Plains, rainfall is particularly appreciated after a prolonged dry spell in spring or summer at a time when crop failure can be averted (*139*). In the arid fringe, departures from the mean annual precipitation are sometimes pronounced. In this belt, deficient precipitation is a hazard that is recorded not only in low yields or crop failures but in higher crop-insurance rates, which increase proportionately with the risk involved.

Occasionally, there are significant departures from what may be considered normal amounts of precipitation. Moreover, average annual precipitation is not a true indication of the moisture supply available for crops. Seasonal distribution of precipitation and temperature, and length of growing season have much to do with the effectiveness of the moisture supply that is derived from precipitation.

Departures from the annual mean precipitation are significant even in the humid eastern part of the United States (*77*), but as a rule they are of little consequence. Crop yields are affected by too much or too little rain, but they are seldom damaged to the extent of approaching total failure. The risk from too much precipitation is not so much the result of seasonal variation as it is of intensity of rainfall. Torrential rains are rather frequent in some sections of the Southern States (*144, 166*). The heaviest concentration of rainfall is found along the gulf coast from Louisiana east to and including northern Florida, where annual precipitation is heavy. On inadequately drained land, the soil remains waterlogged for some time after such rains, and this is a drawback to agricultural use of the land. On well-drained rolling-to-hilly country, these torrential rainstorms, with their sudden increase in runoff, produce damaging floods and accelerate erosion.

The other extreme on the precipitation scale is reached in the western high plains and the intermountain basins and valleys. Aside from the mountains and plateaus, precipitation here is so low that the land can be used only for grazing. If crops are grown, irrigation is required. Some years ago, the Bureau of Reclamation estimated that about 240,000

square miles received less than 10 inches of precipitation annually. Within this area, a good proportion receives even less than 5 inches of annual rainfall, and although this amount may be sufficient to sustain some pasture plants in places, the absence of stock water precludes use of this land for pasture most of the time. Only during the occasional winters in which snow falls and stays on the ground can sheep be driven in to pasture such land.

Changes in precipitation usually pass through a gradual transition, although exceptions to this rule occur. In the western mountains, strong contrasts in relief have produced equally strong contrasts in precipitation within short distances. The strongest contrasts are found near the Pacific coast. Humid onshore winds from the ocean discharge much of their moisture in their ascent over the Coastal Range and the higher Sierra Nevada and Cascade Mountains, while the valleys behind these mountains receive little. In this way, Mt. Olympus in Washington receives the highest precipitation in the United States. According to some publications, it may exceed 140 inches, although no station records apply to the higher levels. Northeast of the mountain on Puget Sound, some 30 miles from the crest, the annual mean precipitation decreases to less than 20 inches. A similar contrast exists farther south between the western slope of the Sierra Nevada, where annual precipitation is about 50 inches, and Death Valley, 40 miles to the east, where it falls to about an inch, the lowest in the United States. Land use must be adjusted to these conditions. The humid western slopes of the mountains support a heavy forest growth, whereas the drier valleys—those between the coastal ranges and the Sierra-Cascade Mountains—have developed into the most diversified agricultural land use areas we have. Where rainfall is too low for the most effective agricultural use of the land, it is supplemented by irrigation. Water is supplied by the runoff from the bordering mountains.

Precipitation differentials between the higher and lower places in the Rocky Mountains are marked, as is effectively recorded by the vegetation. Changes in vegetation from lower to higher elevations indicate that in the mountains more moisture is available for plant growth as a result of higher precipitation and a lower evaporation-transpiration ratio. Tree growth and forest use of the land are therefore confined to the mountains. The lower limit of tree growth, however, is not uniform; it is higher in the south and lower in the north, and it varies also with exposure. In these mountains, forests occupy an elevation belt. The upper limits of the belt are defined largely by temperature, while the lower limits are chiefly a matter of precipitation. Of the two, the lower limit is frequently more sharply defined than the upper (pl. 81).

## Temperature

The influence of temperature on land use in middle latitudes is not as closely related to major uses as is precipitation, but its restrictive power increases with advancing latitude and higher elevation (pl. 11). When the prevailing temperature is so low that frost may occur in any month, use of the land for crops other than hay is almost excluded. The length of the frost-free period and temperatures during the growing season have much to do with the kind of crops that are grown in a region (pl. 4). Within the humid eastern half of the United States, the crop belts known as the Cotton, Corn, and Dairy Belts, are largely the result of temperature. That modifications in temperature through elevation and land relief are involved in delimiting these belts may be observed on the northern boundary of the Cotton Belt. The northern cotton limit skirts the Southern Appalachians and Ozark Mountains, but in the Mississippi Valley, it extends as far north as Cairo at the southern tip of Illinois.

## Elevation

The following example illustrates how differences in elevation modify climate and with it affect the agricultural use of the land. Apparently, Johnson Mesa in northern New Mexico is the highest place in the United States where crops, aside from hay, are grown. On this mesa, wheat, oats, and barley, in addition to hay, are grown at an elevation of 8,200 feet. The frost-free season averages about 110 days (pl. 112). At the other extreme is the Imperial Valley in southern California, the lowest spot in the United States at which crops are grown. Here most of the cultivated land is from zero to 200 feet below sea level (Salton Sea is –240 feet) and the valley has an average of more than 300 days without frost, or practically a year-round growing season. In some years, there is no frost. Subtropical fruits and vegetables for the market are grown in winter (pl. 107). The latitudes of these two areas— Johnson Mesa and Imperial Valley—are only 4 degrees apart.

## Winds

Wind makes the headlines more often as a result of its violent temper and destructive propensities than in recognition of its more gentle moods and beneficial functions as a distributor of temperature and moisture over the earth's surface.

The free motion of the atmosphere provides a many-sided topic for discussion. Early Renaissance cartographers decorated the margins of their maps with wind faces in all quadrants, that is, wind blew from all four corners at the same time. This is about the impression that a casual observer may get at times. So many contingencies affect the movement of air that apparently no order of any kind exists. In reality, air mass drifts follow prevalent directions in response to several factors. In this instance, the cause and effect relationship stems from the heating of the air in lower levels and latitudes, and the cooling off in higher elevations and near the poles. The air movement itself derives direction from the rotation of the earth, the distribution of land and water bodies, and the arrangement of relief features on the land. Not all these factors are constants. The seasonal rhythm of climate usually induces changes in wind direction. In so doing, it may have a compensatory effect on the distribution of precipitation. Some regions are so constituted that no benefits accrue from these changes. As an example, the arid intermountain basins and valleys of the West are parapeted by mountain ranges to the east and west, and little moisture can reach them from either the gulf or the Pacific Ocean.

In some regions, the prevailing winds have produced distinct landscape features. Trees that bend picturesquely indicate the prevailing direction of the wind. In the Western Plains, where there are no obstacles to break the force of the wind, field operations frequently take account of the force and direction of the wind to prevent soil erosion. Stripcropping is often resorted to, and the strips are cut diametrically across the wind direction. The result is a striking land use pattern characteristic of these areas (pls. 65, 73, 74). Shelterbelts are also a form of wind protection in some parts of the Plains. On the eastern prairies, where some trees can be grown, they are planted in protective belts on the windward side of the farmsteads. These windbreaks are an outstanding feature of the landscape in otherwise treeless plains (pls. 54, 62, 67, 70).

## Adjustment to Climate

That land use must harmonize with climate is usually recognized, but the hazards involved are not always appreciated. No area is entirely free from these hazards, but in one form or another certain areas are more exposed to them than others. In subtropical areas, an occasional heavy winter frost may damage citrus fruit. Late spring frosts are a hazard to deciduous fruits. Damage from drought and hail is more frequent and severe in the semiarid belt. Tornadoes are usually confined to the Southern and Eastern States, but heavy rainstorms that cause floods may be expected to occur anywhere within the humid and subhumid zones. In summer and fall when the weather is dry, protection from forest fires is most needed. Heavy snow endangers livestock and wildlife on the open range. These are a few examples of climatic hazards in the United States that are related to use of the land.

The connection between climate and the capabilities of land use, particularly for agriculture, became apparent with the settlement and development of the country. The land became drier and the vegetation sparser as the settlers moved farther west. They called the semiarid plains the "Great American Desert," an indication that reliable information as to weather was needed for development of the country. Agriculture still has particular need for it. Most crops have their own range of climatic conditions under which their growth is most successful. It was obvious that climatic reports and records from stations scattered over the country were needed. The United States Weather Bureau had its inception in 1870, in the Signal Service of the United States Army. Some two decades later, it was transferred to the United States Department of Agriculture, and it was later moved to the United States Department of Commerce. Its functions and the number of reporting stations have expanded steadily. In 1955, there were more than 10,000 reporting stations, of which only about a third were staffed with paid personnel. The rest were operated by unpaid cooperative observers.

The literature on weather, climatology, and meteorology is voluminous. Only a few of the publications that present the subject comprehensively with a land use orientation can be cited here (*74; 118; 135, 1941; 146*).

## Soils in Relation to Land Use

Use of land for primary production is in reality mainly concerned with the use of the soil mantle. Thus, the importance of the soil in relation to land use is highlighted, as not all soils are equally well adapted to specific uses. The economic significance of the many recognizable properties of soil increases when these properties pertain to arable land. Whether the land can be used successfully for production of cultivated crops depends, in many instances, on the nature of the soil. How the soil must be managed to produce the best yields year after year is again related to its characteristics.

Soil characteristics may be thought of as the marks of distinction that evolved in the process of soil development. Usually, they are referred to in terms of soil profile. Fully developed soils consist of a vertical succession of layers, which soil scientists call horizons. These layers may differ in texture, structure, color, and chemical composition. In their stratified sequence from the surface down to the parent material, they compose the profile of the soil. Many factors have contributed to the morphological characteristics of the soil profile. Some of these influences vary with location in the local environment; others are identified with natural conditions of regional extent.

### Parent Materials

To begin with, the parent material of the soil has certain characteristics of its own, which to some extent are transmitted to the soil. The parent material may consist of the accumulated debris produced by weathering and disintegration of the underlying rock. In these instances, the rock may be limestone, sandstone, slate, or granite, to cite only a few petrographic distinctions, so that the soil-developing processes had to act on minerals of differing textures and chemical compositions. As a result, the soil develops characteristics, which in popular parlance are frequently identified with the rocks from which the parent material was derived. This is true also when the parent material consists of unconsolidated glacial, fluvial, marine, lake, or wind deposits. Most of the characteristics inherited from the parent material are recorded in the texture and chemical composition of the soil. Extensive and compact areas can be identified as having soils developed from parent material, which are derived from the same or similar geologic formation. In other areas, the geologic background is more complex; it is this complexity that is usually responsible for a number of soil types in any locality.

### Climate as It Affects Soil

Among the soil-developing agents, climate ranks highest in that it affects the soils both directly and indirectly in more than one direction. The direct action of weather is both mechanical and chemical; soils are affected by precipitation, temperature, wind, and running water. Indirectly, climate operates through the intermediary of vegetation and animal life in that their contributions to soil building are already adjusted to climatic factors.

Two major soil groups, those well leached and those incompletely leached, are produced by humid climates as opposed to those produced under subhumid and arid conditions. All of the incompletely leached dryland soils have one characteristic in common: All have a calcareous zone in the lower part of the profile that rises gradually to the surface with advancing aridity. A gradation of soils brought about by the differentials of temperature, which affect the color of the soil, is particularly noticeable in the forested humid part of the country. When compared with northern soils, well-drained southern soils are more colorful, especially in the subsurface horizons. The latter range from pale yellow to dark red. The former are usually grayish or brownish. The processes that produced these distinctions in color are known as podzolization for the gray-brown soil and laterization for the yellow-red soils.

There are many transitional phases. Soils in the podzolic soil group frequently encroach on the lateritic soils. Podzolization is mainly a process of leaching in a cool to temperate climate under forest cover. Laterization is characterized by the presence of iron oxides and hydroxides of aluminum; it occurs commonly in humid tropical regions. In the United States, only weak stages of laterization have developed. The yellow and red soils of the South fall into this class. Red pebble land, which contains pebbles of iron concretions, furnishes the best example.

## Effect of Natural Vegetation on Soil

Natural vegetation, which is related to climate, has also contributed toward development of the soils. In so doing, it has produced its own marks of distinction. Soils that developed under a grass cover are easily distinguished from those that developed under a forest vegetation. Forests do not produce humus in the upper mineral horizon of the soil as do grasses. The humus produced by the northern forests carpets the forest floor; when dissolved, it is leached to a lower horizon. In southern forests, very little organic matter accumulates. In the warmer climate, decomposition is speeded up to a point at which little organic matter is left from one year to the next.

In contrast to the forests, a grass-type vegetation produces humus in the upper layer of the soil through root decay, which gives these soils their black or dark brown color. Black earth, or Chernozem, is usually cited as representative of this kind of soil. Chernozem, a soil group developed under grass cover in a subhumid climate, is almost black. At a depth of about 3 feet, it has a zone of calcium accumulation. The prairie soils of Iowa, central Illinois, southern Minnesota, and northern Missouri represent a predominantly American kind of soil development, which has much in common with the Chernozems, but which, because they are leached, lack the calcareous zone. In the opposite direction, with the transition from the tall to the short grasses of the steppe type of vegetation, the humus content of the soil decreases and the color changes to brown. Finally, when the grasses give way to desert shrubs, the humus content of the soils becomes so negligible that the soil loses much of its color. Arid soils are ordinarily a light gray.

Animal life both within the earth and on its surface has also contributed to development of soils, but as its action is desultory, it is not discussed here.

## Soils Affected by Land Relief

Differences in land relief also produce differences in soils. These differences are due largely to the reaction of the processes of soil development to drainage. For normal development of soil, well-drained but not excessively drained land is needed. On steeply sloping land, erosion is likely to be too active to allow sufficient time for proper development of the soil profile. Soils of the steeper mountain slopes, therefore, are mainly shallow and rocky. On rugged mountainsites, the rate of erosion may even exceed that of rock weathering and the rocks may remain barren.

Low gradients and level surfaces produce soil profiles of their own as a result of inadequate drainage. The precipitation that falls on such land drains off slowly. It is largely dissipated through evaporation, transpiration, or infiltration into the soil itself. In these instances, the internal movement of water in the soil carries with it the finer particles from the upper horizon and deposits them in a lower horizon. This results in formation of hard or clay pans, which in turn impede internal drainage of the soil. The process is known as eluviation.

In shallow depressions of the humid region, in which water moves only sluggishly or remains standing most of the time, swampland vegetation usually takes possession of the area. Over the years, it builds up an organic soil, which consists of layers of peat and muck. As we now know, the extensive peat bogs in the eastern half of the United States were thousands of years in the making and have their own land use implications (pls. 50, 156).

## Development of Soils Affected by Other Factors

The major factors of soil development have been mentioned. Other factors are more restricted in their fields of operation, but within these limits they are just as effective as the major factors in determining land use capability. The playas of the arid West are examples of this kind. When these basin floors were flooded by the runoff from the tributary watershed, they also received the salts leached out from the rocks and soils of the area. When the water evaporated, the salts remained. In places, these saline accumulations are so concentrated and toxic as to prevent plant growth altogether. In these instances, soil salinity accounts for the desert condition. The Black Rock Desert in Nevada and the Great Salt Lake Desert in Utah are the largest deserts of this type in the country.

Wind as a disturbing element in soil development is most active in the subhumid-semiarid belt. The use capability of extensive areas has been reduced by the action of the wind. The Sand Hills of Nebraska is such an area; it forms a compact area of 19,000 square miles north of the Platte River within the subhumid zone. Here, the sorting action of the wind has carried off the finer particles of the soil but has left the ridges of sand. In contrast to the adjacent country to the north and south, where much of the undissected plain is used for cultivated crops, the Sand Hills can be used only for grazing (pl. 66). The cropland scattered over the Sand Hills lies in the moist depressions, where native grasses are cut for hay to supplement livestock feed in winter. Smaller areas of sandy land in the subhumid belt, in which land use is confined to grazing, are located on the High Plains and the Coastal Plain farther south (pl. 125).

Wind action is no doubt responsible for another type of soil development on the Llano Estacado, which has brought about a similar reduction in land use capability. Rainfall over much of the southern end of the Llano Estacado is sufficient to permit production of cotton, and it is grown in a number of places where the soil is suited to the purpose. In extensive areas, however, the surface soil is sand that was blown in from the Pecos Plains to the west. In other areas, the topsoil is shallow because part of it has been removed by the wind (pl. 120). The largest area with a sandy topsoil abuts the wide breach in the western escarpment south of the Mescalero Rim. The two transverse sand-dune belts formed in the same way are even more impressive in the restrictions they impose on land use. (See figure 20.) In these instances, the best use that can be made of the land is grazing.

## Use Capability Affected

Light sandy soils in the humid eastern half of the country have decreased the utilitarian value of land in several instances. The outwash plains in northwestern and central Wisconsin and the north-central part of the southern peninsula of Michigan seem destined to remain in forests almost exclusively. Outside the glaciated region, well-known parts of the country fall into the same category. The Pine Barrens of southern New Jersey, and the Sand Hills below the Fall Line in the Carolinas and Georgia, are the larger areas for which recreation and forests are the best uses that can be made of most of the land.

Shallow and rocky soils have also eliminated alternative land use possibilities over considerable areas. Rough topography and rocky, shallow soils have made the mountains a stronghold of forests. But there are other areas, like the Superior Upland in Minnesota, tracts in northern Wisconsin and Michigan (pl. 41), and New England (pls. 2, 6), which are not mountainous but which have rocky soils that are a serious obstacle to cultivation. Because of this, forest combined with recreation is the prevailing land use. Outside the forested region, the only major land use left in such instances is grazing. In the Great Plains, the Flint Hills of Kansas furnish an illustration. In the Flint Hills, extensive tracts of grassland dominate the landscape. Cherty soils, frequently shallow, developed from the residuum of limestone, explain the predominantly grazing use of the land in the Flint Hills (pl. 61). The lava flows in the Snake River Plain are similar land use controlling features (pl. 89).

Land use is not always so positive in its reaction to soil distinctions as to eliminate one or the other of the major uses altogether. In a good many instances, land is in a marginal class for certain uses because of the soils, especially when crop production is involved. Handicaps imposed by soils can be overcome to a considerable extent through skillful management, use of soil-improvement practices and soil amendments, and selection of crops best suited to the soil. In the South, soils of comparatively low natural fertility, that would not qualify for common field crops, are in some instances used successfully to grow winter vegetables. Whether or not land is marginal is therefore not entirely a matter of soil and other physical conditions. The human factor also enters into the equation. Use of the land may revolve around questions of land ownership and tenure as well as market demands and prices of crops and products. Areas with soils in the lower productivity brackets, however, are more sensitive to these socio-economic influences. As a result, they show the greatest shifts in major land uses. In New England and the South, where much of the land falls into this class, these shifts are pronounced.

Man's dependence on the products of the soil leads inevitably to the conclusion that the soil should be regarded as a permanent resource base of organic production. As the needs of the country are rising, the preservation and improvement of the soil are essential to ensure not only sustained but increased production. From the national viewpoint, soil conservation is a social obligation that will benefit not only individual landowners but also the community and the Nation as a whole.

## Pioneers Exploited Land

Soils have not always been considered in the light of future needs. Conservation as a concept did not disturb the pioneer settlers. They had to wrest a living from the land with simple implements by dint of hard labor. Their knowledge and experience of the destructive forces of nature were slight. The cultural practices they followed were in keeping with their meager resources. Usually they were calculated to satisfy immediate needs. Although the pioneers usually selected the smoother land for arable use because of its natural advantages and their own physical limitations, they seldom took into account these advantages or limitations when it came to field operations. The usual procedure was to lay out the land in tracts that might be oriented by property lines or might follow the trend of the topography, but in cultivating the land, slope or contour was not followed. All too frequently, continued cultivation in this way induced erosion that not only depleted the soil but in many instances made the land useless for further crop production.

Induced erosion is closely associated with steepness of slope, characteristics of precipitation, erosiveness of the soil, and the cultural practices followed. The most severe erosion damage is found on rolling to hilly land in the humid and subhumid parts of the country. In extreme instances, cropland has been gullied to the extent of eliminating arable use from further consideration. Abandonment results, and the land usually reverts to brush and forest. There are exceptions to the rule. Erosion in the humid grassland soils of the Rendzina group is likely to reduce their use capability from arable to pastoral. The Black Prairie Belt soils of Alabama and Mississippi and the soils of the Black Prairie in Texas belong in this group. These soils developed on soft chalky limestone under grass vegetation. Originally, they were rich in humus and lime, almost black, and very productive. Continuous cropping to cotton and corn, both row crops that induce erosion easily with indifferent methods of cultivation, has greatly depleted the soils. With the removal of much of the humus layer, the soils have become heavier. This retards cultivation in spring. As a result, cotton has become more susceptible to boll weevil attacks. Changed soil and biological conditions have also brought about a change in use of the land. The Black Belt of Alabama and Mississippi, which at one time was the leading cotton-producing district of the South, is now a livestock area. Most of the former cottonland is now in grass, to which the calcareous soil is well adapted, and is used for pasture and production of hay (pl. 150). A somewhat similar trend is noticeable in the Black Prairie of Texas, especially in the southern part (pl. 116).

Soil erosion is not always the result of the action of water. On the High Plains, where rainfall is scanty, wind erosion is likely to be just as active during protracted dry periods, and as damaging to soils as water erosion (pl. 63). Abandonment of cropland has resulted from it in a number of places. With use as cropland eliminated, only pastoral use remains.

Soil erosion from both water and wind has caused permanent loss of soil over much of the country. It has reduced the productive capacity of the land, and in many instances it has damaged the land to the extent of making further use as cropland impossible. Damage incident to erosion is not confined to land from which the soil has eroded. The silt and sand washed from the slopes are carried by creeks and streams to lower levels and deposited in flood plains and stream channels. Eroded, unprotected upland accelerates runoff, and clogged-up water channels slow down streamflow and increase the danger of floods. Reservoirs located on the streams are silted up, their water-storing capacity is progressively reduced, and their span of usefulness is shortened proportionally. Accelerated runoff and increasing damage from erosion led finally to the extension of conservation measures to the soils, which in many parts of the country have produced their own cultural landscape features.

Conservation measures extend to all major land uses, including use for recreation and preservation of wildlife. On the western open range, it means controlled grazing as provided by grazing districts, and improvement of the forage plant cover. In forested areas, conservation is concerned with the proper management of forests to obtain higher and more sustained yields of wood products, and at the same time to preserve the forests, including the natural fauna and flora they shelter. Fire protection, restocking of denuded areas, and watershed protection are some of the measures that serve these purposes. A number of areas have been set aside as reservations to conserve the scenic values of the landscape as historical monuments, areas for preservation of wildlife, or catchment areas to obtain a dependable supply of pure water. In agricultural regions, conservation efforts are directed primarily toward soil conservation. Contour plowing, terracing, stripcropping, and keeping the land under protective cover are practices followed to prevent erosion. Stripcropping is also resorted to in the Western Plains to minimize wind erosion. Wherever soil conservation practices are followed, they produce a new and impressive land use pattern (pls. 13, 18, 53, 65, 73, 74, 114, 121, 126, 143, 149, 151, 163).

The soil regions mentioned in the text can be identified readily in figure 16.

Aside from having acquired local site characteristics, soils also show regional affinities that may be derived from land relief, geologic formation, climate, natural vegetation, drainage, or a combination of these factors. Only the regional associations can be shown in a strongly generalized representation to illustrate occurrence and distribution of different soils on a small-scale map, such as this one.

The map shown in figure 16 and its legend were prepared more than 25 years ago. Thus they do not reflect all the latest concepts in soil classification. They are in general agreement with the soil map in the 1938 Yearbook of Agriculture. The soil regions, as delimited on the map shown here, readily permit tracing

# IMPORTANT SOIL REGIONS

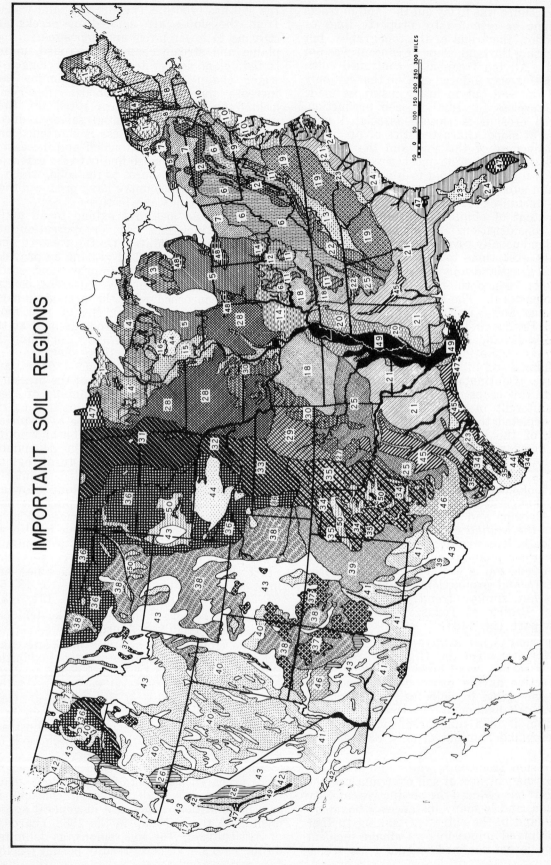

U. S. DEPARTMENT OF AGRICULTURE       NEG. 58(5)-2500 AGRICULTURAL RESEARCH SERVICE

FIGURE 16.—Map showing soil regions. (Prepared in the former Bureau of Chemistry and Soils.)

## Legend for Map

*Podzols.*—The profile consists of a thin organic layer above a gray leached layer which rests on a dark-brown or coffee-brown horizon. The Podzol is developed usually under a coniferous forest in a cool, moist climate. Its inherent productivity for crop plants is low. The figures below refer to area numbers on the map.

1. Rough stony land, including areas of shallow Podzols.
2. Chiefly loams and silt loams, developed from sandstones and shales of the plateau and mountain uplands.
3. Dominantly sands and loamy sands, developed on glacial drift.
4. Dominantly loams and clay loams, developed on glacial drift.

*Gray-Brown Podzolic Soils.*—The profile has a rather thin organic layer over grayish-brown leached soils which overlies a brown horizon. The soils are generally acid, at least in the surface. These soils develop in a moist and cool-temperate climate under a deciduous forest and are inherently more productive than the Podzols.

5. Dominantly loams and silt loams, developed on calcareous glacial drift.
6. Brownish-yellow silty loams or stony loams with hilly relief developed on sandstones and shales.
7. Loams and silt loams, developed on acid glacial drift and composed of sandstones and shale material. Some of these soils are imperfectly drained.
8. Dominantly stony and gravelly loams, developed on glacial drift.
9. Loams and silt loams, developed mainly on the crystalline rocks of the northern Piedmont.
10. Largely sandy loams developed on the sands and clays of the northern Coastal Plain.
11. Chiefly brown silt loams, developed on limestone.
12. Shallow soils developed on interbedded limestone and calcareous shales.
13. Loams and stony loams from granitic material with hilly to mountainous relief.
14. Silt loams with heavy clay subsoils, developed on Illinoian glacial till.
15. Silt loams developed largely from loess.
16. Imperfectly drained grayish silt loams with silty clay loam subsoils, developed from acid glacial drift.
17. Largely loams and silt loams with yellowish subsoils, developed from sandstones and shales.
18. Grayish-yellow to reddish silt loams and cherty sil tloams, developed from cherty limestones.

*Red and Yellow Soils.*—This group of soils consists of two general types of profiles that are intimately associated. Both have thin organic layers. The profile of the red soil is a yellowish-brown leached layer over a red horizon while the profile of the yellow soil is a grayish-yellow leached layer over a yellow horizon. Both developed under the forest in a moist warm-temperate

climate. Generally, the yellow profile is more pronounced under the coniferous forest and the red under the deciduous forest. The inherent fertility of the yellow soils is relatively low and that of the red soils medium.

19. Dominantly brownish-red clay loams and gray sandy loams, developed largely from crystalline rocks of the southern Piedmont.
20. Yellow to light brown silt loams, developed on loess.
21. Dominantly gray to yellow sandy and fine sandy loams with some sands and fine sands, developed from Coastal Plain materials.
22. Largely brownish-red to red silt loams and clay loams, developed from limestone.
23. Grayish-yellow to light brown sands and fine sands of the Coastal Plain.
24. Grayish fine sandy loams, with some gray or black loams, developed in the flatwoods area of the Coastal Plain. Includes areas underlain by coralline limestone.
25. Grayish-yellow to reddish fine sandy loams and silt loams, developed from sandstones and shales. A considerable portion is hilly and stony.
26. Red soils of the north Pacific slopes.

*Prairie Soils.*—The profile of the Prairie soil grades from a very dark brown or dark grayish-brown surface through brown to lighter colored parent material at a depth of 2 to 5 feet. It is developed in a moist temperate climate under a tall-grass prairie. Inherent fertility for crop plants is high.

27. Reddish-brown soils of variable texture, developed on sandstones, shales, clays, and sands.
28. Dark brown silt loams with yellowish-brown subsoils, developed on glacial drift and loess.
29. Dark brown to reddish-brown silt loams and clay loams, developed from limestone and calcareous shales.
30. Dark brown or grayish-brown silt loams, having heavy subsoils or claypans.

*Northern Chernozem.*—The profile has a black or dark grayish-brown surface soil grading below into light-colored material that is calcareous at 2 to 6 feet. It is developed in a temperate to cool subhumid climate under tall and mixed grasses. Inherent productivity is high.

31. Black, silt, and clay loams, developed on calcareous glacial drift and associated lacustrine deposits.
32. Dark grayish-brown loams and silt loams, developed from loess.
33. Dark grayish-brown silt loams with clay-pans developed from loess.

*Southern Chernozem—Dark Brown Soils.*—The profiles have dark brown to reddish-brown surface soils underlain by brown or red horizons, grading below into light-colored material that is calcareous at 3 to 6 feet. These soils develop in a warm, subhumid to semiarid climate under a mixed tall-and short-grass prairie.

34. Heavy or moderately heavy dark brown soils, developed from calcareous materials.
35. Predominantly red and brown sandy loams and sands, developed largely from unconsolidated calcareous sands, silts, and sandy clays.

*Northern Dark Brown (Chestnut) Soils.*—The profile grades from a dark brown surface soil into a whitish calcareous horizon at a depth of 1½ to 3 feet. These soils develop under mixed tall and short grasses in a temperate to cool semi-arid climate.

36. Dark brown soils developed on unconsolidated, calcareous sands, silts, and clays.
37. Dark brown soils, developed on heterogeneous material associated with mountainous and plateau terrain.

*Brown Soils.*—A brown surface soil grading at a depth ranging from 1 to 2 feet into a whitish calcareous horizon. The profile is developed in a temperate to cool, semiarid climate under short grasses, bunch grasses, and shrubs.

38. Northern—chiefly brown loams, developed largely on unconsolidated sands, silts, and clays.
39. Southern—chiefly light brown to gray fine sandy loams to silty clay loams of smooth relief, developed largely on limestone or unconsolidated sands, silts, and clays.

*Sierozem and Desert Soils.*—Grayish and reddish soils, closely underlain by calcareous material. These soils develop in an arid climate under short grass and desert plants.

40. Northern—gray and grayish-brown soils of variable texture, developed largely on loess and alluvial fan material.
41. Southern—gray, brown, and reddish soils of variable texture, developed largely on alluvial fans.

*Soils of the Pacific Valleys.*—42. Includes a number of variable zonal, azonal, and intrazonal soils that are too intimately associated to separate on a schematic map. These soils developed under a range of climatic and geological conditions.

*Intrazonal and Azonal Soils.*—These soils may possess one of the two general types of profile: (a) The profile may express a local condition as drainage or parent material rather than the zonal profile of the region; (b) the profile may be too immature to express a zonal type.

43. Rough and mountainous (azonal).
44. Largely azonal sands, some of which are associated with bogs.
45. Black (or brown) friable soil underlain by whitish material excessively high in calcium carbonate. These soils developed under a prairie vegetation and are known as Rendzinas (intrazonal).
46. Shallow stony soils from limestone (azonal).
47. Marsh, swamp, and bog (intrazonal).
48. Soils largely intrazonal, developed on lake plains.
49. Alluvial soils (azonal).
50. Rough broken land.

55

the influence of soils on land use on a regional basis.

For more localized information, the soil surveys can be consulted. Soil characteristics are mapped by counties with considerable detail. Much of the country is now covered by soil surveys, and the relationship of soil types to land use is discussed in each soil survey report.

The literature on soils is voluminous. A listing of county and areal surveys alone would fill pages. Only a few of the principal publications issued by the Department of Agriculture on the broader aspects of soil development, soil characteristics, and soil distribution can be cited here (86; 73; 135, 1938; 128; 10).

## Natural Vegetation and Land Use

The term "natural vegetation" is sometimes thought to refer to the original vegetative types, which in America belong to pre-Columbian times. However, very little of our present vegetative cover belongs to these types. Some small remnants of them remain, but with the use of the land by civilized man, most of the original plant associations were modified to a greater or lesser extent. For the natural vegetation with which we are here concerned, a somewhat broader concept is implied; in addition to the occasional remnants of the original vegetation, all vegetative types that grow without cultivation are included.

Natural vegetation is one of the chief assets in the economy of the country. Natural vegetation provides the only means of using land that cannot be used or is not needed for cultivated crop production, building sites, service areas, and so on. How significant a part the natural vegetation plays in the national economy may be perceived by comparing the acreages in major uses. In 1954, cultivated crops were grown on about 380 million acres, or 20 percent of the total land area of the United States, while on about 1,314 million acres, or 69 percent of the land area, natural vegetation was used. The rest is made up of urban areas, parks, service areas, desert, swamp, and wasteland. Thus natural vegetation on more than two-thirds of the land contributes to the national economy. This contribution is invaluable to the national economy, as some of our more important industries—the animal industry, the lumber and wood-working industries, the naval store, paper, printing, artificial fiber and leather industries, among others—largely or wholly depend upon it, either directly or indirectly. To the economic contributions made by the natural vegetation should be added the values imparted to the countryside by the voluntary growth of trees, shrubs, and grasses (fig. 17).

To a large extent, the three major types of vegetation indicate the potential use capability of the land. If forest land is well drained, has a smooth, not too strongly rolling, hilly or mountainous surface and a good soil, it can either be left in forest or, when cleared, used for cropland or pasture. Grassland may be used for either cropland or pasture. The only economic use that can be made of arid desert shrub land without irrigation is grazing.

The natural vegetation is a permanent asset to the Nation. However, neither the yields nor the composition of the natural plant cover remains the same with use or even with time. Modifications occur when man takes possession of the land or when the climate and other biological factors change. For instance, the native chestnut, which formerly was commonly found in eastern forests, has almost disappeared as a result of the chestnut blight. In both the North and the South, a number of exotics have been added to the list of trees.

### Natural Vegetation Changed by Land Use

Changes in the composition of the original vegetation that were brought about through man's use were usually accompanied by a decline in productive capacity. Clearing and use of the land for crops, especially in the eastern half of the country, greatly reduced the extent of native vegetation. In addition, the productive capacity per areal unit of the remaining natural vegetation was lowered. This was true of all major vegetative types—forests, prairies, and desert shrubs. Usually the natural vegetation was one of the resources that was first exploited. In the early stages of settlement, the native vegetative cover was used without a proper understanding of the need to safeguard its reproductive ability in order to retain its functional value in protecting the land and the water supply, and its enduring value as a basic economic resource. The result was an increasing deterioration, which makes proper management essential when natural vegetation provides the principal means of using the land.

*Forest.*—Originally, forests occupied a rather compact zone in the eastern part of the United States. Some prairie areas were interspersed, for instance, the Black Prairie of Alabama (pl. 150), the prairie areas of Texas (pls. 127 and 128), and some smaller ones in the Alluvial Valley of the Mississippi (pl. 133). There were also the open areas of Indian origin previously discussed. Aside from these occasional breaks, the forests stretched across hills and valleys without interruption to a park-like fringe (pl. 52), where they gave way to the prairies. In contrast to the East, the forests of the West were confined mainly to the mountains. They did not reach as far as the valley floors (pl. 81). They are identified largely with the central and northern Rockies, and the Sierra-Cascade and

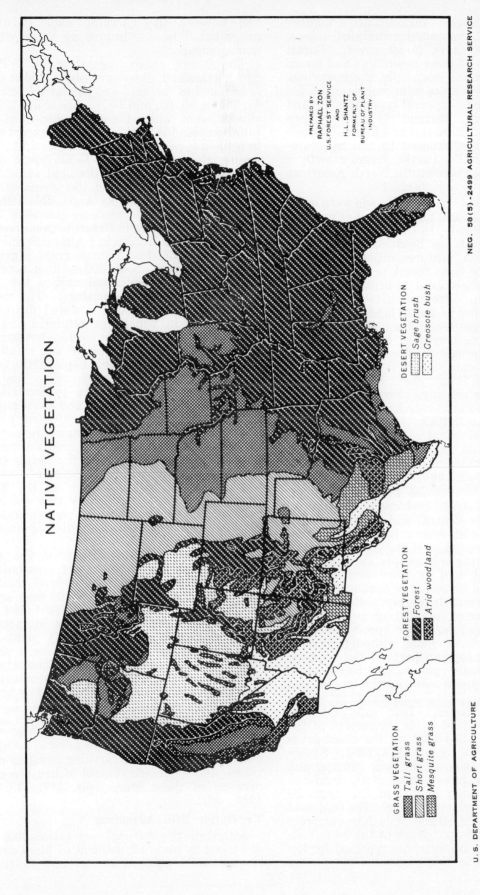

NATIVE VEGETATION

PREPARED BY
RAPHAEL ZON
U.S. FOREST SERVICE
AND
H. L. SHANTZ
FORMERLY OF
BUREAU OF PLANT
INDUSTRY

GRASS VEGETATION
▨ Tall grass
▨ Short grass
▨ Mesquite grass

FOREST VEGETATION
▨ Forest
▨ Arid woodland

DESERT VEGETATION
▨ Sage brush
▨ Creosote bush

U. S. DEPARTMENT OF AGRICULTURE          NEG. 58(5)-2499 AGRICULTURAL RESEARCH SERVICE

FIGURE 17.—What is now regarded as natural vegetation is the successor to the native vegetation found by the colonists and pioneer settlers of the country. The vegetative cover represents an adaptation to the physical environment and consequently mirrors the prevailing natural conditions. The distribution of forest, grassland, and desert shrub is controlled largely by climate.

Pacific coastal ranges. Included are a number of the higher disconnected mountains, mesas, and ranges that have forest cover. Forest growth on many of these mountains and mesas is rather sparse and open. On the lower elevations, it gives way to arid woodland of the pinon-juniper and chaparral types (pls. 83 and 84). On others, particularly the western slopes of the Pacific coastal and Sierra-Cascade ranges, which are exposed to the moisture-laden winds from the Pacific, forest growth is heavier than elsewhere on the North American Continent (pls. 95 and 99).

As the country developed, inroads were made into the more than 900 million acres of original forest and woodland. In the East, nearly half the original forest has been cleared to make room for cropland, pastures, cities, roads, and so on, but shifts from forest to cropland and reversions of cleared land to brush and forest are still going on. Proportionately less extensive is the clearing of forest land in the West. Much of the virgin forest has been cut over by now, some was destroyed by fire, and most of the rest is in the western forests. Restocking of depleted forests to restore the former stands and provide for future needs has not always progressed satisfactorily. Profound changes in the original forest cover have been brought about by man's activities. One of these is the reduction in areal extent with its distributional adjustment to the economic use capability of the land. The other is the frequent modification of the density and composition of tree associations in the second growth (54).

*Grassland and Arid Shrubland.*—The natural grasslands of the Central and Western Plains have experienced an even greater transformation than the forests. Of the more than 500 million acres of the original prairie and plains grassland, about half is tilled and used as cropland. If the appraisal is confined to prairies, the proportion is higher. Most of the subhumid or humid undulating prairie land that is not needed for other special uses has been converted to cropland, although grasses still play an important part in the rotation systems of farmers (pls. 45, 51, 54, 60, 64). The one-time prairies make up the largest and most compact crop-producing farming region in the United States. Less extensive and coherent in its spread is the conversion of the virgin sod into tilled land on the short-grass plains (pls. 68, 73, 80, 111, 113, 120). Severe restrictions are imposed by soil, climate, and physiographic features. Most of the land can be used for grazing only, and this must be supplemented by winter feeding. The feed used for this purpose is largely wild hay cut from native grass meadows. Much of the 14 million acres of native grass meadows reported for the United States is in this region. Overgrazing

had lowered the carrying capacity of the range but it is now improving in response to management.

The desert shrub vegetation, plus Pacific bunch grassland, desert grassland, and savanna, is confined to the arid and semiarid West (pls. 67, 77, 78, 86, 98, and 100). These are types of vegetation on which the encroachment of cultivated cropland is least in evidence, except where irrigation is carried on. Either precipitation is inadequate, or the surface is too rough or the soil too shallow to make the land suitable for tillage (pl. 76). Outside the irrigated land, only grazing remains as a possible use, and even grazing is precluded on extensive tracts in the Mojave-Colorado Desert because no water is available for livestock. Although the area occupied by the desert shrub-grass vegetation comprises in all about 300 million acres, its grazing capacity per areal unit is low when compared with eastern pasture. The natural productivity was further lowered during the half-century in which the semiarid and arid parts of the country were used by herdsmen as free open range. Unregulated use resulted in overgrazing, which not only depleted the forage but deteriorated the range. The best and more palatable forage plants, particularly the grasses, almost disappeared and were replaced by plants less desirable or worthless for pasture use. As a result of these changes, the carrying capacity of the western range area was reduced by about half. A turn for the better in the management and improvement of western pasture set in with adoption of the Taylor Grazing Act in 1934. Under this act, about half of the public domain was included in grazing districts, within which grazing is regulated (164, 136).

A different transformation of the range occurred with use in the desert grassland and savanna country, which is confined chiefly to the southern range. When white men arrived in this part of the country, they found open prairies with occasional clumps of mesquite, live oak, cedar, and other woody plants. At that time, grasses were the dominant vegetation. Today, brush frequently dominates the landscape. No doubt several contributory factors facilitated invasion of grassland by noxious brush, but the chief factor was man himself. Overgrazing destroyed the grass turf that protected the soil and made the spread of brush vegetation possible. The invasion of brush has materially reduced the carrying capacity of the range, and has made control of brush a major problem of these areas (pls. 117, 118, 123) (167, 53).

## Vegetation Still Adjusting

Although the natural vegetation has been disturbed by man, adjustment of plant associations to soils, climate, and ground moisture is still in evidence. There are exceptions, some of which go as far back as the pre-Columbian era. The extension of the prairies into the humid zone of the United States is cited as an outstanding example. Several reasons have been advanced to explain the extension of grassland into the forest area. Repeated burning is one. A temporary eastward extension of a warmer and drier climate in postglacial time is another. Probably both fire and fluctuations in climate occurred before the advent of European settlement, and contributed their share to produce what appears to be an anomalistic distribution pattern of vegetation. But there are also indications that climate as now constituted may tip the scale in favor of grasses. So long as average annual precipitation alone is considered the controlling factor, we find that the prairies of the Central States are located in the humid zone. This conclusion is supported by the absence of the calcareous horizon in the lower part of the soil profile. The climatic aspect changes somewhat when precipitation is considered in relation to evaporation.

As Albrecht puts it, "When precipitation is put against evaporation as ratios according to Professor Transeau, there are suggestions for the prairie conditions in the central states far east of the commonly considered prairie areas of the low rainfall" (3). The relationship between climate and plant distribution is illustrated on the map "Climatic Provinces and Plant Growth Regions of the United States," by C. W. Thornthwaite and F. L. Mulford (118). A similar conclusion may be drawn from a study of climatic fluctuations. In year-by-year fluctuations, as worked out by Thornthwaite for 40 consecutive years, the moist subhumid type occurs sufficiently frequently eastward to make it the normal type for the prairie part of the Central States. It may well be, therefore, that these drier years constitute the critical climatic element in the prairie extension (118). That the controlling forces of prairie and forest distribution have not always been in perfect equilibrium is evident from shifts of the prairie-forest boundary, which occurred before settlers appeared on the scene and which are recorded in soil characteristics. Much of what was formerly the Big Woods in southern Minnesota must have been prairie at one time. To some extent, the soils still show prairie characteristics, but they are changing to the gray-brown podzolic forest soils (86, p. 63).

Even in its modified forms, natural vegetation responds to the forces of nature. In its distributional pattern, it reflects adjustment to climate, physiography, and soils. Changes in these conditions are sometimes sharply defined. To this extent, they also affect land use, which may mean a sharp transition from dual-use capability to unilateral uses or vice versa, depending on the viewpoint from which the subject is approached. The Sand Hills of Nebraska, the Flint Hills of Kansas, and the southern part of the Llano Estacado in Texas and New Mexico have been pointed out as examples in which the soil restricts land use to grazing. In several areas in the humid zone, and especially in the Coastal Plains, the very light or very heavy soils favor forestry as permanent use. A reaction to soils in another direction is noticeable in the semiarid part of the upper Deschutes Basin in Oregon. The eastward extension of the pine forest is almost coextensive with the volcanic pumice deposits of this area. Pumice has a high water-holding capacity, and this may have been a factor in the eastward extension of the forest.

As a rule, land relief and climate favor forest vegetation for mountains but there are exceptions. In the intermountain region of the West, where the amount of precipitation is near the lower limit for forest growth, frequently only the northern and eastern slopes of the mountains are forest clad while the southern and western slopes are covered with grasses and shrubs (pl. 75). Sharp distinctions of this kind are due to a modification of the local climate. The evaporation ratio on the southern and western slopes is higher than that on the eastern and northern slopes. As a consequence, the moisture requirements of trees are not met. A distinction of a similar order, which is caused by diminished rainfall, exists on a larger scale between the eastern and western slopes of the Cascade Mountains. On the western slopes, which receive a heavy precipitation brought in by the onshore winds from the Pacific Ocean, the forest cover is so dense that undergrowth is suppressed and grazing is eliminated (pl. 95). The forest use is the best use that can be made of these western slopes. On the eastern slopes, which are in the rain shadow, precipitation is lower, the tree stand is comparatively sparse and open, and plenty of room is left for grasses to grow (pl. 94). In this instance, land use is a combination of grazing and forestry.

**Effective Use of Range**

When the natural vegetation provides the only opportunity of using the land, obviously land use must be adjusted to the capabilities of the vegetative cover. This is particularly true when grazing is the major use. In this respect, semiarid and arid vegetations have their own use limitations, which are usually low carrying capacities with restriction to certain months of the year. These limitations are again subject to the cycle of precipitation. To use the range effectively, seasonal shifts of livestock are necessary, and they have developed into a migratory movement of livestock

# SEASONAL USE OF WESTERN RANGE, 1947

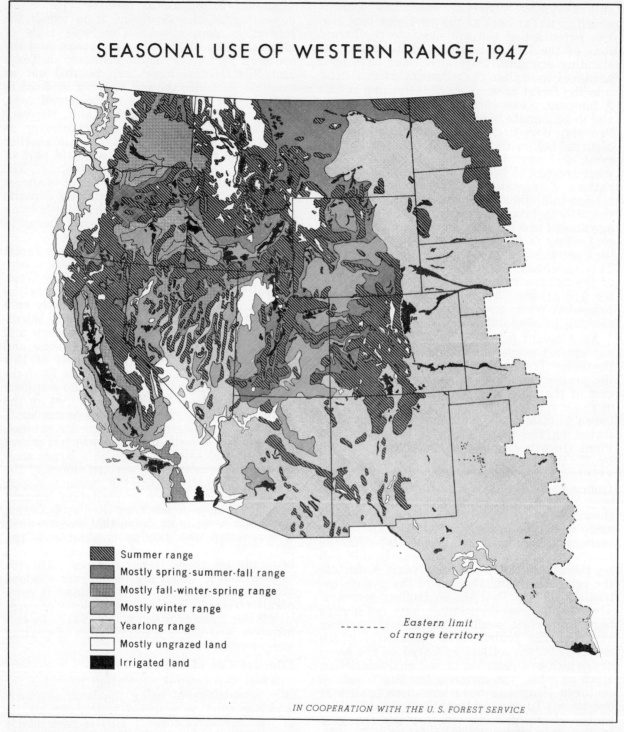

Summer range
Mostly spring-summer-fall range
Mostly fall-winter-spring range
Mostly winter range
Yearlong range
Mostly ungrazed land
Irrigated land

- - - - - - - *Eastern limit of range territory*

*IN COOPERATION WITH THE U. S. FOREST SERVICE*

U.S. DEPARTMENT OF AGRICULTURE      NEG. 58(5)-2502 AGRICULTURAL RESEARCH SERVICE

FIGURE 18.—In our western mountains and basins, grazing depends upon the seasonal movement of livestock. On the higher levels, pasture is available only during the warmer season. On the intermediate levels, the range is used mainly in spring and fall. In the basins and valleys, it is used during the winter and is frequently supplemented by winter feeding. Summer and winter ranges are often more than 100 miles apart.

that is repeated each year. The movement, which is frequently referred to as transhumance, follows a natural trend. It is not unique to the United States. In middle latitudes, where grazing is available in the mountains, livestock is kept through the winter on lower levels, moves with the advancement of spring to higher grounds, and in summer is grazed in the mountains. At the end of the summer season, a reverse movement sets in, which ends in the valleys. Seasonal migration of livestock occurs in most of the western mountains and basins, where yearlong grazing is not feasible. Summer and winter grazing grounds are often far apart so that livestock, and particularly sheep, may have to travel considerable distances, most of which is done by trailing. Motortrucks and railroads are also used to some extent (63). National forests provide about 8 million animal-unit months of grazing in summer. On the winter range, grazing often must be supplemented by feeding, which is done chiefly with forage produced on irrigated land (fig. 18).

In the East, only the Cumberland Plateau is large enough to deserve mention in this connection. The vegetation of the Cumberland Plateau is that of a cutover forest, which is used by the few farmers on the plateau as an open range. Some of the valley farmers drive their livestock to the plateau where it grazes for about 6 months in summer (89). At lower levels, grazing in the forest is still practiced to a considerable extent throughout the South (148). In recent years, however, with the intensification of forest growth over much of the higher ground, the forest range has been reduced. As of 1958, it is confined mainly to the Coastal Plain.

## Use for Recreation

Natural vegetation has so far been considered primarily as an economic asset in the light of the uses made of it. From this viewpoint alone, the improvement and proper management of the natural plant cover assumes paramount importance. Economic uses of the natural vegetation, however, are not the only uses that are vital to the welfare of the people. There are functional uses which, in some instances, transcend in importance the benefits of economic use. With the congregation of people in urban centers, outdoor recreation in scenic places offers its own compensation. Its benefits to society have been recognized by Federal, State, and community governments, which have set aside park areas totaling about 19 million acres for recreational use. Wildlife, too, depends chiefly on natural vegetation for food and shelter. To preserve the species, refuge areas, in which the natural vegetation is usually preserved, have been established in different parts of the country. Together, these areas comprise about 8 million acres. But over much of the land the chief function of the natural vegetation is the conservation of soil and water, which can be accomplished only if the perennial plant cover itself is conserved. Economic and functional uses of the natural vegetation can be combined in most instances, but proper safeguards are essential to preserve its use potentiality in both directions.

The accumulated literature on the natural vegetation, its uses, and its abuses, reflects the importance of the subject in connection with national welfare and development. Only a few publications of national scope can be cited here (109; 135, 1948, 1949).

# Water Management and Land Use

Broadly speaking, the use of land cannot be divorced from the use of water. Water is the complement to land, on which plant, animal, and human life depend. Because of this relationship of water to land, water is a main factor in determining the use capability of the land itself. As recorded in the amounts of precipitation received in various parts of the country, water is unequally distributed in space and frequently in time. Much of the land receives very little; other areas receive a large amount. By force of necessity, the early settlers recognized these conditions. Where water is scarce, settlement is sparse. Conversely, wet and swampy land was avoided also.

## Natural Distribution of Water

That to a certain extent the natural distribution of water can be controlled and improved

was discovered in the early stages of civilization; some of the old cultural centers developed as a result. The Indians diverted water for irrigation. Along with the settlement of the country went the development of its resources, water included. Old drainage ditches, dams, and mill ponds are evidence of regulation and use of water with the meager equipment the settlers had at hand. Management of water has become an integral part of the development of the country. In its advanced stage, water management cannot be regarded as exclusively concerned with the regulation of the water supply on land used for agricultural production. Management of water is essential to obtain a reliable supply for our urban and industrial concentrations so that the health and welfare of the people can be safeguarded. Development of hydraulic energy is frequently included in the water-management projects that serve multiple purposes. But from whatever angle the management of water is approached, the land and its use are involved in one way or another.

As nature's way of distributing water leaves much to be desired so far as human needs are concerned, man has had to improve the distribution pattern. Rainmaking was part of the religious ritual of the Indians, but we have little evidence by which to judge its efficacy. Of late, rainmaking by scientific methods has shown some promise, but whether man can succeed in distributing rain at will where it is most needed and prevent it from falling where it is damaging is debatable. The processes used in desalting salt water for desert irrigation have received attention recently. Research is making progress in reducing the cost of desalting sea and brackish water, but these processes are still in the laboratory stage. Except for such places as Kuwait on the Persian Gulf where conditions for application of one of these processes are exceptionaly favorable, they have not been perfected to the point of making their more universal use economically feasible.

For the time being, we must depend on the available supply of moisture, and efforts toward water management are directed chiefly toward modifying the distribution of water after it has reached the ground. This may be done by either holding water where it is needed or bringing it there, by preventing undesirable accumulation of water, or by checking too rapid runoff and flow. Frequently, the chief function of a water-management project is expressed in its name. Irrigation, drainage, soil conservation, flood protection, use of inland waterways for navigation, city water supply, ground water use and control, water storage, pollution abatement, and hydroelectric power development are the main objectives of water management. Many of these objectives may constitute individual projects, but more often related objectives are combined in multiple-purpose projects, or all of them may form part of a river-basin development plan.

## Water Management

River watersheds are the accepted units of water management. If they had been strictly adhered to, that is, if water use and control had always been confined to the available water within drainage-basin divides, the growth of some of our largest cities would have been inhibited by water shortages. Gravitational flow has always been the chief means of water distribution, but modern techniques now permit the lifting of volumes of water through pumping from one basin into another. This technique is used successfully in some water-utilization projects.

An example is New York. Although the city is on the Hudson River and is partly surrounded by the waters of Hudson Bay, it went to the Catskill Mountains for a desirable source of water. It supplemented this supply by tapping the headwaters of the Delaware.

Denver, which is in a semiarid region, grew until a shortage in the water supplied by the runoff from the eastern slopes of the Rockies began to be felt. To avert a drought in city water, Denver diverted some of the runoff from the Pacific slope of the Rockies through the Moffat Tunnel to the Atlantic slope.

Los Angeles probably had the most serious problem of water supply of any large city. Because of its rapid growth, this city soon reached the limits of the supply of water available from the surface and subsurface of the basin in which it is located. To augment its supply, Los Angeles brought water by means of an aqueduct from the Owens River 250 miles to the north and across the mountains. From a purely technical angle, the replenishment of water in the Los Angeles Basin from such a distance was a remarkable accomplishment, but there were legal complications also. Before the city appropriated the water of Owens River, it had been used by settlers in the Owens Valley for irrigated farming. With the acquisition of the water and land of Owens Valley by the city, the settlers were deprived of their use, and the valley reverted to arid grazing. Meanwhile, Los Angeles and its adjacent communities continued to grow and soon needed even more water. The nearest supply was on the Colorado River. Bringing water from that river to the Los Angeles area required the building of an aqueduct 240 miles long. The water had to be lifted in stages for more than 1,600 feet across the intervening mountains (*129*).

These are three examples of large cities that have solved their water problems by drawing on the resources of additional drainage basins. Not all cities, however, have the same problem. Chicago, for instance, lies on the divide between two large drainage systems, that of the St. Lawrence River and that of the Mississippi River. The city water is taken from Lake Michigan on the St. Lawrence side, and discharged into the Illinois River, a tributary of the Mississippi; in this instance, a considerable volume of water is diverted from one basin into the other.

Diverting water by lifting it across a divide is not reserved exclusively to cities. It is used to some extent in irrigation projects. The Big Thompson project in Colorado operates on this principle, as does the Grand Coulee project in Washington. An inverse procedure is followed in the Central Valley of California. Water of the Sacramento River is not distributed by gravity alone. After it reaches the lower end of the Sacramento Valley, the surplus not used in the valley is lifted again by pumps into the San Joaquin Valley where it is used largely for irrigation (*129*). All these are multiple-purpose projects, in which storage of water, control of floods, generation of power, and use of water are integrated.

River basins as units of water management are affected by the physical and economic conditions characteristic of the area. Also, as they frequently comprise extensive areas, they are composed of political divisions under different jurisdictions. All the larger river basins include parts of a number of States, which sometimes have conflicting interests in water-resource development that must be adjudicated before a project can be undertaken. Rivers that cross or form part of the international boundary, like the Rio Grande, the Colorado, the Columbia, and the St. Lawrence, pose problems on the international level. Distribution of water and development of power are involved in all these problems. Added to the St. Lawrence River problem is inland navigation. Agreements with Canada and Mexico are essential to the working out of equitable solutions to conflicting claims and the preservation of friendly relations with our neighbors.

Water management is essential in most parts of the country where agricultural use of the land is concerned, but it is particularly so where water is scarce and thus becomes the controlling factor in the development of the area.

In the arid West, where production of crops usually depends on irrigation, the valley dwellers should be directly concerned with the management of their water supply. Management of water must start at the source of the water in the mountains, which constitute the main catchment areas of precipitation. Storm or snow water that runs off too fast is likely to do more damage than good. To hold the water in the mountains so it can be delivered steadily when needed is a part of management. This is the function of the vegetative cover. Vegetation retards runoff on slopes and gives water time to infiltrate the soil. Protection of the vegetative cover of the mountains from misuse and depletion is a sound water-management measure. It is needed also to maintain the use capability of the mountains as summer grazing grounds or for production of timber.

As elsewhere, precipitation in the mountains varies considerably over the years, and this variation affects use of water in the valleys. Much of the precipitation falls in the form of snow, which accumulates in winter, melts during spring and early summer, and thus furnishes the irrigation water needed in the valleys. So that operations in the valleys may be adjusted, forecasts of the quantity of water that will become available from accumulated snow are now made successfully from snow surveys. On about 1,000 snow-survey courses laid out over the western mountains the snow is measured monthly in the latter part of the winter. The results obtained provide the basic data for the forecasts (*87*).

## Storage Reservoirs

A dependable water supply cannot be obtained in most instances without storage reservoirs from which the water can be released as needed. The larger irrigation districts, which include much of the nearly 25 million acres of irrigated land in the West, could not have been established without provision for storing a reliable supply of water. (For irrigated land, see colored map in pocket, and plates 79, 82, 84, 87, 88, 98, 101, 102, 103, 104, 106, 107, 108, 110, 122, 124.) A similar need exists for perennial hydroelectric power generation. Hydroelectric powerplants on rivers with uncontrolled flow frequently have steam plants as standby units for emergency use. To a considerable extent, flood control must rely on reservoirs to detain the waters. Catchment basins have been acquired and set aside by some urban centers. The water is stored in reservoirs for the needs of the cities. Water stored or retained in reservoirs, therefore, serves many purposes.

In 1948, nearly 1,000 reservoirs of more than 500-acre-feet storage capacity were in operation (*58*). Almost 200 more have been constructed since then, and others are under construction. These reservoirs cover more than 8 million acres. This does not include natural bodies of water in which control dams have been installed. Most reservoirs submerge the land permanently, and to this extent, they reduce the area of land. Some of the submerged land was good farmland in operation. In such instances, construction of reservoirs meant removal of the farmers from their lands.

Reservoirs of a type about which little information is available cannot be included in any areal or numerical estimates. These are the small artificial lakes or ponds that serve mainly private interests. These homemade bodies of water may serve as fishponds, swimming pools, or basins to hold stock water. No complete count has been made of these ponds, nor is the acreage they cover known. But they are numerous, and more of them are found in the subhumid and semiarid parts of the country than in either the humid or arid regions. Furthermore, their number is increasing rapidly with the expansion of conservation programs. In the subhumid and semiarid regions, where precipitation is not plentiful but gully erosion is severe, the dams constructed frequently serve a dual purpose. Erosion control comes first and storage of water second. As of 1949, about 40,000 dams of this type had been constructed

(140). As an illustration of farm-pond construction in a subhumid region, Lincoln Township in Comanche County, Okla., may be cited. Within this township, which contains 36 square miles, 89 ponds were counted, an average of about 1 per farm (138). Not all of these ponds hold water the year round, but they serve their purpose for most of the year.

Soil conservation revolves around water management, particularly when water erosion is the issue. Control of runoff to check its erosive force and to retain water on the land where it is needed is the chief objective of water management in this instance. Not only is the soil conserved in this way, but the productivity of the land is improved at the same time. Grass cover is one of the most effective erosion-control measures but it cannot always be applied. Such mechanical practices as contour plowing, terracing, installation of grassed or rubbled water runways, construction of dams to control gully formation, or establishing an erosion-resisting vegetative cover on badly damaged slopes must be resorted to frequently if the desired result is to be obtained. All these measures are designed primarily to conserve the soil. However, by controlling runoff, they also help to prevent floods through retention of water on the land so it can replenish the subsurface water supply that nourishes our springs and streams.

## Drainage Installations

Checking the speed of running water and storing and distributing it where it is needed make up a side of water management that has its counterpart in measures designed to accelerate the movement of water and to protect or relieve places that receive an excess of water. Projects of this kind are better known as drainage and flood-protection enterprises.

Distribution of precipitation governs the location of most of the land that usually receives an abundant supply of water. Of the total land area of the United States, about 45 percent receives an annual average of more than 30 inches of precipitation. Aside from the western mountains, most of this land is in the eastern half of the country. Because of slight slope or a combination of slight relief and heavy soils, extensive tracts in the Coastal and Inland Plains have or have had inadequate natural drainage for the best use of the land. To these must be added the relatively broad flood plains of the larger rivers that traverse the Coastal Plains. In contrast to the East, drainage needs in the West are associated not with high rainfall but with irrigation.

Drainage installations may be divided into two categories according to whether they can be or have been accomplished by individual action of a landowner or operator, or whether community action is or was essential. Only small-scale drainage works can be undertaken by individual users, and then only when drainage outlets are available. By far the largest acreage of drainable land requires community action for drainage installations. Community organization may take the form of drainage districts. These districts may extend across county boundaries, in which case they have a legal standing of their own, or they may be functionally integrated with the county government. How these drainage enterprises operate depends, therefore, on legal authorization by the States in which they are located. According to the 1950 census, drainage in 10 States is organized and managed by counties and in 30 States by districts (fig. 19).

Most of the land in drainage enterprises is on the till plains and glacial lakebeds of the North Central States. In many of these areas, drainage is not of the reclamation type because much of the land was used for crops before artificial drainage was installed (pls. 37, 42, 45). Surface and internal soil drainage were deficient, however, and to produce the best yields and reclaim wet spots required drainage improvements. Reclamation was the more prevalent objective of the drainage districts in the South. In most instances, the wet and swampy land required not only drainage improvements but clearing of the forest vegetation as well. In the Mississippi flood plains (61), drainage and clearing were supplemented by levees to protect the land from frequent overflow (pls. 12, 20, 21, 24, 25, 34, 39, 40, 45, 50, 51, 54, 97, 132, 135, 136, 140, 141, 142, 150, 155, 162, 168).

Reclamation and land improvement are the chief objectives of drainage enterprises in the East. In the West, drainage has acquired a third function in connection with irrigation. Seepage from upper irrigation ditches frequently produces alkaline accumulations on the lower levels. To prevent or relieve these areas from the toxic concentrations of salt in the soil requires drainage installations on the irrigated land. In these instances, irrigation and drainage are interdependent (pl. 103).

About 100 million acres of wet and swampy land are to be found in the United States. Most of these lands are along the South Atlantic and Gulf coasts and the Alluvial Valley of the Mississippi River. Although the acreage in drainage districts is expanding—it has now passed the 100-million-acre mark—not all the wet lands and swamps can be reclaimed economically. A considerable part of these lands can be reclaimed, however, when more agricultural land is needed. Some of them are already included in drainage districts, but they have not yet been developed. For the larger swamps, with soils not well adapted to agricul-

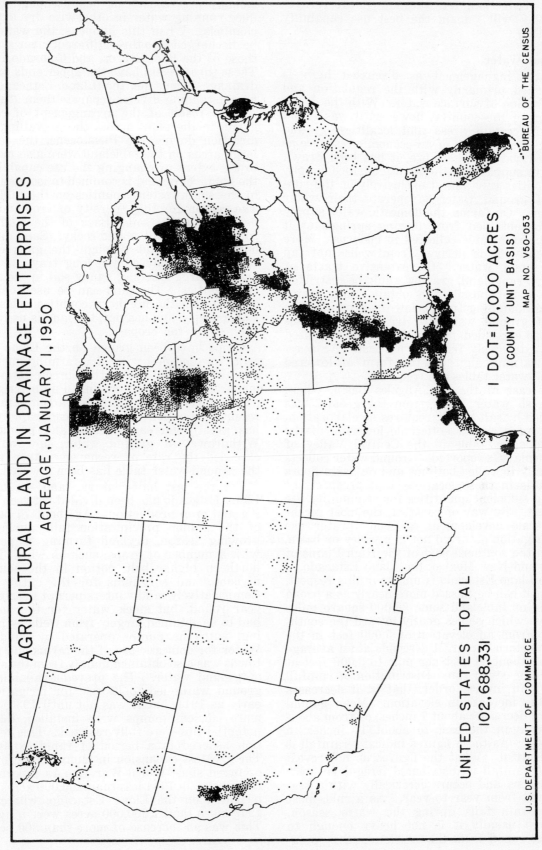

## AGRICULTURAL LAND IN DRAINAGE ENTERPRISES
### ACREAGE, JANUARY 1, 1950

UNITED STATES TOTAL
102,688,331

1 DOT = 10,000 ACRES
(COUNTY UNIT BASIS)

MAP NO. V50-053

BUREAU OF THE CENSUS

U.S. DEPARTMENT OF COMMERCE

FIGURE 19.—Coastal lowlands, interior plains, and humid climate account for the concentration of wet and swampy lands in the East. Reclamation through drainage was started along the Atlantic Coast in Colonial times but little was accomplished. Organized community drainage enterprises are to be found in the Central States, the Alluvial Valley of the Mississippi River, the Gulf and Atlantic coasts, and southern Florida.

tural production, forests and wildlife refuges probably will remain the best use capability (pl. 156).

## Ground Water

Water management as discussed here is concerned primarily with the regulation and distribution of surface water. With the development of the country, however, it was found that in certain areas and localities, ground water was as much of an economic resource as surface water. Therefore, it has been drawn upon to supplement the scanty surface supply. Some cities rely almost exclusively on the supply of ground water to operate their water systems. On farms, the domestic water supply may be obtained from flowing springs, or it may be rainwater collected in cisterns. More frequently, it is derived from wells that tap the ground water. On extensive tracts of western rangeland, grazing would be restricted were it not possible to obtain stock water through pumping from below the ground. The use of ground water for irrigation purposes has also expanded. Ground water is now used more extensively than in the past. As a result, warning signs in the form of lowered ground-water tables are frequent.

The case of the Los Angeles Basin, where the fresh water taken from the ground was replaced by salt water, requires no elaboration. Some years ago, a noticeable lowering of the ground-water table in the Central Valley of California was reported. Ground water collects naturally in valley bottoms and on basin floors and it is in these locations that prospects of finding sufficient quantities for community use are best. By way of contrast, the most recent large-scale development of ground-water use for irrigation occurred not in a valley or basin, but on the southern part of the High Plains of Texas and New Mexico, the Llano Estacado.

The Llano Estacado is unique in this respect, in that it can be classed more nearly as a broad plateau or tableland some 30,000 square miles in area, which slopes gently toward the southeast. From an elevation of 5,000 feet in the northwestern corner, it descends at an average rate of about 11 feet per mile to 3,000 feet at the southeastern rim. Distribution of rainfall follows an inverse order, that is, it decreases with the increase in elevation. Mean annual rainfall decreases about 7 inches, or from about 21 inches in the east to about 14 inches in the west. As these figures indicate, rainfall is not plentiful. What the figures do not reveal is that rainfall is distributed irregularly over the seasons and occurs erratically within seasons and from year to year. As a rule, most of the rain falls during the warm season, although usually it is not heavy enough to produce runoff from the tableland. Only occa-

sionally are rainstorms heavy enough to produce running water in otherwise dry drainage channels. When this happens, the water may be discharged into three different river systems, those of the Red, Brazos, and Colorado Rivers. These three rivers have the upper ends of their drainage basins on the Llano Estacado, and no outstanding divides separate them (fig. 20).

As a result of the arrangement of escarpments in the plain across the prevailing wind direction during the Pleistocene, the soils of large areas on the tableland were also modified to the extent of changing the use capability of the land. Cropland is confined to isolated areas in the southwestern counties on the tableland. The reason for this sparsity of cropland is to be found in the soil. Back of the bluffs, the soil is mainly shallow and rocky. Sand drifting onto the tableland through the gaps of the escarpment produced the long traverse dunes and the large tracts of sandy soil in the southern counties. The land can be used only for grazing. In the northern counties, where the soil is deeper and heavier, the land is used more extensively for crops.

Crops have been grown on the Llano Estacado for decades with dry-farming methods. But the low and fluctuating precipitation has made crop yields uncertain. Pump irrigation as a supplement to rainfall is a comparatively recent innovation; it has spread rapidly and has greatly increased yields and production. Withdrawal of ground water, however, has exceeded the rate of recharge. As a result, the ground-water table has been lowered.

For the last half-century, land use on the Llano Estacado has been divided between grazing and crop production. As about 75 percent of the annual precipitation falls during the growing season, dryland farming is possible with a number of crops, such as wheat in the northern higher belt, cotton in the southern division, and sorghums for the entire area. Comparatively mild winters permit grazing the year round, but stock water for the animals had to be obtained largely from wells by pumping, with the pumps operated by windmills. Water for domestic use of the farms and in the towns was also obtained mainly from the supply of ground water. The proved availability of ground water led to its use for irrigation as early as 1911, but it was not until 1935, when more efficient pumps were installed, that its potentialities were fully realized. This realization ushered in a period of rapid expansion. The greatest expansion in pump irrigation has occurred since World War II. As reported by the census, in 1944 less than 400,000 acres were irrigated on the Llano Estacado, whereas in 1949 more than 1,600,000 acres were irrigated. This was an increase of more than 300 percent in 5 years.

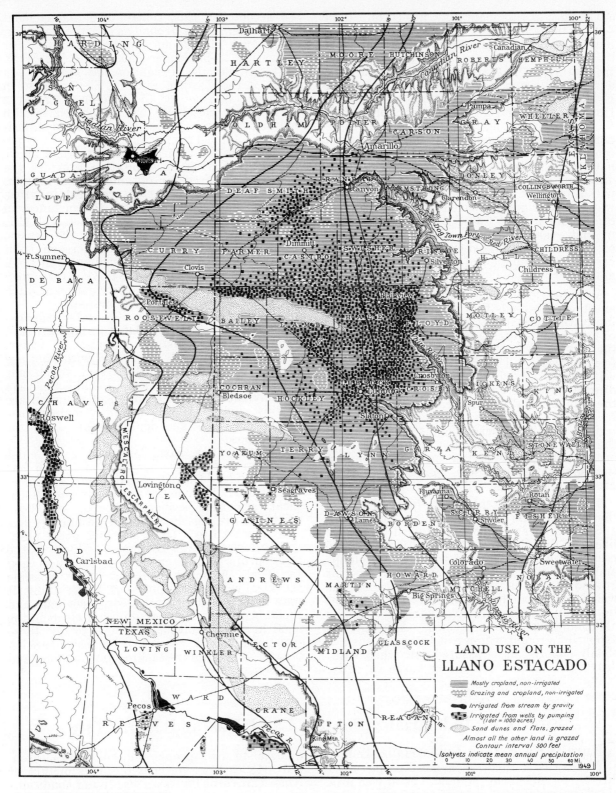

LAND USE ON THE
LLANO ESTACADO

≡≡≡ Mostly cropland, non-irrigated
≡≡≡ Grazing and cropland, non-irrigated

● Irrigated from stream by gravity
▦ Irrigated from wells by pumping
  (1 dot = 1000 acres)
░ Sand dunes and flats, grazed

Almost all the other land is grazed
Contour interval 500 feet
Isohyets indicate mean annual precipitation

0  10  20  30  40  50  60 Mi.
1949

U. S. DEPARTMENT OF AGRICULTURE        NEG. 58(5)-2493 AGRICULTURAL RESEARCH SERVICE

FIGURE 20.—The Llano Estacado consists of the southern part of the Texas High Plains. The Canadian River Canyon separates it from the northern part. It is a slightly tilted tableland defined on three sides by an escarpment and connected on the south with the Edwards Plateau. The eastern rim drops for more than 500 feet in places. On the west, the escarpment is usually less than 200 feet high and is broken at some points.

67

Changes of this magnitude are certain to be felt in the economy of the region. Not only have yields risen to an all-time high, but crops that require more water have also come into the picture. The grain sorghum, corn, alfalfa, and other crops now grown on the Llano Estacado could not be grown without irrigation. How irrigation has affected production may be illustrated by cotton. For 1944, the census reported 555,000 bales of cotton harvested in the counties on the Llano Estacado. In 1949, the harvest had risen to 1,649,000 bales. To produce this crop required, in 1948, an estimated withdrawal of 1.2 million acre-feet of ground water for irrigation, which was about 97 percent of all ground water lifted to the surface in that year. For 1954, the census reported an increase in irrigated cropland of 2.9 million acres, but production of cotton declined to 1.3 million bales.

Withdrawal of ground water to irrigate such an acreage exceeds the rate of recharge from infiltrating precipitation and affects the level of the ground-water table. From 1938 to 1949, the ground-water table was lowered up to 50 feet in places. The greatest recession of the water table occurred in areas of heavy withdrawal by closely spaced pumps. However, the number of wells is increasing. As reported for 1950, 14,000 wells supplied the water to irrigate 1,860,000 acres on the Texas side of the Llano Estacado alone. The pumps were operated by either electric motors or combustion engines using butane, gasoline, or natural gas (pls. 119, A and B) (7, 84).

The lowering of the water table is a sign that withdrawal and recharge are out of balance. It indicates that more difficult times are likely to be ahead. A lowered water table reduces the availability of water to the pumps and increases the cost of pumping. Use of ground water for irrigation has economic as well as physical limitations, and these limitations may become effective before the supply of ground water is exhausted. Although the supply of ground water can be replenished, a steady supply can be assured only when withdrawals do not exceed the recharge capacity.

To accomplish this, control and management are as essential for ground as for surface water.

The use of ground and surface water for irrigation is no longer confined to the West. In recent decades, irrigation has expanded in most of the Eastern States. The increase in irrigated acreage in the rice-growing areas corresponds closely to the expansion in rice culture. In other parts of the humid belt, irrigation is applied mainly during dry spells, when the evaporation-transpiration rate rises above the rate at which precipitation provides the moisture required for optimum plant growth. Irrigation is particularly successful in areas of intensive crop production, for instance, in fruit- and vegetable-growing districts (pl. 19). To cite an example reported by the census, Florida expanded its irrigated acreage from 126,000 acres in 1939 to 485,000 acres in 1954. Deficient soil moisture in these areas may be supplemented through subirrigation or ditch irrigation, or with sprinkler systems.

Aside from the objectives of water management that are directly related to land use and domestic and industrial supplies of water, others only indirectly connected with land use usually form an integral part of the larger water-management projects. Inland waterways for navigation and prevention of pollution are of this kind. In either instance, maintenance of sufficient flow and depth are necessary for the purpose.

Next to cities, rural land use is the chief beneficiary of water management, which has many facets. Only the main ones are mentioned here. Frequently, in its operations, technical, scientific, economic, social, and legal questions are closely related. Technology has now advanced to a point at which great physical obstacles can be surmounted. However, the large projects have many aspects other than technical. Although a project may be possible technically, the feasibility of undertaking it may hinge on questions of cost, economic and social benefits, or the possibility of clearing the legal hurdles involved. Needless to say, these questions should receive prior consideration because of their far-reaching implications and consequences.

# Effects of Industrialization on Land Use and Rural Life

## Rural Life Before Industrialization

There was a time when most people lived directly on and from the land. Food was provided by crops and domestic animals; home industries converted the fibers and lumber into clothing, buildings, and furniture. Only a comparatively small proportion of the crops and animals or animal products were available for disposal to townspeople, and only a few essential articles were purchased. This picture of American rural life describes living conditions of pioneer settlers only a little more than a century ago. This type of self-sufficing economy did not apply with equal force to the southern plantations or northern manors that were organized primarily for cash production.

During the early periods of settlement, the needs of the people were relatively rudimentary. Human labor and animal energy were the forces that cleared and cultivated the land. The implements used and the tillage operations were simple. Nonetheless, the settlers relied on the land to produce a living, although they knew little of the productive capacity of the virgin soil. Nor were they able always to appraise correctly the advantages and drawbacks of the natural environment in which they built their homes. Land was settled where it was unoccupied, and where the settlers thought they could make a living. Some of them expected to find a means of livelihood in the mountains almost as readily as could others in the valleys or plains. Site location was not considered of paramount importance or relevance to the use of the land, nor was it evident that physical factors were endowed with economic and social attributes as later turned out to be the case. In many places in the northern and southern Appalachian Mountains, land that would now be considered submarginal for agricultural production was settled and cleared. The standard of living did not concern the population then to the extent that it does today. But the pioneers cherished the tenets of freedom and the opportunity to establish homes.

## Industrialization of the Country

The old American way of living changed markedly with the westward movement of settlement and the industrialization of the country. Agriculture as the major industry using the land was profoundly affected by these two developments. Settlers who moved to the prairies and plains found the physical conditions for agricultural production more favorable than in parts of the East. Extensive tracts of land with smooth undulating surfaces and fertile dark soils were ready for the plough. On most 160-acre homesteads, much or all of the land was tillable. The settlers were able to produce a great deal more than they could use. The surplus was disposed of on the domestic and foreign markets. Inland waterways at first provided the main shipping facilities. They were soon supplemented and later almost superseded by railroads and highways as connecting links between farms and markets.

With the settlement and development of the Central Plains, a new spatial order in the economic structure of the country emerged. Agriculture, which had been the main occupation of the people, moved westward and established its gravitational center in midcontinent, while manufacturing, service, and mining became the dominant industries in the more populous East. With the opening and development of the West, additional shifts in agriculture and industry occurred though not to the extent of revising completely the outstanding distributional characteristics of these industries. The agricultural character of the Great Plains is evident from the use made of the land. Measured in terms of proportion of land used for crops, the Central Plains contain the largest and most homogeneous area of the country in which crop production is preponderant. The concentration of industries and principal markets is reflected by the urban aggregations of population in the East.

Expansion of settlement and industrialization of production began to transform the country immediately after the Revolution. These two forces operated in the direction of developing resources and improving standards of living. The introduction of labor-saving machinery is largely responsible for development of the manufacturing industries and for the commercialization of agriculture. Although their application was not restricted, not all parts of the country could benefit from these innovations to the same extent. Advantages or shortcomings of location prevented uniform development, and regional differences in economic and social conditions resulted.

To provide a more effective exposition of the disparate distribution of agricultural production and market centers, two maps were prepared. Figure 21 illustrates the relative proportion of land used for crops in different parts of the country. Figure 22 visualizes the distribution of population. A comparative study of these two maps will reveal that concentration of cropland does not necessarily produce a concentration of people, and conversely, that only in exceptional cases is a concentration of people the result of intensive use of the land for agricultural production.

A comparison of the distribution of cropland with that of population will disclose the difference in location of centers of industry and commerce and production centers of agriculture.

Advantages of site account largely for development of cities in different localities. These advantages may consist of transportation and port facilities as they are found along the inland waterways of the Great Lakes and the coast, or the proximity of raw material and sources of energy.

### The Case of Cotton

The relationship of changing land use through expansion of settlement and industrialization of the country may be perceived by considering what has happened in the case of cotton. Cotton is a cultural plant. Its fibers were spun and woven into fabrics by the peoples of India and those of the old civilizations in America centuries before the first European settlers arrived in the New World. Settlers in

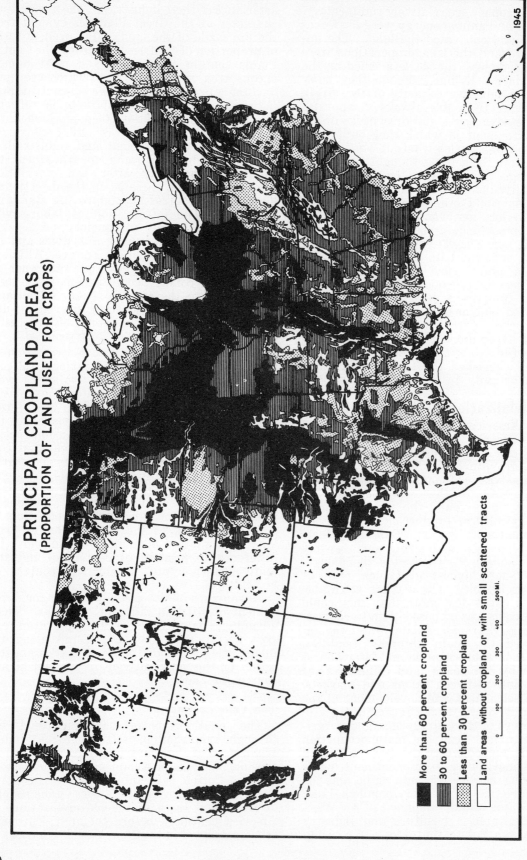

## PRINCIPAL CROPLAND AREAS
### (PROPORTION OF LAND USED FOR CROPS)

1945

■ More than 60 percent cropland

▨ 30 to 60 percent cropland

▧ Less than 30 percent cropland

☐ Land areas without cropland or with small scattered tracts

0  100  200  300  400  500 Mi.

U. S. DEPARTMENT OF AGRICULTURE

NEG. 58 (5)-2494 AGRICULTURAL RESEARCH SERVICE

FIGURE 21.—When the proportion of land in crops is used to illustrate relative intensity of land use in different parts of the country, the relationship of land use to physical conditions becomes evident. Much land in the Western States is arid and irrigation is practiced. Rough mountainous land, poor soil, or inadequate drainage is found in much of the East. The largest concentration of cropland is in the Central Plains.

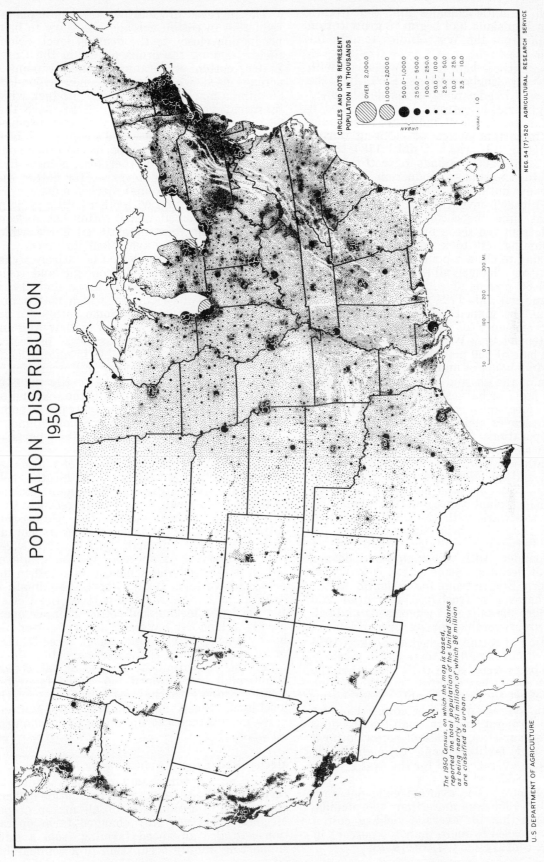

## POPULATION DISTRIBUTION
### 1950

CIRCLES AND DOTS REPRESENT
POPULATION IN THOUSANDS

OVER 2,000.0

1,000.0–2,000.0

500.0–1,000.0

250.0–500.0

100.0–250.0

50.0–100.0

25.0–50.0

10.0–25.0

2.5–10.0

URBAN

RURAL · 1.0

*The 1950 Census, on which the map is based, reported the total population of the United States as being nearly 151 million, of which 96 million are classified as urban.*

U S DEPARTMENT OF AGRICULTURE

NEG 54 (7)-520 AGRICULTURAL RESEARCH SERVICE

50   0   100   200   300 MI.

FIGURE 22.—An outstanding feature of the distribution of population as shown on this map is its unevenness over the country as a whole.  Approximately 85 percent of the total population is east of the 100th meridian.  The greatest concentrations of population are in the North Atlantic and Great Lakes States, which contain sites favorable to the development of large urban centers.

the South Atlantic colonies and the French settlers in Louisiana had begun to grow cotton brought in from the West Indies mainly for their own use.

Cotton textiles had been produced with machinery in England since 1769, but the industry was handicapped in its development by the high price of cotton. In the colonies, it remained more of a home industry; homespuns were an important article of clothing during the Revolution. It was not until 1784 that 8 bags, or some 3,200 pounds of cotton, were exported to England. Production of cotton remained low until, in 1793, it was stimulated by Eli Whitney's invention of the cotton gin. Up to that time, the cotton fiber or lint was separated from the seeds by hand, which was time-consuming. It took an operator a good part of a day to clean a pound of cotton in this way. Whitney changed all this. With his first gin model 60 pounds of cotton a day could be cleaned, and with his 1794 model 1,000 pounds a day could be ginned. Since that time, the operating efficiency of cotton gins has been further stepped up. With present equipment, ginning a bale of 500 pounds of cotton requires from 2½ to 3 hours of man labor, depending on the design of the gin and whether the cotton is picked by hand or harvested with a mechanical stripper. Mechanically harvested cotton contains more leaves and trash, which slow down ginning operations (*114, 90*).

Cotton was the first crop to feel the impact of mechanization. Whitney's invention made it profitable, and the effects were felt in different directions. Not only was more cotton grown on established plantations, but the plant also migrated westward with the advancement of settlement in the Southern States. Except for the War Between the States, production of cotton expanded, with minor ups and downs, until recent decades. Some cotton is grown in all Southern States from the Atlantic to the Pacific wherever a frost-free season of 200 days or more prevails and where soils and soil moisture are favorable for its production.

Production of cotton reached its peak in 1926 when more than 44 million acres yielding nearly 18 million bales were harvested. Since then the acreage of cotton has declined, but the decline has been offset to a considerable extent by an increase in average yield per acre. This increase was brought about through the breeding of improved varieties, the use of better cultural practices and fertilizer, and through insect control. The average yield for the first 2 years on record—1866 and 1867—was less than 150 pounds per acre. The average yield per acre recorded for 1955 was more than 400 pounds, which means that the average yield of cotton per acre increased by more than 100 percent in less than a century (*134, 1952, 1956*).

The increase in yield per areal unit made a reduction in cotton acreage necessary to bring production closer to the demand level. Nonetheless, among the crops grown in the United States, cotton still ranks second in point of acreage used, which fluctuates now around the 20 million mark, and in value of product, which in recent years has amounted to more than $2,300 million. The United States produces more than half of the world's cotton. A large part of this cotton is exported to other countries. Growing cotton, therefore, is more than a strictly domestic enterprise, for cotton that reaches the international market must be produced in competition with other cotton-growing countries. Even at home, cotton has its competitors in the form of artificial fibers, which in many instances have taken its place.

As it is now grown, cotton is entirely a cash crop. This has affected economic and social conditions in the producing areas and also in the industrial districts for which cotton provides the raw material. Some cotton for industrial use had been shipped to New England before the ginning process was perfected. When cotton became available in quantities to furnish the raw material for mill operation, a new industry was born. The textile industry of New England grew with the expanding production of cotton and the increase in population. Cotton textile mills are now found in the South, also, and in many other parts of eastern United States.

Mechanization of field operations also has benefited cotton producers. Of all the field operations, harvesting cotton by hand picking is the most laborious. It is only recently that this process has been mechanized. Harvesting cotton with a mechanical stripper is not all gain, however. Although much labor is saved and the harvest is speeded up, the grade of cotton is lowered and some cotton is left in the field. In western Texas, where the climate is drier than in the eastern part of the Cotton Belt, a 2-row mechanical cotton stripper operated by 2 men can harvest 2 acres of cotton per hour. In North Carolina, about three-fourths of an acre per hour is the average rate. Moreover, the operation of a mechanical cotton stripper is conditioned on both favorable weather during the harvest season and nearly level land. Steep slopes, contour rows, and terraces are obstacles to operation of mechanical strippers (*115*).

## Mechanized Crop Production

More significant than any other change in farming methods was the mechanization of field operations in production of all major crops. Mechanization not only changed farm operations; it also advanced farming from a self-supporting family occupation to a commercial enterprise. That such far-reaching changes resulted from it is due mainly to the increase in efficiency of farm labor. These innovations have found their widest application where crops and physical setting lend themselves to mechanized operations. For instance, mechanized production of small grains on nearly level land, a subhumid or even semiarid climate, and a productive medium-textured soil showed the greatest gains in efficiency of farm labor. A comparison of man-labor requirements for some of the main crops grown with old and new methods will help to explain the significance of mechanization.

*Wheat.*—Around 1800, the man-labor requirements for production of wheat, expressed in United States averages, were about 56 hours per acre yielding 15 bushels, or 373 man-hours per 100 bushels. A century later, these requirements were reduced to 15 hours per acre yielding 14 bushels, or 108 man-hours per 100 bushels. In 1954-56, the average number of man-hours needed to grow an acre of wheat yielding 19.3 bushels was 4.3 hours, or 22 hours per 100 bushels. This is only 8 percent of the per acre requirement in 1800, or 6 percent of the requirement per 100 bushels.

*Corn.*—Corn, the most extensively grown crop in the United States, has a record no less remarkable. Corn grown for grain in 1800 required an average of 86 man-hours per acre producing 25 bushels, or 344 man-hours per 100 bushels. By 1900, these man-hour requirements had been cut to about half, and by 1954–56 they had declined to 11.8 man-hours per acre yielding 41.3 bushels, or 29 man-hours per 100 bushels. The average number of man-hours required to grow an acre of corn, therefore, was reduced to 14 percent, or, on the 100-bushel basis, to 8 percent of the requirement 150 years ago.

*Cotton.*—By means of yield estimates for 1800, a similar series of figures that indicate man-hour requirements has been prepared for cotton. According to these estimates, in 1800 the average labor requirements for growing an acre of cotton yielding 147 pounds of lint were 185 man-hours, or 601 man-hours per bale. By 1900, the average yield per acre had increased to 191 pounds, and the man-hours needed to grow it had declined to 112, so that only 280 man-hours were needed to grow a bale of cotton. For the 1954–56 period, the average yield again increased. It is now 386.7 pounds per acre, which require, on the average, 77 man-hours, or 96 man-hours per bale. The average number of man-hours required to grow cotton has therefore been reduced in 150 years to 42 percent of the former requirement per acre, or 16 percent per bale (*26, 62*).

These three sample illustrations of the increase in farm labor efficiency are averages for the United States as a whole; they cannot be regarded as norms that are applicable to regions, much less to localities. Recent regional studies reveal that under favorable conditions much greater savings in man-hours per acre have been attained than may be suspected.

For instance, in the hard winter wheat region of the High Plains, wheat can be grown and harvested with less than 2 man-hours of labor per acre. Corn is grown for grain in the Corn Belt with from 6 to 20 man-hours per acre. Like corn, cotton has a considerable spread in labor requirements, depending on the region, yield and variety, and the extent of mechanization. On the High Plains of Texas, irrigated cotton yielding 418 pounds of lint picked partly by hand and partly by machine required 34.5 man-hours per acre. On nonirrigated land, an acre of cotton yielding 200 pounds of lint harvested partly by hand and partly by machine required only 21 man-hours. In California, cotton grown on irrigated land producing around 700 pounds per acre of lint picked mainly by hand required 99 man-hours per acre. In the humid East, however, without mechanical picking and moderate yield, cotton usually requires more than 100 man-hours per acre (*125*). Similar departures from the averages of man-labor requirements must be expected in areas in which modern production practices are not or cannot be followed to any extent.

*Other Crops.*—These three crops—the principal crops in point of value—have also contributed proportionally more than the others to the general decline in farm-labor needs as a result of mechanized operations. However, with few exceptions, all other crops follow a similar trend. This is especially true of the grain crops. Some crops are less affected by increased efficiency of farm labor, but more so by the increase in per acre yields. Tobacco is an example of this type of crop. Forty years ago, the average yield per acre of tobacco was 816 pounds, which required 356 man-hours of labor, or 44 man-hours per 100 pounds. In 1954–56, the average yield per acre was 1,461 pounds, with a labor requirement of 490 man-hours, or 34 man-hours per 100 pounds. Per acre yields of practically all crops have increased in the last half-century. This also explains the statistical differences in man-hours required when applied to areal or crop units. These differences help to explain, in most instances, the fact that the increase in labor efficiency cannot be attributed entirely to mechanization of farm operations. Increased yields are also responsible to some extent.

## Efficiency of Farm Labor Increased

Increases in efficiency of farm labor have been recorded ever since the country was settled, but the greatest gains have been made since 1910. Comparison of figures representing average performances for the beginning and end of this period may be helpful. From available records, it has been calculated that in 1910 the man-hours of labor per crop-acre for the United States amounted to 38 hours. By 1955, they had declined to 17 hours. At the same time, the production efficiency index of farm labor per hour on a 1947–49 base had risen from 46 in 1910 to 132 in 1955. In other words, during this 45–year period, the labor requirement in man-hours per acre declined by 55 percent, whereas the productive capacity per man-hour increased by 187 percent.[4]

Changes of this magnitude in the efficiency of farm labor brought about through technical advances in the processes of crop production and increased yields could not fail to react on land and people. These innovations not only modified the old order of farming; they also affected the use of the land in different directions. With the displacement of horses and mules by tractors, the land needed to grow feed and fodder for draft animals became available to grow crops or feed or to be used as pasture for meat and dairy animals. The number of horses and mules displaced in this way ran into the millions. The number of horses and mules on farms reached its peak from 1915 to 1918, when more than 26 million were reported; from then on their number declined. In 1955, less than 4 million were reported. Instead, 4.3 million tractors, more than 2.7 million motortrucks, and more than 4.4 million automobiles were reported on farms. What a decrease of this size in number of draft animals means in terms of land use becomes apparent when the acreages needed to produce the feed for these animals are compared. In 1915, 91 million acres were needed to produce feed for horses and mules. By 1955, only 9 million

acres were needed for this purpose. The livestock–acre ratio is not exactly the same for the two periods because changes in feed rations were taken into account in the computation. As these figures indicate, in the process of mechanizing farm operations, the use of 82 million acres of land almost exclusively in farms shifted from production of horsepower to production of farm products (*134, 1952, pp. 455, 651; 1956, pp. 359, 433, 447*).

The displacement of animated energy and labor by motorpower and machines was not confined to horses and mules. Farm families and workers on farms were also affected. Statistics register a decline for both, despite a substantial increase in the total population. In 1910, the total population of the United States was 92 million, of which 32 million were living on 6 million farms. In 1955, the total population was 165 million, of which 22 million were living on 5 million farms. As indicated in round figures, the total population increased by 73 million in the 45–year period, but the number of farms decreased by more than a million, and the farm population by 10 million. These are not the only instances in which a gain in labor efficiency had an inverse reaction on the man–land relationship. During the same period, even though the number of farms declined, the land in farms rose from 879 million to 1,158 million acres. Cropland harvested, however, rose only from 317 million to 333 million acres. Farm employment declined from 13.5 million in 1910 to 8.2 million in 1955. Expressed in relation to total population, the ratio was 1 farmworker to 7 people in 1910 as compared with 1 to 20 in 1955. This is of profound socio-economic significance. As indicated, a reduced labor force provided the agricultural products for 72 million more people in 1955 than in 1910 and for export as well, and this was accomplished with only a slight increase in acreage of cropland (*134, 1956*).

## Type-of-Farming Areas

The statistical evidence of changes in agricultural production presented so far applies to the country as a whole, but the ratio of change does not apply uniformly to all regions. Some regions are affected more than others, mainly because of specialization. Regional specialization evolved through adjustment of the scope of farming enterprises to the potentialities found within the environmental frame of natural conditions and economic opportunities. This type of adjustment has been going on since colonial days.

That not all colonies were equally suited to production of certain crops became apparent

at the beginning of settlement. Wheat, for instance, was tried by the early settlers of New England but smut soon made its appearance and greatly damaged the crop. In the colonies south of the Hudson, however, wheat was more successful. There, it soon became a commercial crop to be sold in northern markets. These natural advantages and drawbacks of different regions gradually became known with the advancement of settlement and use of land.

Regional specialization involves all products of the land. The supply–demand relationship created by regional specialization is therefore not confined to land and city; it also requires

---

[4] Unpublished data.

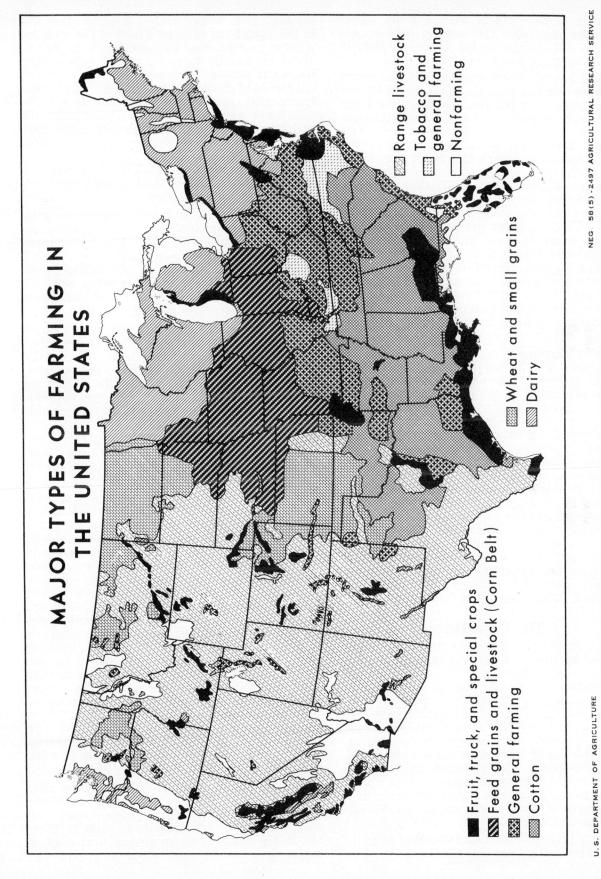

## MAJOR TYPES OF FARMING IN THE UNITED STATES

Fruit, truck, and special crops

Feed grains and livestock (Corn Belt)

General farming

Cotton

Wheat and small grains

Dairy

Range livestock

Tobacco and general farming

Nonfarming

U.S. DEPARTMENT OF AGRICULTURE

NEG. 58(5)-2497 AGRICULTURAL RESEARCH SERVICE

FIGURE 23.—Agriculture is sensitive to advantages of site. Climate, soil, or lay-of-land alone may create a favorable or an unfavorable environment for different types of farming. The regionally specialized production areas shown on this map represent adjustment of agricultural production to natural conditions. But proximity to markets was also a factor in development of the fruit, vegetable, and dairy industries.

exchange of products between regions. This interlocked economic relationship between regions is not limited to the United States; it extends to most countries.

As settlement moved westward, it was found that large regions were so handicapped by low precipitation that the land could be used for a few grain crops only. Farther west, the land could not be used for crops, except with irrigation. From east to west is therefore the main direction in which the major use capability of the land changes because of differences in amount of precipitation. Within the more humid eastern section of the country, changes in type of farming occur mainly from north to south. These changes are due largely to the decrease in temperature, and the shortening of the frost-free season with advancing latitude. Although the character of the soils and the land relief are also involved, terms such as "Cotton Belt" and "Corn Belt" have become popular. The arrangement and distribution of the major type-of-farming areas are illustrated in figure 23 (*123, 38*).

Type-of-farming areas as represented on the map should not be regarded as permanently fixed in outline or internal structure. Change may be expected with the passage of time. For a time, a particular type of farming may constitute the best adjustment that can be made to the prevailing natural and economic conditions of an area, but farming responds also to economic inducements or limitations. These inducements or limitations may stem from changes in market demands and prices, modifications in farming methods, introduction of new crop varieties or new crops, concentration of specialty crops, or reclamation of land. With either inducements or limitations, some changes may be expected. These changes affect the type of farming and social and economic conditions as well. Some of the changes that occur are mentioned in the pages that follow.

## The Corn Belt

The central part of the country is so richly endowed by nature with physical qualities favorable to agricultural use of the land that it has reached a high degree of development. For the most part, the surface is undulating to slightly rolling. Consequently, aside from the short slopes along the incised drainage systems, it presents few obstacles to farming or to construction of transportation and communication systems. Straight-lined field operations, straight highways, roads, and railroads are prevalent features of the landscape, and they represent adaptations to the rectilinear divisions of the land.

No less favorable than surface relief to agricultural production are climate and soils. Climatically, the larger part of the Corn Belt lies in the humid and subhumid part of the country. Annual precipitation averages 25 to 40 inches, of which usually more than half falls during the warm season. Temperatures are warm in summer and moderate in winter. The frost-free period ranges from 140 to 180 days. The soils have developed mainly from glacial till under grass cover and are naturally productive. These features combined produce a physical background that is adapted to farming. As a result, the proportion of all land in crops is higher in the Corn Belt than in any other area of similar size in the country.

Animal industry and crop production with feed crops predominating from the beginning provided the orientation for the agricultural development of the Corn Belt. Corn, which had been the chief crop of the Indians, was transmitted by them to the earliest settlers. The growing of corn succeeded wherever summer temperatures averaged around 65° F.

From experience gained in different parts of the country, it was found that in no other region could corn be grown more successfully than on the central prairies. Thus corn became the dominant crop and earned the region its name. Other crops—wheat, oats, rye, and hay particularly—were grown with corn in rotation, although the composition of the cropland pattern has been altered (*150, 152, 151*). These changes were not confined to farming; they affected the economic structure and social divisions of the population as well.

In the Corn Belt, the technological improvements and scientific methods developed during the last few decades have found ready application. Crop production has become almost entirely mechanized. With the disappearance of draft animals, the acreage of hay and forage crops needed to feed them declined, but production of corn gained in importance. Corn was no longer an exclusive food and feed crop. It had found industrial uses and with them expanded its market demand. As a result, corn is now grown largely as a cash crop. Production of corn was further stimulated by the advent of hybrid corn around 1933. From that time on, hybrid corn has gained in favor. Today, about 90 percent of the corn grown in the United States is hybrid corn. The average per acre yield of corn in the United States was 25 bushels in the 1926–30 period, as compared with 38 bushels in 1950–54, an increase of more than 50 percent (*134, 1956*).

Corn is not the only crop in the Corn Belt that has affected farming profoundly; soybeans have also affected it. The soybean, a native of Asia, was brought to America as early as 1804, but it did not become an agricultural crop of major importance until about 30 years ago

(92). It was only after the soybean had become acclimated and its value as a field crop had been recognized that it started its rise to prominence. In 1925, 1½ million acres were planted, but less than a half million acres were harvested for beans. Average yields were 11.7 bushels per acre. Three decades later in 1955, the total planted acreage for the United States was more than 20 million acres, of which 18 million were harvested for beans. The average yield was 20 bushels per acre, or a total of 374 million bushels. The significance of this figure in this connection arises from the fact that 251 million bushels, or 67 percent of the total, was produced in the Corn Belt (134, 1956). This sudden rise in soybean production not only affected the economy of the Corn Belt; it was felt around the world. It reversed the position held by the United States on the international market. This country had been the world's largest importer of soybeans and its products; it is now the largest exporter. That soybeans made such phenomenal gains in the Corn Belt was due largely to its similarity to corn so far as conditions of growth were concerned. Soybeans can be grown in rotation with corn or as a replacement crop when corn does not get the proper start in the spring.

Changes of this magnitude in yield and kind of crops grown could not fail to affect farm organization as well as the economic status of the region and the social grouping of the people. The large-scale production of crops for industrial use attracted industries to the small towns, the population of which increased rapidly. Up to the early decades of the 20th century, the population of the Corn Belt was predominantly rural, and the country towns grew slowly. With the arrival of industry, especially in the eastern part of the belt, the trend in population growth was reversed.

As indicated by census figures for the last few decades, the urban population is increasing rapidly while the rural population is barely holding its own and, in some instances, is decreasing. This is one aspect of regional development that is of more than local interest and concern. From both national and farm viewpoints, much can be said for the preservation of the fertile land of the Corn Belt for crop production. The extension of urban settlement reduces the land available for crops and often encumbers the remaining farmers with a share of the cost of development and an increase in service charges. This kind of urban extension, moreover, is not confined to one region. It can be found around most urban centers, where suburban development is spreading. In some instances, zoning ordinances have been adopted to guide land development in order to prevent misuse or waste of land and other resources.

# The Great Plains

Large-scale mechanized production of crops had its inception in the Great Plains. Topographically and climatically, the Great Plains represent the most favorable natural environment for mechanized crop production in the United States. Large unbroken rectangular fields on slightly rolling or nearly level land with a minimum of precipitation during the harvesting season provide the regional setting. Small grains, mainly wheat, are the principal crops grown on the Western Plains. They are produced entirely with machine operations. With straight-line operations a mile or more long, a grain grower of the Plains frequently can cultivate and harvest fields that comprise hundreds of acres, an accomplishment that could not be approached with the farm implements formerly available (pls. 62, 63, 65, 74). Without modern mechanical equipment, much of the land in the semiarid plains that is now utilized for crop production could not be used for this purpose with any expectation of economic returns. Because of the cyclical variations of climate over the years, average yields are comparatively low and crop acreages fluctuate.

Because of the low and irregular precipitation, which averages between 15 and 25 inches annually over most of the higher part of the Great Plains, a more diversified cropping schedule is not possible and crop yields are unreliable. Recurring droughts are a hazard to crops. Small grains are the principal crops that can be grown here with any degree of success. Wheat, oats, barley, and rye are grown, but wheat predominates; in some sections wheat farming approaches a monocultural type of agriculture. In the 10 States represented in figure 24, A and B, the acreage now used for wheat is more than twice as large as the acreage used for oats, barley, and rye combined. Recently, despite occasional setbacks and the ever-present hazard of weather, the acreage of wheat has expanded more than have the acreages of other grains.

In other parts of the country, acreages of wheat have contracted. In 1925 in the 10 Plains States, around 32 million acres were in wheat. In 1950, close to 50 million acres were planted to wheat; in 1955 only 42 million acres were seeded. These expansions and contractions of cultivated land on the western semiarid margin of the Plains, however, cannot be attributed to a single cause. Economic factors are involved also. For instance, high prices for wheat provided an inducement to expand the acreage of wheat. The ultimate outcome of the contest between mechanical efficiency, the vagaries of climate, and the changing market prices of the crop is not yet known.

# WHEAT YIELD PER SEEDED ACRE
## In the Great Plains, 1926-48

**AVERAGE**

**VARIABILITY**

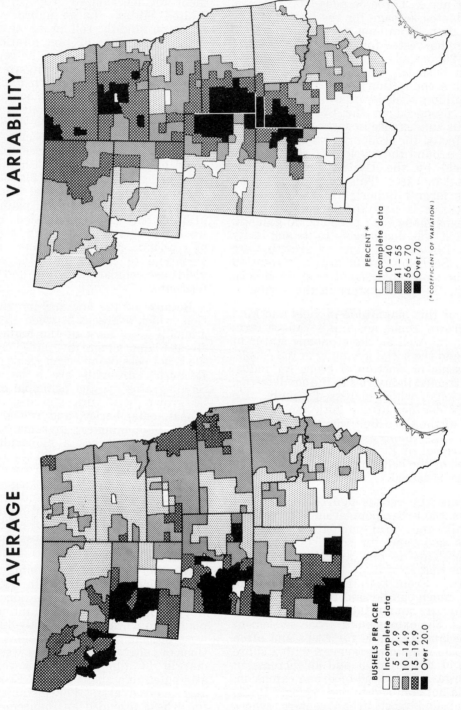

BUSHELS PER ACRE
- Incomplete data
- 5 – 9.9
- 10 – 14.9
- 15 – 19.9
- Over 20.0

PERCENT*
- Incomplete data
- 0 – 40
- 41 – 55
- 56 – 70
- Over 70

(*COEFFICIENT OF VARIATION)

U. S. DEPARTMENT OF AGRICULTURE

NEG. 58(5)-2498 AGRICULTURAL RESEARCH SERVICE

FIGURE 24.—Distribution of average wheat yields, and distribution of variation in wheat yields in the Great Plains are shown in this chart. The two parts of the chart cover the same area; both are based on yields of wheat by counties over a 22-year period. But neither the distribution of average yields nor the variation in yields conforms strictly to climate. In areas where it is practiced, irrigation has its effect.

So far as land use is concerned, the contest may never be decided on a permanent basis (*139*).

Wheat is the most representative and the most important of the small grains grown in the Great Plains. What happens to wheat as a result of changes in weather is shared to a considerable extent by the other small grains. Fluctuations of crop yields from year to year, because of variations in weather, occur throughout the United States but nowhere else is the range as wide as in the Great Plains. Yields of wheat in the Plains may vary from very low or crop failure to a bonanza crop. The uncertain crop yields must be taken into account when the regional economy is considered.

Irrigation is largely responsible for the high average yields and low variability of yields shown in figure 24 for the counties west of the Plains, in southern and western New Mexico, and in counties that contain valleys and basins in Colorado (pls. 78, 82), Wyoming, and western Montana. Even some of the Plains counties on the upper Arkansas, upper Platte, and Cheyenne Rivers are similarly affected. The higher average yields and lesser variability of yields along the eastern margin of the Plains are due primarily, however, to an increased and more reliable occurrence of precipitation.

For the dry-farming areas of the Great Plains, average yields have little significance as an index to prospective harvests. As applied in figure 24 they function as a standard level from which the departures indicate the variability of yields. The percentage used as the coefficient of variation applies to the two-thirds of the annual yields that fall within the indicated percentage range below or above the average. The extremes are therefore excluded.

## Suitcase Farming

Complete mechanization of grain farming also had its reaction on farm settlement, urbanrural population ratio, and economic and social conditions. In the wheat-growing areas, fieldwork is mechanized to the extent that large fields can be cultivated in a comparatively short time. If no livestock is kept on the farms, farmwork is confined almost entirely to seeding and harvesting time. Compared with other types of farming in which a resident operator is needed the year around, this is a real distinction in that mechanized field operations have converted large-scale operation into a part-time occupation. As in most other parts of the country, dispersed farmsteads were the original settlement pattern. This pattern still prevails over much of the area but it is not static.

By force of circumstance, farmers of the Wheat Belt acquired mobility. During the dry 1930's, many farmers had to leave the rural environment but the movement did not stop with the arrival of the wet 1940's. Although the acreage of cropland harvested expanded in the 1940's, the rural population continued to decline and the urban population to increase. Many farmers moved to town. By so doing they could share the amenities of community life and avoid the inconveniences of dispersed settlement. "Suitcase" farmers, as these city operators are sometimes called, now operate their farms successfully from a distance of up to 30 miles or more. In some parts of the Wheat Belt, they cultivate a considerable acreage (*75*).

Operating a farm while living elsewhere is not exceptional, nor is it confined to the grain farms of the Wheat Belt. To a considerable extent, ranching in the Rio Grande Valley of Texas is carried on in this way. Farming and ranching in Utah is conditioned largely by the original Mormon village-settlement pattern. A concentration of nonresident farming is found in southern Florida in connection with production of citrus fruits and vegetables. Cash grains, especially rice, in California are grown chiefly by operators who do not reside on the land they cultivate. The Great Plains, however, have one distinction that is not shared by other regions to any extent—the number of farmers who do not live on the farms they operate is increasing. In most other regions, this number is either more or less stationary or is declining (*9*).

Nonirrigated crop production in the semiarid western border of the Great Plains is now mechanized to the extent that cash grains can be grown in this belt. The choice of land use is therefore confined to either grain production or grazing. In these instances, the physical capabilities or drawbacks inherent in the land determine whether production of grain can yield the necessary economic returns. Adjustment to these conditions is essential. As may be observed on the enclosed colored map of major land uses, it has produced the ragged edge of cultivated land along the western border of the Plains. Cropland appears in detached areas or as jutting-out belts on the smooth upland portions of the Plains, whereas grazing land, as a rule, is confined to the rougher land or to sandy and shallow soils. The Badlands in North Dakota and South Dakota, the breaks along the Platte, Arkansas, Cimarron, and Canadian Rivers, and similar areas are used for grazing (pls. 68, 69, 72, 73, 74, 80, 113, 118). Thus they provide examples of adjustment of cropland to the suface configuration of the Plains.

## Flax a Special Crop

In addition to the grain farming that prevails on the Plains, more diversified production areas on the western margin are made possible through irrigation. Fruits and vegetables and other specialties are produced in these areas. On the eastern border, where the rainfall is somewhat higher and more reliable, other farm crops such as corn and soybeans, are edging in. In the Red River Basin to the north, flax is frequently grown in rotation with grain.

During the last century, flax shifted from one principal use category to another. Originally, it was grown primarily to produce the fiber from which linen textiles are woven. With the appearance of cotton as a competitor, flax has lost ground. Aside from the small quantity of flax grown for fiber in Oregon, the flax grown in the United States is seed flax used mainly for production of linseed oil. The growing of seed flax fits in well with local grain-farming practices; all are mechanized operations. To promote increased production of seed, flax is seeded thinly to give the plants room for branching, which shortens the fibers. Seed flax is not harvested until the seeds are ripe and stalks are hardened. These short, hard fibers of flax straw are unsuited to use for textiles, but they provide excellent raw material for manufacturing paper. Cigarette paper is now made exclusively from the fibers of seed flax. For other high-quality paper, for instance currency paper, flax fiber now forms part of the raw material, as it imparts needed strength. In point of acreage and yield, flaxseed is a fluctuating crop. It varies from 3 million to more than 5 million acres and produces from 30 to 40 million bushels of seed. North Dakota and Minnesota are the chief producers of seed flax (*32*).

# The Dairy Belt

The cool humid region of eastern United States comprises roughly the Lake and Northeastern States, plus Pennsylvania and Maryland. Dairying, the prevalent type of farming, gave rise to the name of the belt. As the climate is humid, the three major land uses are found here. Approximately 50 percent of the total land area of the belt is in forests. Some of the largest compact forest areas in the United States are located in this region. As a rule, the forests occupy mountainous, rocky, swampy, or sandy land. Much of this land is included in National and State forests or parks, or is otherwise publicly owned, but commercial forests on privately owned land are also represented, particularly in Maine. These are the main features the Lake and Northeastern States have in common (pls. 1, 3, 5, 6, 8, 16, 41, 49).

Land use in both sections is also greatly affected by industrial development and urbanization of the population though not to the same extent. The physical backgrounds differ also,

as does farming in some respects, and the land–man relationship is not the same in the two areas. These divergencies are sufficiently marked to make separate discussions of the eastern and western sections of the Dairy Belt necessary.

## The Lake States

Unlike the Northeastern States, the Lake States have no extensive mountain ranges. They are a northward extension of the glaciated plains with their morainic belts (pl. 46), sandy outwash plains (pl. 49), glacial lakebeds (pl. 51), swamps (pl. 50), rough and rocky hills, and uplands (pl. 41). The lakes, which form the international boundary and divide the States, function along shorebelts to modify the climate to such an extent that use of the land is affected. In addition, these large connected inland waterbodies serve as transportation routes for bulky freight to the Eastern States. Completion of the St. Lawrence Seaway will bring ocean traffic direct to the inland ports of the Great Lakes. The economic consequences that may be expected to follow in the wake of this waterway extension cannot be foretold.

Industries and agriculture are well developed in the Dairy Belt. Land use and agriculture have been adapted to the physical environment and to economic opportunities, so far as location is concerned. Crop specialties in particular are more sensitive to physical location than are most field crops. The fruit belt along the eastern shore of Lake Michigan (pl. 39) and the cherry orchards on the Door Peninsula in Wisconsin are examples of adjustment of production to the potentialities of climate. In both instances, the success of growing fruit on a commercial scale depends on the protection from frost provided by the moderating influence of air currents from the lake during blossomtime in spring and near harvesttime in early fall. Production of sugar beets is concentrated particularly on the glacial lakebeds around Saginaw Bay (pl. 40). Green peas, celery, and sweet corn are the chief vegetables grown for sale. All are grown in clustered production areas where physical conditions are favorable and where marketing facilities have been organized. Corn is an important field crop, but it is not grown for grain to the same extent as in the Corn Belt. With advancing latitude, the summers grow shorter and cooler, and corn does not ripen each year. As dairying and animal husbandry are the chief agricultural enterprises, corn is often grown as a forage crop to be ensiled and used as winter fodder.

That agriculture and industry are still expanding may be seen in estimates of population and crop acreage. As reported by the census, population rose for these 3 States from close to 8 million in 1920 to nearly 13 million in 1950, of which 64 percent is now urban. Cropland increased for the same period from 36 million to nearly 38 million acres. The growth rates of population and acreage of cropland, therefore, differ considerably but acreage of cropland does not tell the whole story of agricultural growth. The farmland has been improved, and most of the farm operations are now mechanized. Yields per acre have increased, as has output per animal unit. As this is a dairy region, production of milk is particularly important. Milk production per cow increased in all dairy States during the last decade by approximately 20 percent over the 1941–45 average (76, p. 5).

## The Northeast

The situation in the Northeastern States differs considerably from that in the Lake States. The northeastern part of the country has had a longer period of development and adjustment. In addition, the physiographic background is more varied. Back of the level land along the ocean front are hills, mountains, and plateaus. Differences in climate conform to this arrangement, and settlement and development were greatly affected by these conditions. Population is increasing rapidly, but it is distributed unevenly. Settlement in New England was of the town and village type (pls. 5, 6, 7), and to a lesser extent this was true also of the coastal areas in other States. Favorable sites for large concentrations of population were provided by sheltered harbors. However, when the lowlands were occupied, settlement spread into the hills (pl. 3), mountains, and valleys. With the prevailing way of life in colonial days this was possible, but it proved to be a handicap to advancement in levels of living, which began with the opening of the Western Plains for settlement and the industrialization of the country.

Industrialization in the Northeastern States had an early start, and this too had its reaction on the labor market. Industrial competition for man's labor injected an economic element into the land–man relationship, which produced changes in both land use and distribution of population.

Many settlers in the northeastern mountains discovered that farming could provide only a poor living at best. They soon realized that they were economically handicapped. With the opening of the Central Plains and the West, many of them moved to more favorable surroundings for agricultural production. Others were attracted by the growing industries and towns. These migratory movements did not alter greatly the population total for the Northeastern States as a whole, but they changed markedly the distribution pattern of the people and with it the cultural landscape of the mountains and the coastal belt. Many mountain farmsteads were abandoned, and the land cleared and cultivated by the settlers reverted to brush and forest or was used for pasture. Others are used as summer homes (20, 22, 117, 2).

Migratory movements of people and changes in use of the land in the Northeastern States are not confined to the mountains. They are evident also in the lower coastal belt. Urbanization, industrialization, and trade in these States affect the economic and social status of the people to a greater extent than do topography and climate. Besides the proximity of metropolitan markets, the prevalent village and town type of settlement offered a concentrated labor supply for industry. With these advantages, the population increased rapidly. At the same time, the pace was set for urbanization.

How the development affected the man–land relationship can be told more impressively with a few round figures pertaining to the last three decades. The total population of the Northeastern States in 1920, as reported by the census, was 31 million, which increased by 1950 to 42 million people. Of these, 75 percent lived in urbanized areas. During the same period, the number of farms declined from 640,000 in 1920 to 443,000 in 1950, and with it reduced the acreage of harvested cropland from 24 to 17 million acres. Acreage of cropland is not a true measure of productive capacity, but in this instance, it indicates dependence on supplies from more distant sources. Actually, this concentration of population has produced the largest market for agricultural products in the country.

Not all the land that went out of production was used for urban expansion, nor can all of it be classed as poor. Some of this land is used for pasture and some is used for gardening or part-time farming. Diversion to resort and recreational uses accounts for part of it, but a goodly proportion is reverting to woodland. However, a reduction in crop acreage does not necessarily mean a proportional reduction in production. Frequently, a reduction in acreage of cropland is offset to a considerable extent by an increase in yield per acre, and some of the specialties grown in these States have responded in this way.

### Specialties Produced

Dairying is the predominant type of farming in these States, but in some districts specialty crops are equally or even more important. Along the shores of the Great Lakes stretches a belt in which the land is used intensively for fruits and vegetables. In northern Maine, potatoes are the chief cash crop. The per acre yield of potatoes has more than doubled in the last 30 years. In 1920, the average yield per acre for the entire country was 112 bushels;

by 1955, it had advanced to 268 bushels. Tobacco, another specialty, is grown in the Connecticut Valley, the Piedmont of Pennsylvania, and southern Maryland; it has followed a similar trend. In 1920, the average per acre yield of tobacco was 780 pounds, and by 1955, it had risen to 1,467 pounds. Fruits and vegetables are grown intensively in some districts near the coast. Here, too, production methods have improved and the output has increased.

Poultry farming, an important industry, is also well-established in the region, although it is concentrated more in the lower coastal belt. Until a few decades ago, poultry was almost entirely a sideline of general farming, and to a considerable extent this is still true. But in the meantime, poultry farming has evolved as a special type of animal industry, in which production of commercial broilers has attained the status of large-scale business. Some broiler-growing establishments produce more than a million birds a year.

The indications are that commercial broiler production started in the early thirties on the Delmarva Peninsula. More recently, other production centers have developed. They are scattered over the Eastern, the Southern, and the Pacific Coast States. Within the last decade, production of commercial broilers has expanded to a point at which it exceeds considerably the number of chickens sold on the farm. A few round figures will illustrate this point.

The number of chickens produced in 1955 on the farms of the country totaled 377 million. Iowa led with 30 million. In the same year, commercial broiler production in the United States amounted to 1,078 million birds. Georgia led with 178 million. The commercial production of broilers in this country is therefore nearly twice the farm production of chickens.

A comparison of these figures becomes even more impressive when confined to the 11 Northeastern States of the Dairy Belt. Chickens produced in 1955 on the farms of these States totaled 67 million. Pennsylvania led with 18 million. Production of commercial broilers in these States in 1955 amounted to 261 million birds, of which 70 million were produced in Delaware. This made Delaware the leading State of the region.

Broiler production has increased rapidly as has its feed efficiency. To produce a 3-pound broiler 20 years ago required approximately 12 pounds of feed. As of 1957 less than 9 pounds was required. Improved strains of birds, feed of better quality, and more efficient operational practices largely account for the improvements.

An equally significant increase occurred in egg production. In the United States, about 40 billion eggs were produced in 1940. In 1955, 59 billion were produced. This increase in egg production was accomplished without a corresponding increase in the number of fowls, which totaled 296 million and 309 million, respectively, for the 2 years. The higher rate of production of laying hens accounts for most of the increase. The average number of eggs produced per layer in 1940 was 134; by 1955, it had advanced to 192 (*134, 1940, 1956; 93; 57*).

Pointing out the highlights of the poultry industry with a few figures pertaining to chickens and omitting mention of turkeys gives a distorted picture. The turkey is part of the native American fauna; to the early settlers, it was a game bird. Turkeys are respected members of the barnyard congregation and are raised in great numbers on turkey farms. Most of the turkeys are grown in the Dairy Belt; in 1956, they totaled 77 million birds (*72*). Finally, ducks and geese are also produced to some extent, but they do not approach chickens and turkeys in either number or value.

The large concentrations of population in and near the Dairy Belt provide not only the chief market outlets for dairy and poultry products, but in addition they profoundly affect land use. Urban development has progressed rapidly, and, by taking advantage of modern transportation facilities, it has sprawled far out into rustic territory (pl. 8). Aside from the land actually used as building lots, advanced real estate values and speculative holdings have eliminated from farm use much of the land in the ragged suburban fringe. This land lies idle, waiting for the homebuilders to come. There are also developments in the opposite direction, where the proximity of urban centers has promoted more intensive use of the land for truck farming and horticultural production (pls. 19, 20). Instances of this kind may be found along the warmer coastal region from Boston south into the Delmarva Peninsula. In the northern Piedmont, farming is diversified; both livestock farming and crop production are carried on (pl. 22).

## The General Farming Belt

Between the Corn Belt to the north and the Cotton Belt to the south, lies a belt from which cotton is eliminated because of the cooler climate. In this belt, corn, although it is one of the principal crops, cannot be grown in proportioned quantities as in the Corn Belt. The chief drawbacks are the extensive hilly to mountainous surface and the less productive soils. The Ouachita (pl. 131), Ozark (pls. 58, 130), and southern Appalachian Mountains (pls. 27, 28, 30, 31, 145, 146) comprise a major part of the belt, but valleys and rolling country, like the Pennyroyal Plain (pl. 33), the Bluegrass Region (pl. 32), the Nashville Basin (pl. 144), the Great Appalachian Valley (pl. 29), parts of the Piedmont (pl. 26), and the Coastal Plain (pl. 25), are included also. In an aggregation of varied land characteristics of this kind, adjustment of land use and farming to the capabilities of the land is a necessity.

Much of the rugged mountainous land is included in national forests or parks; forest and recreation are the best uses that can be made of such land. This does not mean, however, that the hills and mountains are uninhabited, or that this belt is sparsely populated. Actually, some of the hilly sections have a denser population than the broad valleys (88). That so many people live in the hills is due largely to the conditions that prevailed at time of settlement. Over much of the eastern section of this belt settlement occurred during the colonial period or shortly thereafter, and even the part of the belt that was in the public domain was occupied before mechanization made farming a commercial enterprise.

Settlers in the hilly country, however, cannot take full advantage of operational improvements. Usually their fields are small and frequently they are too steeply sloping to permit the use of modern tools. Furthermore, the farm income of these settlers is insufficient to provide either capital or credit for the purchase of mechanical equipment. In this respect, the mountaineers have a permanent economic handicap. Farming in these surroundings provides no more than a subsistence level of living. There is no opportunity for economic advancement but these families own their lands and have homes (126). Many of the younger people look for off-the-farm employment, which may be found in mines or more recently in the manufacturing industries that have located in the area.

The mountaineers represent an extreme example of low-income farmers, but their level of living does not prevail throughout the belt. In those areas in which the surface of the land permits more extensive farm operations, the economic status of farmers is higher. In a number of districts, specialties are produced in commercial quantities. Fruit, tobacco, peanuts, and livestock, which in the Bluegrass Region and the Virginia Piedmont includes purebred horses and some other specialties, are all represented. Over much of the areas, woodland and pasture predominate. Only in exceptional instances has farming been able fully to utilize modern equipment for crop production.

## The Cotton and Subtropical Fruit Belt

Economic and social conditions in the South are rooted in the history of early settlement. These conditions were touched on in the discussion of the role cotton plays in this part of the country. Equally important are the rela-tionships between cotton growing and the land and between cotton and man. Cotton, which is produced largely by tenant farmers, is grown entirely for the market. Where plantations were the dominant socio-economic institutions for use of the land, large holdings were the rule. A number of these plantation holdings are still intact, but they are operated by tenants under unified management (pl. 140). The majority of tenants, however, are independent operators. Tenant farms are numerous in the South; in many counties, more than 50 percent of the operators are tenants (68). As a rule, tenants or sharecroppers operate small farms to produce a cash crop, chiefly cotton. Occupancy of these tenant farms is more frequently on an annual agreement basis, and consequently it fluctuates with economic conditions. In recent years, tenancy in the South has declined considerably, partly as a result of the reduction in the acreage of cotton.

### Cotton

Among the crops, cotton is the most widely grown. It has also experienced the greatest decline in acreage, which is particularly noticeable in the humid cotton States of the East (pls. 129, 150). According to the census, the acreage of cotton in these States declined from 43 million acres in 1929 to 17 million acres in 1955. A movement in the opposite direction is reported for the 3 western cotton-growing States (pl. 119, *A*, *B*), where acreage rose in the same period from 645,000 to 1,498,000 acres. The reduction in cotton acreage in a quarter-century, therefore, was approximately 17 million acres for the United States. Curtailment in acreage did not bring about a proportional decrease in production. Using census figures for comparison, in 1929 production was 14.6 million running bales of lint. In 1954, with a 56-percent decrease in acreage, it was 12.8 million bales. The average yield per acre increased from 164 pounds in 1929 to 341 pounds in 1954. The decrease in acreage did not affect production as much as it affected the number of tenant operators.

Tenant operators are not rooted in the land by ownership or long-term lease. They move freely from place to place or to and from nonfarm employment. Consequently, they have only a transient interest in the land itself. Improving the land and adopting conservation practices to preserve the soil for generations to come are not concepts that would influence a cotton-growing tenant to change from straight furrows to furrows that follow the contour of the land. Furthermore, as cotton was the chief consideration of the rental, this crop was frequently grown for years on the same land without rotation or changes in the practices followed.

If not properly cultivated, cotton can easily induce erosion on rolling and hilly areas. Erosion induced in this way has brought drastic changes to parts of the South. For instance, the use capability of some of the cotton land that was originally the most productive, like the Black Prairie of Alabama (pls. 142, 150), and to some extent the Black Waxy Prairie in Texas (pls. 116, 128), is used only for grazing. Damage from erosion severe enough to change the use capability of the land has not always attained regional proportions, but it has eliminated many tracts from further cropping or has reduced markedly the productivity of the land.

Erosion damage of this kind is not confined to the Cotton Belt; it extends over much of the arable land of the United States. Conservation measures devised to combat erosion are followed widely. However, because of the cropping practices in the Cotton Belt, the greater frequency and intensity of thunderstorms, and the mild winters in which the ground seldom freezes, erosion is a year-long process. Thus, it is a greater hazard to land in the South than in other parts of the country (166, 145).

## Large Holdings

In the part of the Texas Coastal Plain that was settled during the Spanish period of government, land use is still affected by the land-acquisition system in operation at that time. The early settlers could obtain land in large tracts. A settler who cultivated land and raised stock could get a sitio grant—4,428 acres, or nearly 7 square miles—for a nominal sum (82, p. 31). Land in the coastal belt of Texas is still held in large tracts and is used predominantly for livestock ranching. Some of the largest stock ranches of the country are in this part of Texas. Large-scale mechanized rice culture is now established on the eastern half of the Gulf Coast Prairie (pl. 127). Much of the land used for this purpose, however, is under lease to the operators. The oilfields located in the lower Coastal Plain have injected additional complications into questions of land ownership and use. Farther inland, in the eastern Texas pine region, much of the land that was cleared and used for crops by tenant farmers is now reverting to forest as a result of low productivity of the soil and industrial labor demands (pl. 129).

That land tenure is related to use of the land is apparent from the examples cited. In some places, size of holdings is equally important. In the Atlantic and Gulf Coastal Plains, where many large tracts are held by absentee owners, the use capability of the land cannot be fully developed without drainage improvement. Absentee ownership of these large tracts, however, is not conducive to initiation of the community action needed for the purpose. Community action is essential to installation of a drainage system. A drainage district must first be organized and later maintained. In these instances, large holdings by absentee owners impose a real handicap to development of the land resources.

## Fractionalization of Holdings

If in this respect large holdings have their drawbacks, so also have the holdings at the other end of the landownership scale. In some eastern sections of the country, the Old World custom of breaking up land holdings and transmitting parcels of equal size to heirs has become a more or less accepted practice. The parcels of land that result from these divisions frequently are too small to provide economic units for farming. Fractionalized farms of this kind may lie idle, or they may be used in conjunction with adjacent farms. In some instances, they may revert to woodland (59). In the West, the oldest agricultural district in the United States is affected in the same way. This district is located on the Upper Rio Grande in north-central New Mexico (pl. 110). When the early Spanish explorers visited the valley in the 16th century, they found the Pueblo Indians cultivating irrigated land. Irrigated agriculture has been the cultural land use ever since. Individual land ownership was no doubt established during the Spanish colonial regime. With it was introduced the custom of dividing the family holdings equally among the children at the death of the parents. Many of these farms have become too small to provide an adequate family income (67, 23). In these instances, there are two possible ways to increase farm income. One is to consolidate these small farms into larger units; the other is to specialize in high-value crops. Consolidation is more in line with the present tendency of enlarging operational units.

Fractionalization of land holdings to obtain more farm units is contrary to need. Technological advances have increased the efficiency of labor to such an extent that the old family farm units are frequently too small to provide economic units for mechanized operations. In land use, the impact of mechanization has been felt in two main directions. The machines increased the acreage that a farmer could cultivate or operate. By so doing, a good many farmers were displaced. Stated in another way, the number of farms decreased but the average size of farms increased. In 1920, there were close to 6.5 million farms, which comprised nearly 956 million acres and averaged 148 acres per farm. In 1954, the number of farms had decreased to less than 4.8 million and the land in farms was close to 1,158 million acres, or an average of 241 acres per farm.

The increase in the average acreage per farm is not uniform throughout the country; it is higher in the Great Plains and lower in other parts of the country; nevertheless, it indicates how farming has been affected by mechanization. A similar movement has occurred in forestry. If lumber or paper mills are to operate on a permanent or sustained-yield basis, they must control the output of lumber from a considerable acreage of forest. To be able to do this, either ownership of the forest land must be acquired, or contractual agreements of management must be entered into with other owners.

## Woodland and Forest Uses

In the humid eastern parts of the cotton and subtropical fruit belts, the chief land uses are woodland and forest. The area usually is identified by foresters as the southern pine region, in which approximately 60 percent of the land is still in forest and woodland (pls. 138, 152). Farm woodland comprises about half of it, and the rest consists of commercial forest with some National and State forests included. The proportion of land in forest is an indication of the important part played by forests in the local economy. Distribution of forests within this pine region, however, is not uniform, nor are forests in this environment of the timber-producing type only. Concentration of forests in large tracts is more prevalent in the lower parts of the Coastal Plain, where the land is too flat to drain adequately. The heavy rainfall and poor natural drainage make the land unsuited to agricultural development without artificial drainage improvements (pls. 152, 161). In places, sand, heavy clay, or hardpan soils are often deterrents to cultural use of the land.

The forests of the Coastal Plain region usually consist of rather open stands, which permit growth of grasses and other forage plants. Here, production of lumber can be combined with grazing. Because of this, grazing of forest land is common in the South. Only about a sixth of the total forest land remains ungrazed. Moreover, on the extensive forest tracts in the lower Coastal Plain, grazing of livestock on unfenced forest land is not legally restricted, and for all practical purposes this land constitutes open range. In keeping with these conditions, forest owners frequently are cattle owners also and their land would be grazed anyway.

*Naval Stores.*—A year-long dual use of the land for forest and grazing is more characteristic of parts of the South than of any other section of the country. Southern forests produce a diversity of products. In addition to logs, poles, and pulpwood, the naval stores belt also furnishes rosin and turpentine. In the early days of settlement, naval stores were produced farther north on the Atlantic coast. At that time, pine gum was used mainly to caulk the seams of wooden ships and to preserve the ships' ropes and riggings. As a trade name, the term "naval stores" dates back to that time. It is still in use, although industrial requirements have largely replaced naval uses. Production of naval stores in the United States is now confined almost exclusively to a belt of the lower Coastal Plain, which extends from western Louisiana into South Carolina. The greatest concentrations are in southern Georgia and northern Florida. In this area of around 90,000 square miles, longleaf and slash pines are the chief forest trees. Both slash and longleaf pines are pine species with needles up to 12 inches; they are also the gum producers. This combination of extensive forests and high-yielding species accounts for the annual production of more than 600,000 50-gallon barrels of turpentine and about 2 million drums (520 pounds net) of rosin, which is more than half the world's output of naval stores (*131, 1956*).

Several methods are used to produce naval stores. The older method consists of cutting streaks through the inner bark of living trees in the form of V's to induce and maintain the flow of gum; this chipping operation, which is repeated weekly during the growing season, produces the face on the tree. Below each face, the gum is caught in a cup from which it is collected each month and hauled to the distillery. A sulfuric-acid solution sprayed on the freshly chipped streak increases the efficiency of labor and lengthens the productive life of the tree. This stimulates the flow of gum to the extent that chipping can be delayed for an additional week without reducing the yield.

A more recently perfected process of obtaining naval stores from wood has advanced so rapidly in the last three decades that it is now the leading process. Pine stumps and dead branches, most of which are remnants of earlier lumbering operations and formerly were regarded by the lumber industry as waste, constitute the resources on which the wood naval stores industry depends. They are collected and transported to central plants where they are shredded or ground in preparation for the steam distillation process. Rosin and turpentine are produced mainly, but the output ratio differs considerably from that of gum distillation. Steam distillation of wood produces about 5.5 drums of rosin (520 pounds net) to 50 gallons of turpentine. Proportionally, this is about twice as much rosin as is obtained from gum. There are other processes of producing naval stores from wood. One is destructive distillation, in which the wood is heated to the

85

point of carbonization. The commercial output by this method, however, is comparatively small. More important is the process by which naval stores, particularly turpentine, are recovered as byproducts of the sulfate paper industry (122, 36, 124).

As a perennial natural resource of the South, the forests have an interwoven use pattern that requires internal correlation if a sustained high-level yield is to be obtained. In the early stages of the country's development, the forests were exploited. Since then, their permanent economic resource value has received fuller recognition, and considerable progress has been made in introducing proper management and operational practices. A few National and State forests are scattered throughout the area. They serve as research and demonstration stations in sound forest management.

## Other Crops Grown

Although cotton is the most widely grown crop, and forests occupy the largest acreage in the cotton and subtropical fruit belts, they do not everywhere provide the most important products of the lands. In certain sections and localities, specialty crops dominate the agricultural economy (pl. 165). Deciduous fruits, peaches particularly, are important in some Piedmont counties (pl. 163). In some sections of the Coastal Plain, peanuts, and in others, tobacco (pl. 166) have supplanted cotton as commercial crops (pl. 157). Production of small fruits and vegetables are important enterprises in other localities. Along the Gulf Coast, especially along the coastal prairie of Louisiana and Texas (pls. 127, 136), rice is the chief crop. This is true also of the Mississippi terraces in Arkansas (pl. 133). Rice growing, which in this country is completely mechanized, is usually a large-scale enterprise. In this part of the country, rice is grown in rotation with pasture.

In the United States, the growing of sugarcane is confined to this subtropical belt. The cane is grown for commercial sugar production, chiefly in the lower Mississippi Delta of Louisiana (pl. 137) and in a smaller district on the shores of Lake Okeechobee in southern Florida (pl. 155). As a farm crop for sirup, it is grown over much of the southern humid part of the Coastal Plain. As a commercial crop, sugarcane provides an example of how science came to the rescue of industry. In the early twenties, the mosaic virus was introduced into Louisiana with stem cuttings from the Orient. The disease spread rapidly, and the yield of cane was reduced to such an extent that the industry came almost to an end. But plant breeders succeeded in breeding mosaic-resistant varieties of sugarcane and thus saved the industry. At the same time, they produced higher yielding plants than had been in use before (12). What happened can best be told in figures. In 1926, production of cane sugar in the United States was down to 48,000 short tons. By 1955, it had climbed to 574,000 short tons. In 1926, the per acre yield of sugarcane was at its lowest—6.8 tons—and for the last 15 years, it has averaged more than 20 tons per acre.

Pecans are a tree crop peculiar to the South. Pecan groves are found from eastern North Carolina westward to the edge of the prairies of Texas and Oklahoma. Production of pecans has advanced considerably in recent years. In 1930, 57 million pounds of pecans were produced; in 1953, production rose to 211 million pounds; in 1954, it declined to 95 million pounds; and in 1955 it rose again to 147 million pounds (134, 1950, 1956). This increase in production was due mainly to the development of improved varieties with larger nuts and higher yields.

A more recent contribution to the tree crops of this region is the tung tree. The tung tree is a native of China from which seeds were brought over shortly after the turn of the last century. Its name is derived from the heart-shaped leaves; in Chinese, tung means heart. The climatic requirements of the tung tree restrict commercial plantings to the 100-mile humid belt along the Gulf Coast and northern Florida, where a long growing season permits the nuts to ripen and a short cold spell of 2 to 3 weeks with temperatures of 45° or lower provides the requisite dormant period. Tung plantings were first made in Florida in the middle twenties (pl. 153). Since then, more tung plantations have been added, and the production center has shifted westward into southern Mississippi and Louisiana. Tung oil, a quick-drying oil extracted from the fruits or nuts, is used in a number of industries.

Although production of tung oil is a young enterprise in the United States, it has made considerable progress. In 1939, 3 million pounds of tung oil were produced. In 1954, production had advanced to 32 million pounds (but fell back to 10 million pounds in 1955). The older orchards are still in production, but neither yield per acre nor oil content of the nuts is as high as in the more recent plantings. Higher yielding varieties with fruits that contain a larger proportion of oil have been developed. With greater per acre yields in addition to expansion of orchards on suitable land, the domestic tung-oil needs of the country for the near future may well be met by home-grown trees (99).

*Citrus Fruits.*—The specialties mentioned thus far for the Cotton and Subtropical Fruit Belts are confined to the warm temperate zone. In the lower latitudes where the climate is subtropical, other specialties take the place of those mentioned. The most prominent subtropical crops are citrus fruits, of which oranges, grapefruit, tangerines, lemons, and limes are the better known members. Citrus fruit was first introduced into Florida by Spanish settlers, who planted groves that consisted mainly of trees producing sour oranges. These plantings were near the coast and on the banks of the St. Johns River. The sweet orange and the grapefruit were brought over from Mediterranean countries by later settlers.

Commercial production did not begin, however, until Florida had become part of the United States in 1819. At first, shipments of citrus fruit to northern markets were made by sailing vessels. When railroads were extended into the peninsula, citrus groves were planted inland. As a result, production expanded rapidly. By 1886, a million boxes were produced. Progress was not steady, however. Heavy frosts in the 1890's reduced the crop to a few hundred thousand boxes. New plantings were started immediately farther South where heavy frosts are not the hazard they are in northern Florida. Commercial citrus plantings are now confined largely to the higher land south of Ocala (pl. 154). Production of Florida citrus fruit has increased fairly steadily since then. It has now passed the 130 million boxes a year mark. About three-fourths of these are oranges (*17, 154*).

The records of Florida's citrus fruit industry are remarkable in themselves but they are only a part of the national picture. Citrus fruits are grown in other Southern States. Some groves are found in Louisiana on the natural levees of the Mississippi that jut out into the Gulf. Citrus fruits are a major crop in the Lower Rio Grande Valley of Texas (pl. 124). But the more important production areas of citrus fruit next to Florida are the subtropical areas of the West. Until a decade ago, California was the leading producer of citrus fruits in the United States. The slowing up in the West and the more sustained rate of expansion in the East are related to the natural distinctions between the eastern and western production areas. All of the western citrus fruit areas, the Lower Rio Grande Valley included (pls. 104, 106, 108), are in semiarid country. Consequently, they depend mainly on irrigation, which is a controlling factor in the expansion of production. When production from the different citrus fruit areas in the United States is totaled, the 1955 figure is 195 million boxes, 35 percent more than the 1940 total. In weight, the 1955 harvest of citrus fruits exceeded the total of all the deciduous tree fruits produced in this year in the United States (*134, 1956*). Considered in relation to population, it is more than one box per capita.

As may be surmised, the achievement of the citrus fruit industry, as disclosed by production records, is not purely accidental, nor is it only a matter of accommodating enlarged markets. Solution of many problems required the sustained effort and vigilance of scientists, technicians, and economists. As per capita consumption of citrus fruit was low a few decades ago, the creation of markets and organization of trade channels from producers to consumers, usually over long distances, were involved. Most citrus fruits are grown for domestic consumption; only 5 percent of the total production is exported.

Some of the problems in the development of the industry have been mentioned. These problems differed between East and West, but no valid answers were available for any of them. Research studies and experiments had to supply solutions to the problems of protection from frost, prevention of alkali accumulation in irrigated groves, proper cultivation and treatment of orchards, application of fertilizers and trace elements needed for different soils, control of fungi and insect pests and diseases, breeding of new and better varieties, propagation through budding on desirable rootstock, and grading and packing of fruit for the market, to mention only a few (*153*).

The marketing of citrus fruit brought its own problems. The main citrus fruits were agreeable to the palates of young and old, but as citrus fruits were seasonal and reached the market in limited quantities only, they were regarded largely as a luxury. It was not until the rich vitamin content, particularly vitamin C, of citrus fruit was discovered that the public became aware of its nutritious properties. As a result, the value of citrus fruit in the diet received a public reappraisal. Citrus fruits now form part of the daily diet of millions of people. To promote wider distribution, processing methods were introduced that made citrus products available for ready use at any time of the year. These products may appear as canned, pasteurized juices—orange, grapefruit, tangerine, or blends. They may be in the form of canned citrus salads, which consist of orange or grapefruit sections. But of all the processed citrus products, frozen concentrated juices are most important. Orange juice also leads in this group. These concentrated juices are poured into cans, are then quick frozen, and transported and stored in refrigerated cars and warehouses at 10° F. Currently, about 45 percent of the citrus fruit harvested is marketed as processed products.

The processing of agricultural products usually results in byproducts. What is waste in the family kitchen accumulates in processing plants in prodigious quantities, and most of this material contains valuable substances that can be recovered and used. The pulp and peels from processing plants are converted into feed for beef and dairy cattle. From the peels of the citrus fruits, an oil sought for its flavoring qualities is extracted. Citrus juices are now converted into table wines. An oil pressed from the dried seeds of oranges and grapefruit has many uses; salad oil is only one of them.

*Small Fruits and Vegetables.*—The warm winters of the subtropical belt are utilized to produce off-season crops. Fresh vegetables, lettuce, tomatoes, potatoes, celery, and strawberries are grown on a commercial scale for northern markets. In this respect, the deciduous fruit and vegetable industries are allied with the citrus fruit industry. Unlike the latter, however, they are concerned with many different products and are not confined exclusively to one climatic belt. The fruit and vegetable industries take advantage of the whole range in seasonal conditions from South to North. In winter and early spring, fresh fruits and vegetables come from the subtropical areas, but with the advancement of the seasons, harvesters move northward along the string of trucking areas. In this way, the larger markets are provided year round with fresh vegetables and seasonal fruits.

Obstacles appeared in the production as well as the marketing of the fruit and vegetable industries. Desirable varieties had to be developed, protection from insect pests had to be carried on, soil fertility and moisture content had to be maintained or improved for maximum production, and perhaps most important, as these crops are highly perishable, processing methods and transportation and storage facilities to preserve the quality and value of the fruits had to be developed. Scientific knowledge, technical skill, commercial acumen, and organizational skill played their parts in the development of these industries. Both old and new methods of food preservation are now used. An idea of their growth may be obtained from the figures cited in the paragraphs that follow (*70*).

As the citrus fruit industry is considered separately here, citrus fruits are excluded from the following figures culled from Agricultural Statistics (*134*). These figures do not include fruits and vegetables grown for home consumption; they refer only to those grown for the market. The figures cited for quantitative comparison begin with 1940 and end with 1955. It was during this period that the impact of the quick freezing process, as a new method of food preservation, began to be felt more fully. Fresh fruits and vegetables are still grown for the market, but the quantities grown for this purpose are declining. In 1940, 134,000 carlots of fresh fruits reached the market as compared with 90,000 carlots in 1955. The quantity of fresh vegetables that reached the market increased at first from 459,000 carlots in 1940 to 696,000 in 1946, then declined to 492,000 carlots in 1955.

The decline in consumption of fresh fruits and vegetables, therefore, indicates that a large proportion of these staples now reaches the market in processed form. The drying of fruit is an old device; it holds its own despite new methods of preserving. During the last decade, production of dried fruits hovered around a half-million tons annually. Canning was perfected in America for commercial application in the latter part of the last century. Since then it has made great strides in providing the market with fruits and vegetables at all seasons. Fruits canned in 1940 amounted to 37 million cases containing 24 No. 2½ cans each. In 1955, 72 million cases were canned. Canned vegetables advanced from 117 million cases in 1940 to 230 million cases in 1955. Quick freezing, the latest process of food conservation, has recorded the greatest advances. The first frozen packs were sold in 1930 (*18*). In 1940, the frozen pack of fruit put on the market totaled 172 million pounds. By 1955, it had increased to 660 million pounds (exclusive of citrus juices), or more than 3 times as much as in 1940. Vegetables made an even better showing. The frozen pack of vegetables produced in 1940 amounted to 83 million pounds, but by 1955, it reached 1,140 million pounds, nearly 14 times as much as in 1940.

Impressive as these increases in production of fruits and vegetables are in themselves, they are even more remarkable when the acreage on which they were accomplished is taken into account. The acreage used for commercial production of fruits and vegetables did not change greatly during the last decade and a half. Compared with other crop acreages, it is relatively small. For the commercial production of 22 fruits and nuts, citrus fruit included, the acreage used in the United States was 3,827,000 acres in 1940, and 2,917,000 acres in 1955. A similar acreage was used for commercial production of 28 vegetables—3,262,000 acres in 1940 and 3,827,000 acres in 1955 (*134, 1956*). Of these acreages, the larger proportions are in the Atlantic and Gulf States. These States have ample room for expansion of trucking, especially if market demand should increase beyond the capacity of the established trucking areas.

The warmer climate of this region is an advantage in the growing of several vegetable and fruit crops. To this extent, climate was an aid to establishment of these industries in the South. In contrast, the development of diversified farming, in which animal husbandry functions as a major line of production, was handicapped by the warm climate. This handicap has been surmounted to a considerable extent through the breeding of livestock less sensitive to warm summer temperatures; improvement of pasture through drainage, clearing, or fertilization; and introduction of new pasture plants that provide palatable feed during most of the year. The beef-cattle and dairy industries are the chief beneficiaries of these improvements.

## The Semiarid and Arid Western Plains and Basins

The restricted use capability of the land and the drawbacks to denser settlement and fuller development of the semiarid and arid areas of the West were included in preceding discussions of climate, natural vegetation, and water management. The conclusion reached, that the cultural use of land in the western semiarid and arid plains and basins depends on water for irrigation, will hold true so long as the prevailing distribution of precipitation remains as it is. Exceptions are some relatively small areas in which precipitation is slightly higher and grain can be grown with dryfarming methods (pl. 90). Large and small irrigation systems have been installed in many places where water and land suitable for the purpose are available. Irrigated agriculture, however, varies with the project. Adjustment to the local climate, the potentiality of the soil, and the economic needs of the community, is essential.

Irrigation in its simplest form—diversion of the water of a creek to a ditch—usually is done to improve grazing or to grow hay as winter feed for livestock (pls. 98, 121). On the larger irrigation projects, specialty crops are frequently the chief source of income. On most irrigation projects, livestock is well represented, especially when dairying for nearby markets is an important part of the farm economy. In the warmer areas of southern Arizona and California, subtropical fruits, grapes, and winter vegetables are the main products of irrigated land, but cotton and flax are also important (pls. 107, 108). Deciduous fruits are the best-known products of some of the northern irrigation projects, for instance, the Yakima Valley in Washington and the Grand River Valley in Colorado (pl. 82). Truck crops are a major product of irrigation projects in Idaho (pl. 88), Utah (pl. 84), and Colorado (pl. 79). Sugar beets are one of the most widely distributed cash crops on northern irrigation projects.

### Sugar Beets

For several reasons, sugar beets are well adapted to the western irrigated areas. In semiarid regions, irrigated land frequently contains some alkali, which with increasing concentration becomes more and more toxic to the plants. In extreme instances, the land cannot be used for crops. As sugar beets are not especially sensitive to alkali, they can be grown with little risk and good results on irrigated land. Also, they supply raw material that can be converted into consumer goods by processing plants in local communities. A third reason is that pulp and beet tops as by-products of sugar mills provide a valuable livestock feed, which is in demand during the winter. Because of this, winter quarters for ranch livestock are usually found in sugar-beet-producing areas. By taking advantage of the interrelated benefits that accrue from sugar beets on irrigated land, the beet-sugar industry can almost be identified with western irrigation projects. More than 80 percent of the beets for sugar are produced on irrigated land.

Production of beet sugar is a fairly well established and stabilized industry. During the last decade, the annual crop was around 10 million tons of sugar beets or nearly 1½ million short tons of sugar. In the meantime, the per acre yield has increased somewhat, and this has been offset by a similar reduction in acreage. Before this stability of production had been achieved, however, the beet-sugar industry went through a period of trial and uncertainty, much as did the cane-sugar industry in Louisiana. Both sugar plants were introduced from overseas, and both had to be bred to adapt them to American conditions. Sugar beets were introduced from Europe, but early attempts to produce sugar from beets on a commercial scale failed until, in 1870, a sugar mill in California succeeded in getting a start. For some time, sugar beet growers depended on seed from Europe. But this seed was susceptible to attacks of virus diseases and blights, particularly curly top, which reduced the yield and quality of the crop and sometimes resulted in complete failure. Sugar mills in some of the infected areas had to move to new sites.

Varieties of sugar beets resistant to curly top and leaf spot were needed. Plant breeders succeded in producing both. By so doing, they saved the beet-sugar industry and, at the same time, laid the foundation for a new industry, the growing of sugar-beet seed. When production of seed of disease-resistant sugar-beet varieties got underway in America, imports from abroad gradually declined. In 1940, they ceased altogether. During the succeeding decade, seed of disease-resistant sugar-beet varieties was exported. How this branch of the beet-sugar industry has advanced in the meantime is apparent from the yields of seed obtained. In 1940, the average per acre yield of seed from these new varieties of sugar beets was only 1,127 pounds. By 1955, it had increased to 3,004 pounds. The American beet-sugar industry provides, therefore, an additional example of how science and technology came to the rescue, and how at the same time other sugar beet growing countries were benefited (*25, 116*).

## The Pacific Valleys and Basins

Land use is more diversified along the Pacific Coast than in any other part of the country. Broadly speaking, this is a region of low coastal ranges and broad interior valleys flanked on the east by the high Sierras and broken in places by the drainage outlets of interior basins. Because the mountain ranges stretch across the prevailing direction of the moisture-carrying winds from the Pacific, the distributional arrangement of precipitation, if plotted as a graph, is almost a counterpart of the relief profile. A moderate amount of moisture is discharged on the coastal ranges; the interior valleys are comparatively dry; and the Sierras receive the heaviest discharge of precipitation on the western slopes. This decreases rapidly on the eastern slopes and is low in the adjoining basins. As the region has a midlatitudinal extent of more than 16 degrees, differences in temperature influence greatly the cultural development of the region.

In the northern part of the region, except for the Snake River plains and some sections of the Columbia River Basin, land use is closely adjusted to the potentiality of the physical environment. No major modifications have been brought about by the collective action of man. The exceptions in the Snake River plains and the Columbia Basin are irrigation districts in which agricultural specialties are grown to a considerable extent. Diversified nonirrigated production of crops and the growing of fruit are confined largely to the Willamette Valley (pls. 96, 97) and the Puget Sound Basin (pl. 95), where moisture is adequate to permit the diversification. Mechanized dry farming of small grains is the prevailing land use on the Columbia Plateau (pls. 91, 92, 93). Forest use of the land is confined to areas in which the rate of precipitation is high. These are the mountains and part of the Puget Sound country, where much of the land is in national forests and where lumbering can be organized as a permanent industry (pls. 95, 99). Grazing is the chief use of the arid land where no water is available for irrigation, and in the rougher parts of the country, where tree growth is scanty because precipitation is too slight to support a commercial forest stand (pls. 94, 100).

A different situation prevails in California. Very little land could be used by the early settlers for intensive crop production under natural conditions. The land of the valleys

was dry; small grains could be grown on the valley floors, and livestock could graze in the hills. Such extensive land uses, however, cannot support many people. Yet people moved into the South Pacific valleys, which had attractions and resources that could be developed. Not the least of these resources is the Mediterranean climate with its long summers and mild winters. Also, ground water in the lower levels and water in the streams could be used for irrigation. This combination of pleasant climate and available water supply has been developed. It supports an estimated population of more than 12 million. However, gigantic engineering works, some of which are not fully completed, were necessary.

### Water Important in Land Use

The land use patterns that evolved under these conditions are closely associated with use of water. When no additional water can be applied, extensive uses, such as grazing and dry farming (pl. 105), prevail. With water, the land produces many different crops, fruits, and fibers for the market. In the Sacramento Valley, where sufficient water is available and soils and surface are favorable, rice culture utilizes an extensive acreage (pl. 101). The growing of rice in the valley is commercial and all its operations are mechanized. It differs from many types of farming in that, as a rule, the operators do not reside on the land they cultivate. In contrast to the traditional method of rice growing, which requires much hand labor, all operations connected with this type of rice culture are done with machines. Ditches, levees, and seedbeds are constructed and prepared with machines; seeding is done from airplanes; and harvesting is mechanized. Large fields of regular shape make this type of rice growing possible. Other local characteristics of the landscape are just as striking. In the districts in which either table wine or raisin grapes are produced, the land is used intensively (pl. 104). The farms are usualy 10 to 40 acres in size, and each is a farm home. Orchard farms of fruits and nuts are frequently larger (pl. 106).

Quite distinct are the lower areas that border the San Joaquin River. Irrigation on the higher levels has brought about a rising of the water table in the lower areas and has resulted in an accumulation of alkali in the soil. Thus, the use capability of the land has been reduced (pl. 103). Reclamation of some of these areas through drainage is now in progress, but land use is confined largely to the feed crops needed by the dairy and stock farms of the area. Former tule marshes also have been reclaimed for intensive agricultural production. These marshes are composed mainly of islands at the confluence of the Sacramento and the San Joaquin Rivers (pl. 102). To do this, the natural levees were raised to protect the land from overflow, as much of it is near or below sea level. Vegetables are grown in this area.

Only a few examples of the diversity in agricultural land use found in California can be mentioned here. Edaphic differences, climatic potentiality, origin of land ownership, and agricultural specialization have left their imprints on the land use patterns. Land use distinctions in California, however, are not all derived from agricultural use of the land even in agricultural districts. Manufacturing industries have moved to the west coast, particularly to California, and have located in the valleys. Scattered oilfields have added their characteristics to urban and rural landscape features. Moveover, the climatic and scenic amenities attract not only tourists but also residents with independent means. As a result of the influx of people, industrial and urban centers and those of the garden city type have expanded rapidly and are still growing. In 1955, more than 64 percent of the population was listed as urban.

So far, there are no indications within the region of a sustained population movement from the land to the city that would compare with that in New England. The number of farms is slowly increasing, as is the rural population. Apparently agriculture will remain a major industry of the State, and as many of the high-per-acre-value crops are grown here, California is likely to remain one of the leading States in value of farm production. But strains and stresses in the relationship of population to natural environment have developed, especially in some districts. In this instance, it is not the frequently mentioned increase of "population pressure on the land," but a decrease of pressure in the water mains. Water shortages recur in this part of the country, and large engineering works are necessary to obtain a better distribution of water.

Distribution of water is a perennial problem in California. People and industries continue to locate in the southern coastal valleys. No sooner has one section received additional water than deficiencies are noted in others. In no other part of the country is the distribution of water the problem it is here. Nowhere else has it been given the public recognition it has received in California. The water supply, a basic natural resource, fluctuates. In the end, the safety limit of dependability controls development. According to recent estimates, water use in California now exceeds the safety limit of the developed water supply by about 3 million acre-feet a year. This does not mean that the water resources of California are exhausted; it does mean that they need development.

Plans for the Feather River project are completed, and a master plan has been prepared to chart possible future utilization of the waters from other rivers. In a scheme of this kind, the watershed-unit approach to development can hardly be adhered to if the water is to reach the places where it is most needed and can be used most effectively. Transfer of water from one watershed to another is not the problem it used to be. With the assistance of engineers, the rivers do it themselves by providing the power that operates the lifting pumps. Waters that originate outside the State, as do those of the Klamath and Colorado Rivers, are included, but State compacts for their utilization are necessary. The remaining projects are extensive in scope and require large engineering installations. Technical, legal, and financial difficulties must be resolved before water can be made available for the fuller utilization of California's land resources (16).

# Yield-Improving Practices

How scientific and technological advances have affected land use, and agricultural use in particular, was illustrated by comparing former and recent production records in the discussion of regional conditions. Although this method offers striking examples, it does not provide all evidence that has a bearing on the subject, and it was not used to create the impression that all benefits derived from improved methods of land use can be enumerated separately, expressed in definite quantum figures, and accredited to one or the other factor. Improvements in land use practices may function in more than one direction, or they may supplement each other.

## Conservation Practices

In this respect, conservation practices can be as effective in increasing the productive capacity of the land as any other yield-improving biological or technical innovation, but neither can be always fully evaluated separately and converted into volume measures of improved yield. It would be hard to say, for instance, just how many thousand board-feet of lumber have been saved annually from burning as a result of the fire protection provided by the watchful observers of the lookout towers. Similarly, the exact results of applying control measures to white pine blister rust are not known. However, proper forest management, of which fire protection and blister-rust control are only phases, increases the output of forest products and is essential to maintain forest yields. Controlled grazing as opposed to free grazing operates in the same direction when the grazing capacity of the depleted range is to be restored. Although in itself controlled grazing helps to remedy exploitation, it is even more effective in many areas if brush is controlled also (pl. 117) and reseeding is practiced. But benefits of good forest and grazing management cannot be fully appraised in terms of gains in grazing capacity or greater productive capacity of forest land. In either instance, the benefits derived from retarded runoff and conservation of water and soil may exceed in importance the gains in improved grazing or forest growth.

Soil conservation practices are essential in many parts of the United States if for no other reason than to preserve the productive capacity of the land for further use. When followed, they too have a multiple benefit reaction in that by holding the soil in place, they also help to retain moisture in the soil and thus increase its yield. However, increases in yield that come from soil conservation may be difficult to evaluate correctly. Wherever soil conservation practices are followed, it is evident that the use of land, particularly for farming, is not pursued indifferently, and that almost certainly other yield-improving methods are followed also. High-yielding crop varieties, fertilization, and use of pesticides contribute to attainment of higher yields, but how much each of these factors has contributed to the increase in production for the country as a whole is an open question.

## Use of Fertilizer and Pesticides

The quantities of fertilizer and pesticides used indicate their importance in agricultural production. Only in recent years has consumption of commercial fertilizers reached its present proportions. From almost 9 million tons of fertilizer used in 1940, consumption rose to more than 22 million tons by 1952. It has remained at that level since. This includes all the main plant foods—nitrogen, phosphoric oxide, potash (of which the fertilizers contain less than 10 percent)—and the minor elements needed by certain plants. Not included, however, are liming materials, of which more than 30 million tons are used annually, and phosphate rock, of which close to a million tons are applied directly to the soil (134, 1955).

Although the use of fertilizer is widespread, the opportunities for improvements in yield are not exhausted. As has happened in some instances, a reduction in acreages of crops and pasture can be offset by efficient use of ferti-

lizer. Production can be maintained or even increased on fewer acres with higher yields. Not all regions can benefit to the same extent from use of fertilizer, nor is the same fertilizer combination sufficiently effective in all instances. Efficiency of fertilizer varies considerably on different soils. Field experiments are needed to establish the requirements for different soils and crops, and when correlated to regional conditions, they provide indexes of what can be accomplished in this direction (94).

Pesticides do not promote increased yields directly, but they contribute materially to increased production by saving the crops from destruction. Pesticides include insecticides, fungicides, and weedkillers. Large quantities of these materials are used in the United States to keep insect and fungus pests and weeds under control. Consumption fluctuates around 300 million pounds a year (134, 1956).

From the quantities of fertilizers and pesticides used in the United States, it is apparent that production of these materials supports a farflung industry. To this must be added the manufacturing of the machinery and implements needed to apply the materials to the land. Until recently, this was done almost exclusively with ground equipment, but lately airplanes have been used, particularly in applying pesticides and fertilizers. As of 1952, more than 2,000 aerial applicator firms used approximately 7,000 pieces of aircraft in these operations. Dusting and spraying are the main operations and seeding from the air has been added as a new technique. In 1952, these firms treated approximately 40 million acres. They service all major agricultural areas of the country, but they are concentrated largely where the land is intensively used. In addition, the Forest Service uses airplane sprays to control such insect pests as the gypsy moth. Airplanes used for the purpose were at first converted training models, but special airplanes are now built for agricultural use (155, 71).

Side by side with these new developments are the time-honored methods. Crop-rotation systems, which may include shifts from crops to pastures, are more or less integrated with the regional type of farming. Types of farming in which livestock farming is represented usually have well-established rotation systems also, in which the use of manure and green-manure crops as soil-improving agents is of recognized value. This is not true to the same extent of cash-crop farming areas. For example, in cotton-growing areas, producers rely chiefly on commercial fertilizers to maintain or increase soil fertility. In semiarid areas, where only small grains can be grown, summer fallow is an established practice. It is combined with stripcropping to check wind erosion.

# Impact of Changes on Land and People

How mechanization of agriculture and industry has reshaped socio-economic conditions becomes clear when we compare the urban-rural population ratio of a century ago with the present ratio. In 1850, the total population of the United States was only 23.2 million people, of which 19.6 million, or 85 percent, were classed as rural. This plurality has been reversed. Of the total civilian population of 161.5 million people in 1955, the largest segment, 103.5 million, or 64 percent, was urban, and only 58.0 million, or 36 percent, was rural (132).

## Rural Population Changing

Revealing as these figures are, they do not tell the whole story because the traditional meaning of the word "rural" has become blurred. In its original meaning, the rural population, in contrast to city dwellers, was made up primarily of tillers of the soil, herdsmen, and woodsmen. Under the current definition, of the 58 million people classed as rural in 1955, only about 22 million are members of farm families; the rest are nonfarm residents who have occupations other than farming. Broadly speaking, it may be said, therefore, that in 1955 about 22 million, or 14 percent, of the total population were farm people (121).

The change in the internal composition of the rural population may be accounted for by several reasons. Among them are the spread of urban conveniences and services to rural areas, and land use combinations that minimize the urban-rural distinctions. On the urban fringes of the larger cities, detached real estate development projects or manufacturing plants are occasionally located in rural surroundings and are sometimes combined with part-time farming. In the western irrigation districts, where the regional population is congregated and the land is used intensively, villages, towns, and industries have grown up. Thus, urban living has been projected into the country.

Urban settlement areas have expanded to represent a sizable acreage, which is increasing. This is true also of service areas, which include rights-of-way of railroads, highways and roads, and airports. Expansion of acreage in this category is not uniform, however. The acreage in railroad rights-of-way is decreasing slightly. Some branch lines have suspended operation because of competition from buses, motortrucks, and automobiles. Thus, the land has been freed for other uses (pls. 38, 64). Parks, playgrounds, country clubs, and golf courses have also been developed. In the aggregate, however, these service areas are expanding.

## Regional Specialization

The changes and shifts in land use make up only one phase of the all-embracing process of internal development and economic growth. The haphazard method of settlement, in which individual choice of location was determined largely by availability of land with too little attention paid to adaptability to intended use, has made land use adjustment a perennial process. Adjustment of land use to natural advantages and shortcomings has developed regional land use characteristics that are not confined to the proportional acreages of land in cropping, grazing, and forest uses. It has also evolved production areas specialized by regions. Regional specialization represents an adjustment to the prevailing physical and economic factors that influence land use. Ordinarily, it is identified with type-of-farming areas. "Cotton Belt," "Corn Belt," "Wheat Belt," "Dairy Belt," "Fruit and Truck areas," and "Western Range," are all names that have regional connotations so far as land use and type of farming are concerned. Forestry adds its regional distinction. In extensive areas, forests provide the best use of the land (fig. 22).

Regional specialization in agricultural production usually is not practiced to the extent that crop production is a monocultural enterprise. Only where the climate eliminates other crops, as is the case in parts of the wheat-growing areas, is the regional specialty the only crop produced in the area. In other specialized areas, only a single major use of land may be possible because physical conditions eliminate competitive major uses. The western grazing land is of that type. There the only possible land use is grazing; crops can be grown only in restricted areas where irrigation can be carried on. In the Sand Hills of Nebraska, cultivated crops are eliminated by the nature of the soil. A rugged topography makes the mountains the stronghold of the forests. Corn and cotton are regional specialties in the Corn and Cotton Belts, respectively. Both belts are defined by physical conditions. Nearness to market is frequently the decisive factor in making dairying the farm specialty within the milkshed areas of cities. Specialization in land use, whether it was brought about in response to natural restrictions or to man's needs, usually promotes greater efficiency in production. At the same time, it creates economic group interests of regional extent.

Certain regional aspects of specialization in land use have national implications also. Considered from the national viewpoint, it is obvious that because of specialized production in one direction or another, none of these regions produces foods and fibers in balanced proportions even for their own needs, much less as surpluses for the market. Our large city markets receive farm products from all parts of the country. However, the production–consumption relationship is not a one-way traffic between rural and urban populations. It means an exchange of products among the people of all regions in the country. In their place of origin, the products of the land may be of greater or lesser regional importance, but they form an interlocked and integrated part in the national economy as a whole. In fact, they may even transcend the national boundary.

## Our Changing Diet

Dietary habits are not the same throughout the country. We have regional favorites, for instance, potatoes, beans, or grits, to mention only a few. Diets no doubt vary between country and city people. Frequently, this variation is based on preference rather than economic necessity. But in neither instance is the diet of our people restricted to the products of the locality or region in which they live. With extension of transportation facilities to all parts of the country, improvement in speed and refrigeration equipment for fresh products, and advances made in the food freezing and packing industries, the products of any one region are available to any other region. With these developments, the rise in standard of living, and a better knowledge of the requirements of proper nutrition, the per capita ratio of the different foods consumed has changed considerably, as may be observed in figure 25. The products taken into consideration in the chart

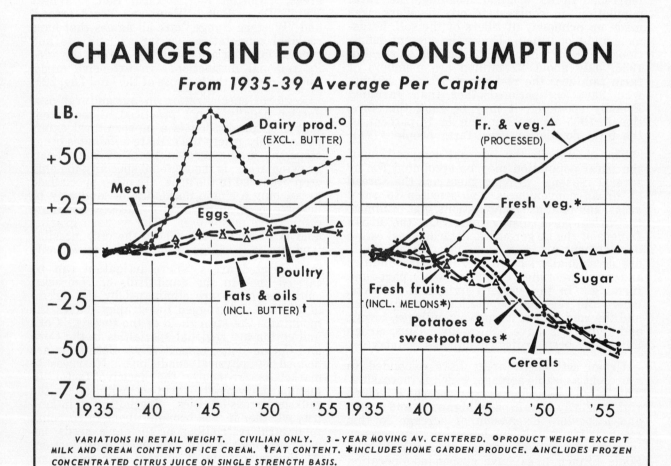

FIGURE 25.—This chart illustrates the mutation in dietary wants from 1936 to 1956. Most impressive were shifts from such starchy foods as cereals and potatoes to animal products, and from fresh to processed fruits and vegetables. Higher standards of living, more information as to balanced diets, new methods of production and processing, and improved marketing methods, account largely for the development of these trends.

are not entirely of domestic origin. As our tastes are cosmopolitan, some of the foods in our daily fare must be imported. This is true also of some of the fiber and forest products and the other raw materials we need. In the opposite direction, we have a flow of surplus products from our own lands to other countries. Economic interdependence of regions and nations is the result.

An additional aspect of the interrelationship between the places of origin of the food and its consumers has been given little attention. With our food supplies coming from all corners of the country or even the world, a balanced diet that will satisfy the energy requirements and will contain in addition all the needed vitamins and minerals for proper nutrition can be arranged readily from the variety of foods available. That a proper diet safeguards the health of the people is well known. By the same token, it may be assumed that it also contributes to the prolongation of life and reduces the death rate correspondingly. Vital statistics reveal what has been accomplished in that direction. In 1900, the death rate in the United States per 1,000 population was 17.2; by 1955, it had fallen to 9.3 (*131, 1956*). Longevity is a phenomenon for which medical science and sanitation usually receive credit; improved diets are overlooked.

## Social Implications of Land Use

The relationship of land use to physical and economic conditions are the more obvious ones, but land use has its social implications also. During the first century of our national existence, land was so abundantly available that occupancy and use of land resources was the first consideration in the public mind. Under these circumstances, the land resources were exploited to satisfy immediate needs and little thought was given to the generations to come. Ordinarily, after ownership was acquired, use of the land was determined by the owner or operator. Often the economically more rewarding use was decided upon, even though alternatives were possible. Private land ownership is an established principle in the United States. For some years, it was thought to give proprietors the undisputed right to use or abuse the land as would serve best their own interests. That land ownership is a trust fraught with social obligation to the community and the Nation became apparent with closer settlement and wasteful use of the land.

Land uses not in keeping with the welfare of the community were most objectionable in crowded cities. To obtain relief, the State legislatures passed enabling laws that permitted local administrative units to adopt regulatory measures of how the land could or could not be used. Zoning ordinances, as these regulatory measures are usually called, therefore, are the product of city environments. In most urban centers, they constitute a regulatory function of the local administration.

Although zoning was originally devised to fit urban needs, it has not remained strictly an urban device. With the expansion of cities, undesirable land uses became a problem in suburban fringes. At the same time, the centrifugal influence exerted by large urban centers was felt in the open country, and land use was affected by it. As now used, zoning ordinances may be intended to regulate settlement in rural districts, regulate urban and suburban development, or protect the land that borders highways from obnoxious uses. Zoning ordinances usually derive their legal status from enactments of local governments, to keep land use within channels beneficial to the economic and social well-being of the people in the area (*112*).

Land use regulation of privately owned land, with conservation as its main objective, is a comparatively new device that is used in some Soil Conservation Districts. As in zoning, the power to regulate land use is derived from the consent of the voters in the districts. As the districts that adopted these measures are on the Western Plains, the hazards of wind erosion have received special recognition. On the whole, the ordinances are designed to protect the land resources of the districts. Control provisions are directed mainly toward regulating grazing on the open range, preventing the plowing out of sodland without permission, and preventing wind erosion through specified cultural practices. So far, these land use ordinances are in operation in only a few districts. They are still in the experimental stage (*147*).

When land is kept in, or acquired for, public ownership to implement public welfare, social considerations also arise. In the continental United States, approximately a fourth of the rural lands are in Federal, State, or county ownership. Most of these lands are in the West. They represent remnants of the public domain or were set aside as national forests, national parks and monuments, and wildlife sanctuaries. An Indian reservation can hardly be classed as public land, as much of it is used by the Indians in common.

Why has so much land remained in public ownership? The answer can be found in the arid and mountainous nature of the country. Land in the western basins and valleys has a low seasonal grazing capacity, and the migratory movement of livestock is necessary. Even under the enlarged homestead act that permitted a settler to claim a full section of land, this acreage could not support a settler and his family. Scattered ranches are found only where an adequate supply of stock water is available and winter feed can be grown under irrigation. A considerable area of the public domain is desert, which excludes economic use. Most of the mountainous lands were included in national forests and national parks as a conservation measure. In the Eastern United States, most of the land had been transferred into private ownership. Nearly all had been cut over but not all could be converted into farms. To protect public interest, a considerable acreage of rugged mountainous land or land with poor soils was bought by Federal and State governments and established as National or State forests and parks (figs. 7 and 8).

Uses that can be made of public lands are usually designated and are frequently multiple in purpose. In contrast to privately owned land, which is often exploited, use of public land is controlled. Conservation through proper use is the main objective. To attain this end, the western range is organized into grazing districts, in which grazing is controlled by the permit system. In publicly owned forests, a number of uses must be accommodated and coordinated. One of the chief functions of publicly owned mountain forests is watershed protection as a regulatory measure in water management. To prevent storm waters from rushing down the mountainsides to form floods in the valleys is one objective. Related to the first is the second—the gradual release of water to furnish a reliable water supply to population concentrations and irrigation districts on the lower levels. Lumbering and grazing in National and State forests must be regulated in accordance with these objectives. Recreation and protection of wildlife are additional functions.

These are the main contributions that National and State forests make to public welfare so far as actual use of the land is concerned. Equally important is their educational value. They provide a practical demonstration of proper forest management. National and State parks and monuments are mainly areas of scenic attractions or historical associations reserved for recreational use, in which conservation measures are essential to preserve the designated use potentiality. The national wildlife sanctuaries have as their objectives the protection and conservation of the native fauna; they are managed accordingly.

Public land has an impressive position in the totality of our land resources. This impression is modified when the potentiality of economic use is considered. When the public lands, particularly those in Federal ownership, are classified according to use capability, it is found that most of them have a characteristic in common; very little public land is suitable for

arable use. These findings do not apply in the same degree to State-owned lands. In the public domain States and Texas, certain lands were reserved for the benefit and support of education. Not all these lands have been alienated; some are still in State or county ownership and are used for production of crops.

In any general survey of land use development and its changes, only the major phases can be cited. But from even the cursory treatment given here, it must be apparent that the continuous advances of science and technology bring in their wake chain reactions that penetrate the entire socio-economic structure. These reactions are felt with greater or lesser force, depending on whether or not the people can apply the innovations to the use of the land. There are two extreme instances. In one, the people have used these innovations. Here the result may be prosperity with a high standard of living. In the other, they have not been able to use all the new devices to keep up with the modern trend. As a consequence, they cannot raise their standard of living above the subsistence level. Economically progressive areas versus stagnating or problem areas are the result.

If users of the land are to share in the good things of life, land use, whether it is in the form of agriculture, forestry, or ranching, must be sufficiently rewarding to permit operators to raise their standards of living above the subsistence level. However, not all parts of the world or even all parts of our own country can benefit to the same extent from use of labor-saving devices and improved methods and practices in land use. Frequently, natural and social impediments are so strong that economic advancement of the people becomes almost impossible.

## Low-Income Areas of Land Use

Those who live in a mountainous or rough country and who try to make a living from agricultural use of the land, as in parts of the Appalachian and Ozark Mountains, are permanently handicapped. Although recent road extensions may have brought markets within accessible distance, on their small and frequently steep fields these mountaineers can produce only a little more than they need for themselves. In some instances, greater improvements in crop-production methods, whether technical or scientific, have only a negative reaction. They widen the economic gap between the areas that can and those that cannot use them. After a country is developed, therefore, natural site advantages or disadvantages have far-reaching economic consequences on the lives of the people.

# Better Land Use

Obviously, such low-income areas can only develop when at the time of settlement, the inherent disadvantages of the natural environment are not recognized and land use advances to a point at which it must be considered a commercial enterprise in which a large part of production is grown for market. When land use reaches this stage, it must be implemented properly if it is to function as a major part of the economic structure of the country. Transportation facilities are necessary to tap the land resources of the country and bring land and people into contact with the rest of the world. Furthermore, if the commercial transactions are on the scale that they are in the United States, service organizations are needed to act as intermediaries between producers of raw products and consumers. With more than 60 percent of the population living in urban centers, a steady flow of products to market is essential. To accomplish this, storage and transportation facilities, frequently combined with refrigeration, must be available. By converting the many raw products into usable commodities, the processing and manufacturing industries act as service agencies. The arteries of commerce through which the products of the land reach their final destination, therefore, may be long and tortuous. They may also experience internal stresses and complications as a result of fluctuating volumes, variable demand, reduction in volume of old and addition of new competitive products. Many of these variations can be traced directly to the use of land, or inversely, land use is affected by them.

Major fluctuations and shifts in the supply of farm products especially may be related to several causes. The vagaries of climate cause the yield of crops to vary from year to year. Climatic departures from normal sometimes reach disastrous proportions, but usually they are not national in extent. Floods, droughts, unseasonal frosts, and hail usually are of only regional occurrence, although they may cause considerable damage and a crop deficit in the afflicted region. But a crop deficit in one section of the country may be offset partly or wholly by surpluses in other sections. This has happened at times, but it cannot be relied on to occur always.

More lasting results, particularly in the direction of better, bigger, and more diversified farm production, have been brought about by using scientific methods, that is, through a better knowledge of the land and its soil, how to preserve and improve it, adjustment of actual use of the land to its potential use, use of fertilizers and pesticides, the breeding of more productive crop varieties and livestock, the introduction of new crops, and the technological implementation of labor.

## Through Science and Technology

Mechanization alone has increased agricultural production in two ways: By making large acreages of land formerly needed for the support of draft animals available for economically more productive uses, and by making possible the extension of crop production, chiefly of wheat, into the semiarid plains. Technology must be credited also with engineering projects in reclamation and flood control. Reclamation, which may be in the form of either irrigation or drainage, has added to crop production other millions of acres that formerly were of little or no use for that purpose. But irrigation and drainage cannot always be designated as reclamation. As functions of water management, irrigation and drainage are frequently used to correct moisture conditions on land already cropped. Supplementary irrigation by means of the sprinkler system is now in use to some extent in the humid sections of the country. This type of irrigation is rewarding when intensive cropping is involved, and the practice is likely to be more widely followed in the future. Flood control has reduced the danger of floods in the Alluvial Valley of the Mississippi to a minimum. Extension of drainage and reclamation of much of the fertile bottom land in this area is now possible.

If technical know-how has stimulated and increased production in different ways, scientific knowledge and production methods are no less conspicuous with their contributions. The two are frequently so closely related in their operations that no clear-cut distinction can be made between them.

A fuller knowledge of the genesis of soil development, the different characteristics acquired by the soil in the process, and the relationship of these characteristics to soil productivity have helped to adjust methods of soil management to the needs of the land. Frequently, deficiencies in plant nutrients and in water-holding capacity, and excess of alkalinity or acidity, can be corrected by applying soil amendments and improved cultural practices. With improved soil-management practices adopted over much of the country, and application of fertilizer, yields have increased. Cultural practices are closely connected with soil conservation, but in its broader sense conservation includes more than soils. The protective and productive plant cover of range and forest is also included. Conservation of these natural resources has as its main objective the prevention of their depletion. However, proper use of the land, which implies conservation, frequently increases output. Soil conservation increases crop yields, range conservation increases carrying capacity, and forest conservation increases output of lumber and other forest products per areal unit.

Remarkable gains in production of food and feed have resulted from the contributions made by the biological sciences in animal husbandry, plant breeding, and introduction of new crops. Through proper care of domestic animals and improvement of breeds, our dairy, poultry, cattle, and sheep industries have increased production considerably so far as input–output relationships and quality of animal products are concerned.

Equally significant are the increases in yields per acre of crops produced as a result of plant breeding, and the diversification of agricultural production through the introduction of new crops. Most of our cultivated plants originated in the Old World. Some were brought over by early settlers, although frequently their crops were attacked by disease or did not succeed in the New World. To fit them into the new environment, disease-resistant varieties and improved strains adjusted to biotic conditions had to be developed through breeding. This process is still going on.

In this respect, the soybean provides an outstanding example. It took this Asiatic immigrant more than a century to become properly adjusted to American conditions. Only after this was accomplished did its phenomenal rise to prominence as one of the major crops of the country begin. A second example is provided by corn (maize), our principal crop, which is American born and reared. Through the development of hybrid corn, average yields per acre have increased by more than 27 percent.

Improvements in production through the use of labor-saving devices and scientific methods have affected agriculture more or less on a regional basis. But aside from the regional distribution of benefits, the districts in which specialty crops are grown usually receive additional attention and incentives to production of quantity and quality crops from the processing industries and marketing organizations with which they are connected. These specialties are mainly small fruits and vegetables, exclusive of white and sweet potatoes, commercial production of which is largely concentrated in certain districts. The total acreage devoted to production of vegetables and small fruits for the market averages less than 4 million acres.

However, in this instance, acreage is not a reliable measure of productive capacity or importance of the industry in the national economy. Land use in these districts is intensive, and frequently more than one crop is grown on the same land. In order to provide the market the year round with fruits and vegetables, these districts are scattered from north to south, so that full advantage can be taken of the range in climate. Most of these crops are perishable, and different methods of preserving them are in use. Drying or dehydration is the oldest method. Canning is a modern device that has met with public favor; and in the last 70 years it advanced to a point at which it holds the leading position in the processing industry. The quick freezing industry is only a little more than a score of years old, and it is still growing. Both the canning and quick freezing industries have become characteristic of the American mode of living.

Only a few of the more noteworthy examples are cited here to show how the tools of science and technology have affected land use. But even from this brief discussion, it must be apparent that these efforts are directed mainly toward increased production of better products, and, as the results show, they have been successful. Increase in production has been attained in two directions. One is increased productive capacity of the land; the other is increased output per acre or per animal unit. Essentially the same principle is followed by the manufacturing industry. To produce new, more, and better products with less effort is the leading motive of both. Usually it is associated with progress.

So far, the increase in crops and animal products has not only kept pace with the needs of an increased population, but in some instances, it has run ahead of the needs. Although in general, crop yields per acre and output per animal unit have increased, the increase has not been uniform. Some of the crops have lost ground that is taken up by others. Many products of the land occupy a competitive position on the market; demand for them is influenced by the buying power of the people. Also, the change in the social composition of the population, and the advancement in the standard of living have modified the buying habits of the people. A significant change in this connection is found in the American diet, as recorded for the last 20 years in the changes in per capita consumption of farm products. Changes of this kind necessarily reflect changes in the use of the land that go back to the land use patterns of our farms. They do not necessarily imply shifts in major land uses; they can be confined to changes in the rotation system and in the composition of crops in the field pattern.

Changes in land use are an inevitable part of the adjustments required to gear our national productive plant to meet new needs. During the wartime emergencies, the process of increasing production was accelerated. In more normal times, an increase in population, variable export needs, hazards of climate, new industrial developments, and contributions of science and technology are factors that are likely to continue to be felt in the national economy. All inject dynamic elements into the land use situation. Adjustments in land use to conform to individual and national needs have been in progress ever since the early settlers arrived. As the United States is still a growing country and its land resources are not yet fully developed, future generations will need to grapple with land use problems. These problems are of public concern. With the physical resource base of the country better known and the techniques more fully developed, it should be possible to evaluate areal advantages and shortcomings properly and to deal effectively with these problems in the future.

## Land Use Patterns as Recorded by Aerial Photography

Aerial photography has become a valuable tool for engineers, administrators, teachers, investigators, and those who carry on research. By recording on a horizontal plane on a reduced scale but with considerable detail and precision, the visible natural and cultural features on the earth's surface, aerial photography furnishes documentary evidence of local settings that could not be obtained with the same completeness and speed from ground observation. Occurrence, distribution, areal extent, and spatial relationship of the features are recorded. Of the many purposes aerial photography may serve, recording the major distinctions in the use of land is a main objective.

Most of the agricultural areas in the United States have been covered by aerial photography at least once. The fund of information provided by these photographs was drawn on heavily in the preparation of this publication. In addition to the contents of the land use map, some of the special features represented on the regional maps are derived largely from aerial photographs. Moreover, with the use of these photographs as a research tool, a new approach to the solution of old problems was made possible. To some extent, the text of this report received its orientation from aerial photography.

When land use is visualized on a national scale, local complexities disappear in the generalized picture. Even in a regional treatment, local land use patterns cannot be set forth adequately, although distribution, composition, or dominance of one or the other major land uses in the regional complex may find fuller recognition. The presenting of a variety of factual evidence in the spatial order and composition of localized environments, and the illustrating of the cause and effect relationship of land use adjustment to historical, physical, and economic factors have been left to the aerial photographs.

Within the more localized environments, land use adjustment to physical factors to a considerable extent is as evident as it is in the national picture. That it is not carried out consistently everywhere is chiefly because of influences that emanate from, or impediments imposed by, economic, social, and historical factors, which frequently have produced the outstanding characteristics of the local setting.

From the many local land use patterns, representative examples recorded by use of aerial photography were selected and described. Rural land use, with which this publication is concerned, received prior consideration in the selection of these pictures. In only a few instances have urban fringe scenes been included to illustrate urban impingement on rural land uses.

The chief criterion in selecting the aerial photographs was their instructive value as illustrations of how under different conditions men have arranged and organized the cultural landscapes of their surroundings, and how they are using the land. As figure 26 indicates, these examples were from various parts of the country; all States are represented in the collection. The number of photographs that could be included was limited; therefore, the site locations are widely scattered. These locations are dissimilar so far as the composition of the land use pattern is concerned; each has its own story to tell.

Most of these photographs were obtained from the Aerial Photography Division of the Commodity Stabilization Service; some were obtained from the Soil Conservation Service, both of which are in the U. S. Department of Agriculture, and a few were furnished by the U. S. Geological Survey of the Department of the Interior.

The information in the legends of the aerial photographs is derived from many sources. Topographic and geologic surveys, climatic records, soil surveys, census reports, type-of-farming studies, and other State publications were used for the purpose. In some instances, county agents have furnished pertinent information relating to their localities.

These photographs were not taken at the same time or even in the same year or the same season of the year. Seasonal peculiarities caused by local cultural practices are sometimes noticeable in the fields. Although an effort was made to obtain late coverage, the only available photographs of some areas were taken 15 years ago. No doubt some changes have occurred, but as these photographs usually pertain to well-established rural districts or cultivated land confined to restricted areas, no radical changes should be expected in the land use pattern.

To permit ready comparison of areal and linear features among photographs, all are reproduced on a scale of 1:25,000. To facilitate comprehension of areal dimensions of farms, fields, pastures and woodlots, some of the metric and English measures are as follows: On this scale a 1.42 inch square represents ¼ square mile, which equals 160 acres or 64.75 hectares. A 4-centimeter square represents 1 square kilometer, which equals 100 hectares or 247.1 acres.

# Guide to Aerial Photographs

# SITE LOCATION OF THE AERIAL PHOTOGRAPHS

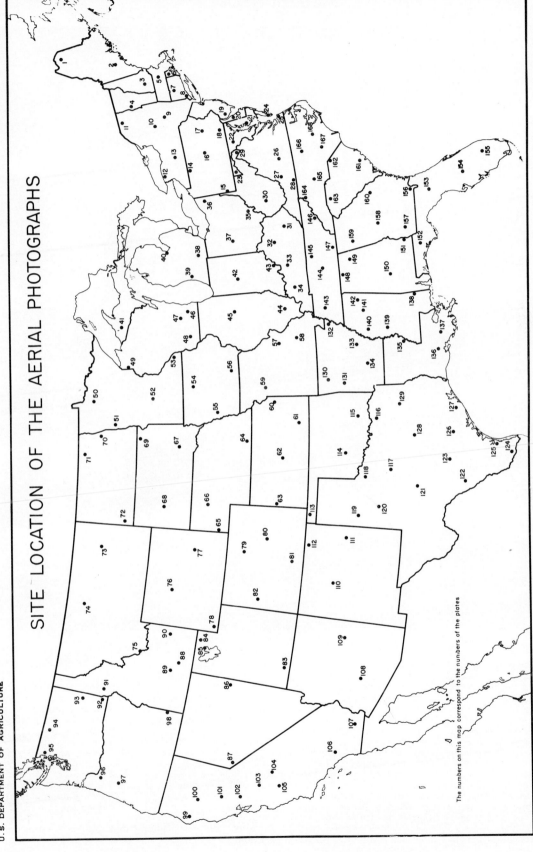

The numbers on this map correspond to the numbers of the plates

FIGURE 26.—The aerial photographs that follow illustrate land use patterns from all States of the Union. Spot location and distribution of the areas included are indicated on the map. The numbers used correspond to the plate numbers of the photographs and consequently provide a ready reference for consultation on individual photographs.

# Northern Maine

DN—1369

PLATE 1.—In Northern Maine, forestry and farming are confined to separate areas with little or no transition between them. In the so-called "Potato Empire" to the east, most of the land is suited to crops, whereas the "Big Woods" area to the west has remained a solid expanse of commercial forest. This marked distinction between the two areas is due primarily to type of land ownership. The forested area is held mainly in large tracts by lumber companies, which retain ownership of the land to ensure a sustained supply of forest products for the wood-processing industry. A section of the contact line of field and forest, near St. Agatha on the shore of Long Lake in Aroostook County, is shown. Aside from the sharp division of farm and forest, the farming area shown has points of interest derived from the land use pattern, which reveals that this is a French settlement. The location of the farms and the arrangement and shape of the fields as long lots extending back from the road along the lake are characteristics of French settlement. This glaciated smoothly rolling country has lakes, swampy depressions, and detached rounded hills and mountains scattered throughout. The fields shown in the photograph are laid across a hill that rises 200 to 300 feet above the lake level of 581 feet. The upland soils, developed from glacial till, are mainly loams and are easy to cultivate. The climate is cool. Summers are mild and the frost-free period is around 122 days. Winters are cold and the snow cover lasts for months. The annual average precipitation is 34 inches. Farming is organized on a cash-crop basis. Potatoes are the chief cash crop, although forage crops are grown also. Livestock farming, and particularly dairying, is gaining in importance.

# Southern Maine

DN-1413

PLATE 2.—In some respects, southern Maine is similar to other parts of Southern New England. The irregular combination of hills and plains is interspersed with lakes and swampy depressions. Drainage is largely of postglacial origin; it has not had time enough to develop fully. The soils, which are usually medium textured, developed from glacial till. In some places they are stony, and, as a rule, they are only moderately fertile. Roads and settlements received their principal orientation from the larger rivers that traverse the area, as may be seen in the illustration, which comprises a section along the Kennebec River between Vassalboro and Waterville in Kennebec County. The Kennebec connects the forested hinterland of Maine with the settlements near the coast. In their descent, these rivers serve as carriers to bring logs from the forests to the saw and paper mills, and also generate power for the industries. In the pictured section, the Kennebec flows in a "canyon-like" channel about 100 feet deep. Highways follow the river on both sides. Settlement and clearing are continuous, and the elongated land divisions are laid out perpendicular to the river. Land use and agriculture have been adjusted to the prevailing economic and physical conditions. Because of the comparatively cool summers, not all crops grow well. Cropland has been reduced to about half of what it was 50 years ago; old fields are now used for pasture or revert to woodland. The main agricultural enterprises are now dairying and poultry. Hay is the leading crop and is supplemented by other feed crops. Some vegetables are also grown for market.

# Southern New Hampshire Hills

DN-1424

PLATE 3.—The mountainous parts of New Hampshire and Vermont have undergone profound changes since the time of settlement. Settlers had gone into the hilly and mountainous country and established homes in many places. They had to clear the land not only of forest, but frequently of stones. Stony loam soils of medium productivity are the most extensive types. However, in the more remote locations, especially, the settlers found it hard to make a living on the land. They could not reach the markets because of distance and difficulties of transportation over rough terrain. Discouraged, they abandoned the farms, and moved to the West or to the towns. Only a fraction of the cultivated land in the hilly and mountainous section that was in use 60 or 70 years ago is now used for crop production. Some is used for pasture, but much is growing back into forest. Because of the pleasantly cool summers and the attractive scenic setting produced by the hills and the many lakes, called ponds, many farmsteads have been converted into summer residences. How little farming is being done in the rougher parts is shown by the tract of hilly land which lies on the Hillsboro-Merrimack County line about 3 miles east of Hillsboro. Farming in this part of New Hampshire is centered on poultry and its products. Dairying is second in importance. Hay is the leading crop but other crops, like potatoes and apples, are grown to some extent for the market. Production of maple sirup and sugar was formerly a more important home industry than it is today.

# Champlain Valley, Vermont

DN-1412

PLATE 4.—In Vermont, land use for agricultural production is concentrated more in the Champlain Valley than in any other part of the State. The land of the valley is a smooth slightly rolling plain. During the glacial period, the southern end of the valley was a glacial lake, which has imparted its own characteristics to the soil. The soil is a heavy clay loam with a calcareous substratum. The area shown lies on the glacial lakebed in Addison County, north of Chimney Point on Lake Champlain. Land use here has gone through a number of stages. This part of Vermont was first settled in the 1730's. The early settlers concentrated on wheat and other small grains, but rust soon invaded the area and destroyed the crops. Cool summers and heavy soils, which warm up late in spring, are not favorable to many of the crops grown farther south. Grasses succeed better than crops and the land is better adapted to livestock farming. Purebred Merino sheep were imported early in the 19th century from Portugal and Spain, and later from France. Thus an improved breed was produced and within a few years, sheep raising became the chief industry of the valley. Merino sheep were not grown for wool alone; many were sold as breeding stock to western settlers. This created competition, which at first impaired and in the end destroyed the sheep industry of the valley. With the decline of the sheep industry, farmers turned first to hay as a cash crop, and with improvement in transportation, dairying gradually became the main farm enterprise. Hay is harvested from more than 80 percent of the cropland. An even larger proportion of the cleared land is used for pasture. Woodland is confined chiefly to wet spots or to rough and stony ground.

DN-1426

PLATE 5.—Land use in central Massachusetts is affected by the physical quality of the land and the presence of an industrialized population centered in towns. The land surface has been sculptured by glaciers into smoothly rounded hills interspersed with lakes and sandy outwash plains. For cropland use, the strongly rolling morainic country, much of which is rough stony land, has its own limitations in addition to the shortcomings of the soil. The upland soils, which developed from glacial drift material derived mainly from coarse-grained crystalline rocks, are chiefly sandy loams or loams that are more or less stony and of moderate productivity. The climate is affected by the proximity of the ocean. The frost-free season fluctuates around 160 days, and annual precipitation averages from 42 to 46 inches. Land use has changed considerably with the industrialization of this part of New England. In the competition for labor, industry gained while agriculture lost. During the last half century, the number of farms and the acreage used for crops declined markedly. Urban expansion has encroached on some of the cropland, but in other instances former cropland is now used only for pasture or is reverting to brush. Cropland is scattered, and small irregular fields are the rule. The photograph shows the eastern end of Clinton and its environs. The stretch of woodland north of the Nassau River bend is a sandy terrace on which a golf course and a sewage-disposal plant are located. Agriculture is diversified. Dairy, poultry and truck farms, and orchards are represented. However, many farms are only part-time enterprises.

# Narragansett Basin, Rhode Island

DN-1425

PLATE 6.—Although Providence and its environs were settled in the first half of the 17th century and therefore make up one of the earliest settled parts of the country, most of the land has remained in forest of little commercial value. The virgin forests have been cut, and the second growth is composed of different kinds of oaks, pitch pine, largetooth aspen, gray birch, and white pine, with blueberry, sumac, bull brier, bracken fern, and laurel underbrush. Cordwood is almost the only product furnished by these forests. The climate is milder here than in most parts of New England. The frost-free period is approximately 180 days, and the annual precipitation of around 46 inches is ample for all crops that can be grown in this latitude. The state's large city population would provide nearby markets. The unfavorable surface relief and the stony, sandy loam soils largely account for the scanty agricultural development. The tract shown, which lies near Chapachet, a village 10 miles from Providence, is a representative example of land use in the interior of Rhode Island. Part of the village may be seen in the upper left-hand corner. As in much of New England, the landforms and soil materials are largely products of glaciation. Smoothly rounded hills, both large and small, but usually not more than 100 to 200 feet high, interspersed with lakes and swampy depressions, are the prevailing surface features, although in places steep slopes flank the watercourses. The scattered farms and orchards are usually identified with tracts of smooth land having a nonstony soil. Farming is largely specialized. Dairy products, poultry and poultry products, horticultural products, and fruits and vegetables are the chief cash products.

# Connecticut Valley, Connecticut

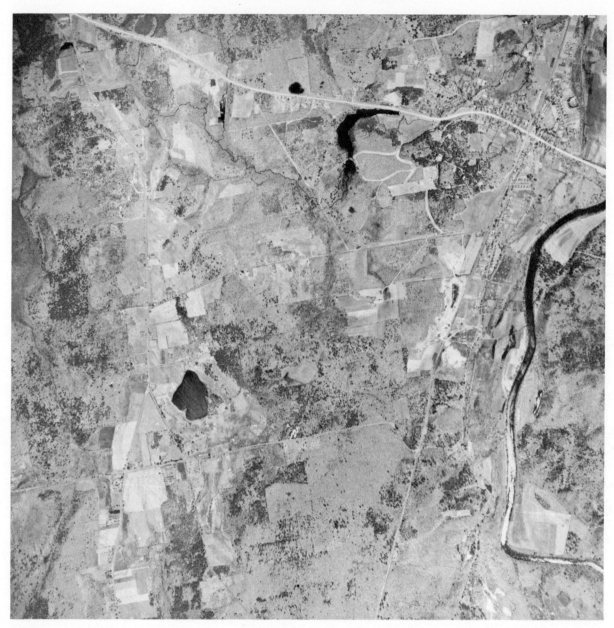

DN-1423

PLATE 7.—Agriculturally, the Connecticut Valley with its tributaries is the most highly developed area in southern New England. Farms and cropland are concentrated, and agriculture has been established since colonial days. Since then, industrialization has left its mark on both land and people. In Connecticut, the valley has an overall width of about 20 miles but is divided by the Talbott Range, a low narrow ridge, into parallel sections—the Farmington Valley and the Connecticut Valley proper. Much of the valley land is smoothly rolling and the lower parts are nearly level. These landform characteristics were inherited from the glacial period. The lower portion was covered by a glacial lake, and the upland was overridden by the ice. Soils within the valley range in texture from sand to loam and are gravelly or stony. The valley averages 46 inches of precipitation annually and has a frost-free period of 160 to 180 days. In the last 40 years, industrialization has reduced the number of farms in Hartford County by more than 40 percent. How industrial development has affected land use is illustrated in the photograph of Avon, a small town in the Farmington Valley, 6 miles northwest of Hartford. Much of the land formerly tilled is now used for pasture or is reverting to brush. As now constituted, farming in the area may be classified as part-time in the small fields south of Avon and as predominantly dairying in West Avon. Tobacco, the principal cash product of farmers in the Connecticut Valley, is also grown in the Farmington Valley.

110

# Urban Fringe Area, Connecticut

DN-1427

PLATE 8.—The reaction to the industrialization of the country is felt in many directions, even in the use of land. The congregation of people in cities and towns requires expansion of urban centers, which is not always confined to the immediate surroundings. Modern transportation facilities permit daily commuters to travel considerable distances from rural areas into the cities and back again. Around the larger cities, branches of suburban developments frequently extend far into the country. An example shown takes in the surroundings of New Canaan 6 miles north of Stamford. Suburban developments follow the main roads leading northward from Stamford in Fairfield County. These suburban extensions are again connected crosswise by the Merritt Parkway, and thus commuting from these suburban districts to Metropolitan New York is feasible. In such instances, urban life is frequently combined with part-time farming, as shown. Urban fringe areas pose many administrative problems. Proper development, taxation of real estate, and service expansions are frequently problems on the agenda of the locality. A peculiar problem arises when urban and rural populations receive recognition as such in the process of enumeration, or when urban land uses must be segregated from the rural uses of the land and considered as separate entities.

# Fultonham Basin, New York

PLATE 9.—The shale and sandstone formations of the Appalachian Plateau bordering the Catskill Mountains to the north are deeply incised by creeks. The valleys eroded by these waterways are deep and also wide in their lower reaches. Thus they provide desirable locations for farm communities. Farms, villages, and towns are strung along the valleys as almost continuous settlements. The basin shown lies on Schoharie Creek in Schoharie County, where the village of Fultonham is located. Here the valley is so wide that the plateau elevation is not reached in the photograph. The road in the valley at the foot of the slope follows an elevation of nearly 700 feet while the plateau above it rises to approximately 2,000 feet. Because of the difference in elevation the climate also differs. Available records indicate an annual mean precipitation of about 40 inches for both levels, but the mean monthly temperatures in the valley are 4 to 6 degrees higher than on the plateau. This also affects the length of the growing season. The frost-free period of around 150 days in the valley is about 3 weeks longer than the similar period on the plateau. On the whole, summers are pleasant but winters are severe. The snow cover lasts from 3 to 4 months. Valley and plateau soils are distinct also. The alluvial bottom soils are chiefly sandy loams, while the soils on the plateau and its slopes are of the heavier types. They vary from loam to silty clay loam and are stony in places. Land use is adjusted to these conditions. Forage crops, small grains, and some corn are grown on the valley land, while pastures, hay land, and some orchards are located on the valley slopes or plateau. Dairying is the main type of farming and poultry raising contributes a good share to the farm income.

# Mohawk Valley Section, New York

DN-1429

PLATE 10.—The Mohawk Valley, between the Adirondack Mountains to the north and the Catskill Mountains to the south, was one of the first gateways opened between the East and the Middle West, and it has remained one of the chief connecting links. The gap in the mountains made possible construction of the Erie Canal, now called the New York Barge Canal. The canal, which was opened in 1825, provided the first constructed transportation channel between the Lake country and the settlements on the Atlantic Coast. Since then, railroads and highways also follow the Mohawk Valley. The valley is also the only belt across the eastern mountains in which much of the forest has been cleared. On the lower elevations of the uplands on both sides of the valley, woodland is confined largely to the steeper slopes and the rough or wet lands. The section shown lies between Utica and Frankfort in Herkimer County. Dutch Hill, a flat-topped hill extension of the plateau to the south, is outlined by a belt of woodland, which marks the slope of more than 500 feet that separates the plateau from the valley. The soils are mainly medium to heavy textured. Because this section is near the divide of the valley, it is somewhat cooler than the portions east or west. On the lower levels, the frost-free period is close to 150 days, but it decreases to 140 or 130 days on the plateau. Precipitation is around 40 inches annually and snow remains on the ground throughout the winter. Agriculture consists chiefly of animal husbandry, mainly dairying. Hay and forage crops and pasture are the chief uses made of the land.

# Northern Slope of Adirondack Mountains, New York

DN-1430

PLATE 11.—Near the Canadian boundary in northern New York, physical conditions restrict alternative land use possibilities. On the northward sloping foothills of the Adirondacks, the advanced latitude, elevation, and northerly exposure lower the temperature and shorten the growing season to a point at which crops cannot be grown successfully. With increasing elevation, farming leaves off and the forest takes over. The change from farming to forest occurs near the 1,700-foot level, as illustrated. There is no really sharp dividing line but the ragged transition is confined to a rather narrow belt. The section of this belt shown lies near the lower Chateaugay Lake, elevation 1,310 feet. The outlet of the lake may be seen in the photograph. Sandy loams, some of which are stony, are the predominant soil types. This border belt is characterized by short mild summers and long cold winters. Although the average length of the frost-free season is from 110 to 130 days, occasional late frosts in May and early frosts in September are hazards to crops. Precipitation averages around 36 to 38 inches annually, of which much falls in the form of snow. On the lower levels, agriculture is largely confined to dairy farming and hay is the chief crop. Irish potatoes are also grown to some extent for the market. Much of the cleared land is used for pasture.

# Lake Ontario Plain, New York

DN-1431

PLATE 12.—The plain that borders Lake Ontario is part of the extensive glacial lakebeds in the Great Lakes country. The surface is so nearly flat that drainage improvements had to be installed over much of the plain before the land could be used efficiently for crops. Some swampy depressions have been left in woods. The rest is now mainly in crops or orchards. The agriculture of the area has changed profoundly since the settlers cleared the land of the heavy hardwood forests. Until the 1890's, agriculture depended mainly on production of grain and livestock. Improvement of the soil and better transportation and marketing facilities made possible adjustment of use to the capabilities of the land. The physical setting of the area has its own advantages. As a rule, the soils, which developed from stratified lacustrine deposits and to some extent from glacial till, are medium-textured, productive, and fairly easy to cultivate. The modify-ing action of Lake Ontario greatly reduces the effects of the late spring and early fall frosts. In spring, the temperature is held down and thus the blossoming of fruit trees is retarded until the danger of frost is past, while the frost-free season, which averages around 170 days, is extended in the fall. The annual average precipitation is 30 inches. Agriculture is greatly diversified and the land is used intensively. As shown, the roads and fields follow rectangular divisions. Originally, the land was part of the Holland Land Company purchase and was subdivided into rectangular tracts for sale and settlement. Animal husbandry is now centered on dairying, with poultry and its products second in importance, followed by cattle and hogs produced for meat. Tree fruits, grapes, and vegetables are the main cash crops, but grains and hay are also important.

# Cohocton Valley near Atlanta, New York

DN-1422

PLATE 13.—The Appalachian Plateau of western New York is dissected by broad, deep valleys, some of which are 1 to 2 miles wide at the bottom. Because of the differences in elevation, climatic differences in some parts of the plateau are sufficient to influence crop production. In the Cohocton Valley near Atlanta, the area shown, the length of the frost-free season averages close to 150 days. Some 20 miles farther south on the plateau, the frost-free period may drop to around 130 days or less. Precipitation varies with elevation—the annual average is around 30 inches on the lower levels and around 40 inches on the higher levels. In addition, upland and valley soils contain some constituent differences. Although both soils developed from glacial drift material, derived mainly from shale and sandstone, and are medium in texture, the valley soils frequently contain limestone and other rock material brought in by the glaciers and water from the north. Much of the land is used for crops and pasture, but woodlots are scattered over the region, especially on the higher plateau. Wooded belts usually outline the steep slopes that separate the plateau from the valley floors. Fields are derived from rectangular land divisions, as the land here was bought by the Holland Land Company and subdivided into rectangular tracts for settlement purposes. However, to prevent erosion, field operations on the strongly rolling upland had to be adjusted to the contour. This did not obliterate the field boundaries, which are still in evidence. Farming is centered on dairying, but some cash crops, like potatoes, are grown. How glaciation affected land use on the Appalachian Plateau will be more apparent when plates 13 and 14 are compared.

DN-1432

PLATE 14.—Land uses in the glaciated and unglaciated parts of the Appalachian Plateau in northern Pennsylvania differ notably. (See Plate No. 13.) On the unglaciated side, where much of the land is gently rolling, very little land is used for production of crops. Most of it is covered by a scrubby forest growth and little real timber is left. A number of reasons explain these differences. One is that in this part of the plateau along the divide, the highest elevations are well above the 2,000-foot level. On these elevations, the growing season is short; frosts occur up to the middle of June and again in early September. The average annual precipitation of 35 to 40 inches is ample but the temperatures are drawbacks. The soils are also a deterrent to more intensive use of the land. They developed from sandstone and shale and are of only fair fertility. Thus cultivation is not especially rewarding. A third handicap to the surface use of the land is the exploitation of the subsurface resources, which extend over a considerable acreage. Where subsurface resources are exploited, as shown, surface use becomes secondary. The section shown is part of the Bradford oilfield in the environs of Rew village, 7 miles southeast of Bradford. This is one of the oldest fields in production. The wells are closely spaced at regular intervals and are flooded in order to increase production. When an area has been flooded and abandoned, vegetation again takes hold of the land and gradually obliterates the well-installation pattern. As shown, agriculture is not highly developed. The few farms on these high levels depend mainly on dairying.

# Dissected Northwestern Border of Appalachian Plateau, Pennsylvania

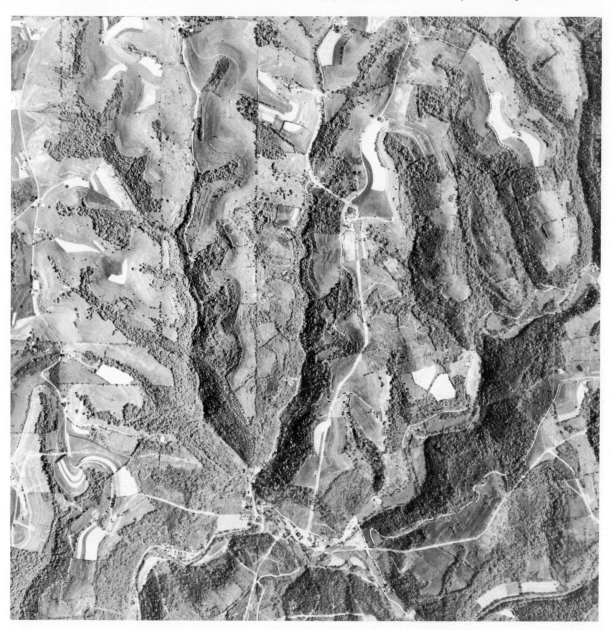

DN—1433

PLATE 15.—The hilly country in western Pennsylvania outside the glaciated zone is a thoroughly dissected portion of the Appalachian Plateau. Narrow ridges, 300- to 400-feet high, separated by equally narrow valleys, prevail. Very little level land is found in the valley bottoms and even less on the ridgetops. The soil of these hills usually is a silt loam that erodes rather easily. Although the mean frost-free period of 150 to 160 days and the nearly 40 inches of annual average precipitation would be favorable to production of a number of crops, the physiographic environment poses problems of production. Cultivation of the slopes is difficult, especially when it must be done in competition with farmers in more favorable locations where mechanization is common. Much of the land was used for crops at one time, but within the last half century the harvested acreage of crops has been drastically reduced. In places, it is only half of the former acreage. More land is used for pasture, and other fields are reverting to brush. Only the steepest slopes have been left in woods. The situation is illustrated by the area shown, which lies on the boundary between Pennsylvania and the panhandle of West Virginia in the southwest corner of Washington County. The straight line that runs north along the crest of a ridge from the confluence of two creeks, stopping fields and woodland tracts from protruding across the line, denotes the State boundary. Farming is centered largely on livestock. Sales of dairy products, poultry, and livestock—mainly cattle, sheep, and hogs—account for most of the farm income. Alfalfa and clover, timothy hay, corn, wheat, and oats are the main field crops.

118

# Appalachian Ridges and Valleys of Central Pennsylvania

DN—1434

PLATE 16.—In central Pennsylvania, the northeast to southwest orientation of mountain ridges and interspersed valleys is the controlling factor in the arrangement of the cultural landscape features. Settlement, agriculture, forestry, transportation, and communication facilities are all affected by it. The railroads and roads that connect the cities and farms follow the valleys, using the gaps in the mountains as gateways to link the valleys together. Property lines are usually drawn at right angles or parallel to the mountain ridges. Distribution of farm and forest land follows closely the mountain-valley pattern. Little woodland is left in the valleys, which frequently have productive soils developed from limestone. Conversely, little cropland is found in the mountains, where the land is steeply sloping and much of the soil is rocky and stony. Larger tracts of mountain land are included in State forests. Precipitation and temperatures are favorable to all crops that can be grown in this latitude. The average annual precipitation is approximately 40 inches, well distributed over the seasons. The frost-free season averages around 160 or 170 days in the valleys. The surroundings of Spangler Gap in the Nittany Mountains near Tylersville are shown. This is the gap that connects Sugar Valley in Clinton County with Brush Valley in Centre County. Crop production, with corn leading, is largely adjusted to the needs of dairy farming, the dominant type of farming in these valleys. However, livestock, and poultry and poultry products are also important, and some crops are grown for the market.

# Strip Mining of Anthracite Coal in Eastern Pennsylvania

DN–1435

PLATE 17.—As a rule, land use is concerned only with surface use. There are instances, however, in which mineral deposits are so near the surface that they can be mined with daylight operations. To this extent, the surface of the land is used also. Open pit operations to quarry building stones, limestone, slate or clay, sand and gravel were known from ancient history. Surface coal mining, usually referred to as strip mining, is a comparatively recent development. With the improvement of power equipment to remove the tremendous loads of overburden and the coal seams as well, within the last 30 years strip mining has expanded rapidly. A comparative study of the two methods indicates that nearly 100 percent of a coal seam can be recovered through strip mining, while only 40 to 60 percent of a seam can be mined with underground operations (91). Strip mining, however, produces problems of land use. If agricultural land is involved, its productive use is almost entirely destroyed. The spoilbanks left by strip-mine operations cannot be cultivated. They regain a vegetative cover slowly, and, as a result, they are unsightly for a long time. The area shown lies south of Hazleton at the junction of the Luzerne, Carbon, and Schuylkill County boundaries. Some of the strip-mine pits in the photograph are more than 150 feet deep. Some of the spoilbanks are equally as high and consist of a scramble of holes and hills. Strip mining is carried on even more extensively in the bituminous coalfields of western Pennsylvania and other Appalachian fields as well as in the interior coalfields, which include lignite fields.

# Lower Piedmont of Pennsylvania

DN—1436

PLATE 18.—Before William Penn received title to the land in 1681, some Dutch and Swedish settlers had already arrived in eastern Pennsylvania. The German and Scotch-Irish immigrants did not arrive until later (1718-32). Of the two groups, the Germans preferred the rolling Piedmont, while the Scotch-Irish occupied the hills. In time, with development, the rolling Piedmont became agriculturally the most productive section of the Colonies and of the Eastern States. Until recent years, Lancaster County led all counties in the United States in value of agricultural products. The lay of the land in the area is not uniformly suited to crop production. Low ridges divide this part of the Piedmont into belts within which soils and land relief differ. In the limestone belt that crosses the northern half of Lancaster County, the land is gently rolling and the soil is a productive brown silt or clay loam. In the southern end of the county, the land is strongly rolling to hilly and the soil is a productive light brown loam that developed from the weathered material of metamorphic rocks. As this is the lowest part of Pennsylvania and usually does not exceed 400 or 500 feet in elevation, the climate is also milder than in other parts of the State. The frost-free season averages from 170 to 200 days or more. Precipitation, which averages from 40 to 42 inches annually, is well distributed seasonally. Land use in southern Lancaster County is illustrated by the environs of Mechanic Grove, 4 miles south of Quarryville. Agriculture is diversified; corn, small grains, tobacco, and potatoes are included in the rotation system. Horticultural specialties are also grown for market. However, dairying and poultry are the principal sources of farm income. In this hilly country, the soils are subject to erosion, and soil conservation practices are followed extensively. Stripcropping has produced the grotesque pattern in the spatial order of the cultural landscape features shown.

121

# Coastal Plain of Southwestern New Jersey

DN—1437

PLATE 19.—All of southern New Jersey is in the Coastal Plain, but land use is far from uniform. A large and rather compact area on the east is woodland covered with scrub oak and pitch pine. This area is usually referred to as the New Jersey Pines, or the Pine Area. On the west are areas in which most of the land is used intensively for crops. That such contrasts exist is due partly to the character of the soil. The soil of the pine area is a light sand, while much of the western part has soils that range from sandy to silt loam. On the Delaware side of southern New Jersey, a combination of natural and economic factors has produced an environment that favors intensive use of the land. Aside from the marshes on Delaware Bay and some wet spots on uplands and creek bottoms, the land is gently rolling. It rises not much more than 150 feet above sea level and is well drained. The soils are easy to cultivate and with proper management and fertilization are rather productive. The proximity of the ocean makes the climate equally fav-

orable. The frost-free season averages nearly 200 days, and the annual precipitation of around 42 inches is well distributed over the seasons. But during the dry spells that sometimes occur during the growing season, sprinkler irrigation is extensively applied on high-value crops. The concentrations of population along the middle Atlantic Coast provide the nearby city markets. In much of this area, land use is intensive and diversified. Farming may be centered on vegetables, poultry and poultry products, dairying, nurseries, or fruits. The area shown lies between Bridgeton and Deerfield at the northern end of Cumberland County. Farming in this section is organized to supply the canning and freezing industry. Harvest of high-quality products is continuous during the growing season. The more important products grown here are fruits and vegetables, which are marketed in frozen packs. A large processing and packing plant may be seen in the photograph.

# Coastal Plain of Delaware

DN-1421

PLATE 20.—Except for the small portion north of the Wilmington–Newark line, practically all of Delaware is Coastal Plain country and lies less than 100 feet above sea level. The surface of the land is either flat, undulating, or slightly rolling near the drainageways. A considerable acreage has a flat surface and consequently drainage is inadequate. The inadequate drainage is an impediment to cultural use·of the land. Many drainage improvements have been installed, but a large acreage of wet land has been left in woods or in marshes along the coast. The better drained land, of which a sample is shown, is used chiefly for crops or orchards. Soils and climate are favorable to intensive use of the land. Soils range in texture from sandy to silt loams, which are easy to cultivate. A mild maritime climate provides a long growing season, which averages around 190 frost-free days. The annual average precipitation of 42 to 44 inches, half of which normally falls during the warm season, is ample for all crops. The tract shown lies about 2 miles south of Smyrna, where farming is greatly diversified. Corn, wheat, and other small grains are grown; considerable hay is cut; vegetables are grown for the market and for canning plants; and orchards are a feature of the landscape. Livestock enterprises, particularly dairying and poultry, are important in the agricultural economy. Delaware was one of the first States to construct dual highways, a stretch of which may be seen in the photograph. Improved highways and roads connect all parts of the State; nearly 2 percent of the total land area of the State is taken up by rural roads and highways and their rights-of-way.

# Chesapeake Shore of Eastern Maryland

DN-1411

PLATE 21.—Tidal marshes are an extensive feature of the shores of the Delmarva Peninsula. On the eastern shore of Chesapeake Bay, especially, tidal marshes are entwined with the lives of the people. These marshes may separate islands from the mainland, or they may follow the rivers inshore for many miles. In the aggregate, they occupy an area of nearly 300 square miles on the Maryland sector alone. The nature of the tidal marshes and of land use on the bordering firm land are illustrated in the photograph, which shows Little Blackwater River at its junction with the main river in Dorchester County. The bridge over Little Blackwater River, in the center of the picture, is about 8 miles inland from Fishing Bay, but the tidal marshes follow the river inland another 4 miles. For a considerable distance away from the tidal marshes, the adjacent land is flat and rises only a few feet above sea level. The soil is predominantly a silt loam, which must be drained for agricultural use. Usually, agricultural development follows the edge of the tidal marshes where the rise of the land is more pronounced, and where drainage installations can be made more readily. Farther back, much of the land is swampy and has been left in woods. Converting the land to agricultural use would mean installation of a more elaborate drainage system. The climate on these Chesapeake Bay shores is mild. The frost-free season usually lasts for more than 200 days and the annual precipitation averages 42 inches. Corn, wheat, soybeans, and tame hay are the chief crops grown on these lowlands. Most of the farmers who live on the shore operate part-time farms. They are also engaged in fishing, oystering, and muskrat trapping. The tidal marshes are used by migratory waterfowls; to sportsmen they are well-known duck-hunting grounds.

# Upper Piedmont of Maryland

DN-1438

PLATE 22.—In the Upper Piedmont of Maryland, the land is used chiefly for agriculture. The interspersed distribution of fields, pasture, woodlots, and farmsteads on the strongly rolling land has produced an attractive landscape. The soils have developed from the decomposed material or rock formations, most of them of the crystalline or semicrystalline kind. In texture, the soils range from loam, or gravelly or stony loam, to shale and silt loams, and their distribution is patchy. They are of medium fertility but respond to good management and fertilization. Elevations of 400 to 500 feet and distance from water have modified the coastal climate. Summers are warm but they are shorter than those on the coast and winters are comparatively mild. Snow seldom remains on the ground. The frost-free period averages 180 days, and precipitation averages from 40 to 42 inches for the year. General farming suited to the physical environment is carried on for the most part, although adjustments to the demands of nearby city markets are evident. Corn, wheat, barley, oats, and hay are the principal crops grown. Considerable quantities of these crops are used as feed on the farms. Cattle, hogs, and poultry are the usual livestock combination, and dairying is the chief source of farm income. Sales of livestock and of poultry and poultry products are also important. Some field crops and vegetables are grown for the market. A typical pattern of land use is presented in the tract shown, which lies about 4 miles northwest of Mount Airy in the eastern part of Frederick County. Most of the farms are medium-sized to large, with land in fields, pasture, and woodlots. Pastures are usually near the farmstead and in the creek bottoms, while woodlots occupy the rougher spots.

# Allegheny Plateau of Western Maryland

DN-1439

PLATE 23.—Western Maryland extends to the divide plateau of the Appalachian Mountains. On the strongly rolling to hilly plateau back of the Allegheny Front, where elevations frequently rise above the 2,500-foot level, only the smoother portions can be used for farming. Of the total land area, about 50 percent is in farms, and only comparatively small portions of this land can be used for crops and for pasture. The remaining acreage is mainly in forests; timber production is the best use that can be made of this land. The forest belt shown covers Negro Mountain, and the farms to the west are 2 to 3 miles south of the village of Accident. Soils developed largely from the weathered material of sandstone and shale, and gravelly or stony types prevail. These soils are not strong, but they respond well to fertilization. Compared with eastern Maryland, the climate is cool. Summer temperatures are moderate in daytime and cool at night.

The frost-free season lasts 4 to 5 months. Winters are cold and the snow cover lasts for some time. As comfortable summer temperatures attract vacationists, some resorts are located on the plateau. The annual mean precipitation of 42 to 46 inches is higher than in the low country to the east. Agriculture on these highlands shows its reaction to climate. Corn is not grown to the same extent as on the lower levels. Hay, oats, corn, and wheat are the more important crops. The chief sources of farm income are dairying, meat animals, and poultry. The tract in the picture is from an agricultural section. Some of the farms have rectangular boundaries, as contrasted to the divisions commonly used in this part of the country. These divisions indicate, however, that the land was subdivided before it was settled. No doubt it comprised part of the unappropriated land that was deeded to soldiers at the end of the Revolution.

# Eastern Shore of Virginia

DN-1440

PLATE 24.—In the Eastern Shore counties of Virginia, the land is generally flat and most elevations are below the 50-foot level. Tidal marshes are extensive on both sides of the peninsula. In this narrow stretch of country, land use is adjusted to a number of physical and economic factors. Frequently the land is not well enough drained for agricultural use and must be improved through ditching or tiles. Physiographically, the land is part of the Lower Coastal Plain. Soils are light and usually range from sandy to fine sandy loams. As a result, they are fairly easy to cultivate. The maritime influence on temperature, which has prolonged the growing season considerably, is felt from the Atlantic Ocean on the east and Chesapeake Bay on the west. Winters are mild; summers are warm and long. The frost-free period averages 210 to 220 days. Precipitation, which is around 44 inches annually, is sufficient for most crops, although sprinkler irrigation systems have been installed in a number of farms to insure maximum yields. Aside from the tidal marshes, land use is almost exclusively divided between cropland and forest, which usually occupies the wetter ground. The photograph shows the environs of Cheapside, a village in Northampton County. Intensive farming is carried on, and production is concentrated on cash crops. Vegetables, Irish potatoes, sweetpotatoes, and strawberries are the chief crops grown for eastern city markets. Woodlots provide lumber for the manufacture of containers in which the farm products are shipped. Cattle and poultry are of minor importance in the farm economy.

# Lower Coastal Plain of Virginia Drained

DN-1441

PLATE 25.—Inadequate drainage is one of the chief drawbacks to fuller economic development of the Lower Coastal Plain on the mainland of Virginia. Swamps and wet lands are extensive. As far back as George Washington's time, attempts were made to drain the Dismal Swamp but failed. For much of the marsh and swamp lands, reclamation through drainage is not economically feasible. For another large acreage, however, drainage improvements are possible. Some areas have been so improved and are now used intensively for crop production. Farm drainage can be installed by the owners if drainage outlets are available on the farm or if outlets can be secured through permits from adjacent owners. This was evidently the working arrangement in the area shown, which lies about 5 miles out of Norfolk, near Kemps- ville at the head of the eastern branch of the Elizabeth River. The silt loam soils have been brought into a high state of productivity through the use of manure and fertilizers. A long, warm summer with an average of 230 frost-free days, a mild winter, and around 44 inches of annual precipitation are favorable to diversified agriculture. The nearby markets in Norfolk and the beach resorts provide the orientation for agricultural production. Dairying and truck farming are the prevailing types of agriculture. The principal field crops are corn, small grains, and hay, and the chief truck crops are strawberries, Irish potatoes, sweetpotatoes, and vegetables. Workers from Norfolk supply most of the labor needed in truck farming, and this has produced an inversion in the movement of commuters.

128

# Upper Piedmont of Virginia

DN-1442

PLATE 26.—No local land use pattern can be regarded as typical for the Piedmont of Virginia. Irregular farm boundaries and fields prevail in the region, but they are not peculiar to the Piedmont alone. The spatial order of fields, pastures, and woodland may be an adaptation to the physiographic background, associated with the customs of the original settlers or the type of farming practiced in the area. In some parts of the Piedmont, farms and fields are arranged along the divide between the streams; in other parts, small fields are the rule, and in the North, where large estates with cattle and horses are found, extensive pastures are a dominant feature. The land use pattern of that part of the Upper Piedmont shown does not approach the extreme in either direction. The area is near Concord, or about 8 miles southeast of Lynch-burg in Campbell County. The land is strongly rolling to hilly and the elevation is approximately 800 feet. Soils vary from sandy loams to clay. The sandy loams are usually found on the smoother upland; and the red stiff clays occupy the steeper slopes where erosion has removed the more friable surface material. Summers are long and warm with an average frost-free period of 200 days, and winters are moderate. Farms are openly scattered and fields occupy a relatively small proportion of the land. Farming is diversified. Tobacco is the principal source of farm income. Corn, wheat, and hay are other important field crops. Cleared pastures occupy a considerable acreage, an indication that livestock enterprises are an important part of the farm economy. Dairying, livestock sold, and poultry contribute their shares to the farm income.

# Catawba Mountain and Valley, Virginia

DN—1443

PLATE 27.—It is not always evident that geologic history and structure are the underlying causes of edaphic peculiarities or that they act as advantages or drawbacks in the development of local land use patterns. The geologic structure and the petrographic nature of the underlying rocks usually influence land use indirectly through land relief and soils. However, in the mountains are localities in which the geologic structure is reflected in the land use pattern. Here land use is adjusted to land relief and rock formations, which are defined and recorded in aerial photography. A sample from the mountains of Virginia—a section of the Catawba Mountain and Valley at the headwaters of Catawba Creek in Roanoke County—is shown. Because of the general arrangement of the landscape, the small acreages of land used for cultivated crops are found in the smoother portions of the valleys and basins. Pastures are usually found on the more sloping lands while the forests occupy the mountains. There are exceptions to the rule. On the northern slope of Catawba Mountain, the pasture zone is divided by a belt of brush and woodland which follows a row of knobs on the mountainside. The belt and knobs define the outcrop of a sandstone formation. Above and below this belt, shales with interbedded limestone provided the parent material from which the soils developed. These valleys have a pleasant climate with a frost-free season of around 180 days and moderate winter temperatures. Annual precipitation averages approximately 40 inches and is well distributed seasonally. The mountainous topography and the distance to markets prevent a more diversified type of farming. As much of the farmland is best suited to pasture, livestock farming is the main industry. Cattle, dairy products, and poultry and its products are the chief sources of farm income.

# Rim of Blue Ridge Plateau, Virginia

DN-1420

PLATE 28.—The Blue Ridge as the separating mountain range between the Great Appalachian Valley and the Piedmont does not retain the characteristics of a ridge from north to south. South of the Roanoke Gap, the Blue Ridge broadens out into a rolling to hilly plateau with the highest spots protruding above the 3,000-foot level. The plateau is bounded on the east by a well-defined rim from 1,000 to 1,500 feet high, of which a section along the Carroll-Patrick County boundary is shown. Along the rim runs the Blue Ridge National Parkway, which offers panoramic vistas over the detached mountains and the hilly country below the rim. In this part of the Blue Ridge, only the plateau rim has recreational value. The plateau itself is largely agricultural. Because of the elevation, the climate is cooler than on the Piedmont below. The growing season in these elevations averages around 6 months. The annual precipitation of approximately 44 inches is ample for agricultural needs. Most of the soils are medium-textured and fairly productive. Land use on the plateau is almost evenly divided among cropland, pasture, and woodland. Cropland usually occupies the smoother land and woodland the steeper slopes. Corn, wheat, and alfalfa are the main crops. Livestock farming dominates the agricultural economy. Cattle, dairy products, and poultry and its products are the chief sources of farm income. On the rim escarpment, most of the land is in woods, although some good-sized orchards, mainly apple, have been planted on the lower slopes. Air drainage on these slopes is frequently sufficient to prevent damage to the trees from late spring frosts.

# Great Appalachian Valley Section, West Virginia

DN-1444

PLATE 29.—Only two counties of West Virginia are far enough east across the mountains to share the resources of the great Appalachian Valley. The valley lies between the Blue Ridge on the east and the Appalachian Plateau and Mountains on the west, and extends south from Pennsylvania to Alabama. Throughout its length, it is known for its fertile soil, pleasant climate, farm specialties, and scenic attractions, particularly the many caverns. The section of the valley shown lies in Jefferson County. A bend of the Potomac may be seen. The smaller river farther south is the Shenandoah. Harpers Ferry lies at the junction of the two rivers. The lands of the valley are gently rolling, with fertile soils; they range from silt to clay loam and were developed from limestone. In places, the soil is shallow and rock outcrops protrude above the surface. Where these rock outcrops are numerous, they interfere with cultivation and the land is best suited to pasture. As a result of its sheltered position, the area is warmer and drier than the mountains. The growing season averages 180 days, and annual precipitation averages 36 inches. Of this, slightly more than half falls during the warm season. Most of the land is cleared and used for agricultural production. Woodland is confined to the steeper slopes. Farming is diversified. Orchards, mainly apple, are extensive, and apple blossom time attracts many visitors. Of the field crops, corn, wheat, barley, alfalfa, and clover are important. Fruit, dairy products, and livestock are the chief sources of income.

# Dissected Appalachian Plateau, West Virginia

DN-1445

PLATE 30.—Most of West Virginia lies in the physiographic region of the Allegheny and Cumberland Plateaus. When used as a geographic term in this connection, "plateau" is more closely associated with geology than physiography, for the plateau is thoroughly dissected. But when viewed from the crest of divides, no outstanding mountain serves as a landmark. Some divide flats in the northern part of the plateau are used for farming. In the southern section, as shown, the land is more maturely dissected. Practically no level land is found on the divides or in creek bottoms. Settlement is scattered along the creeks, and a little land is cultivated on the lower slopes and in spots on the divide. Although differences in elevation between the ridge crests and the valley bottoms are frequently less than 500 feet, the land is rugged. The photograph was taken about 4 miles south of Charleston, but the proximity of a city of 75,000 people is not reflected in the cultural features. Urban influences have not penetrated the mountains to the extent that they greatly modify the land use pattern. Climatically, land use is not restricted. The growing season averages around 180 days, and the annual mean precipitation of 46 inches is more than sufficient for all major uses. Most of the soils developed from weathered material of shale and sandstone and are only moderately productive. In most instances, farming in this part of the country cannot rise above the subsistence level. Frequently, it is only a part-time occupation of the miners. The mining of coal is the chief industry of the area. Forestry is the best use of the land in that it protects the watershed and provides lumber and pulp for the industry.

# Eastern Kentucky Hills

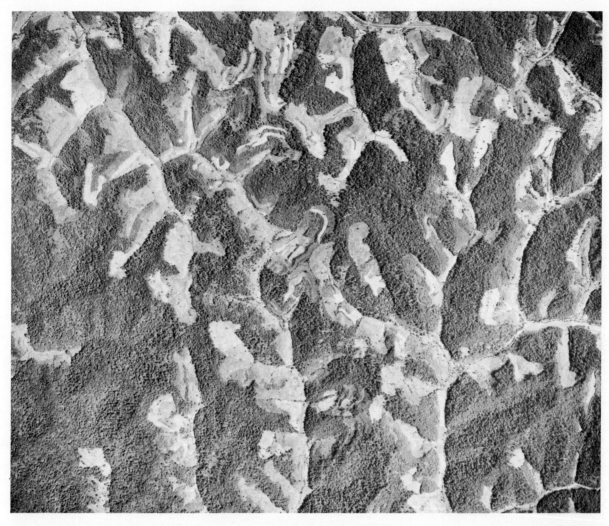

DN—1419

PLATE 31.—The eastern Kentucky Hills represent a maturely dissected plateau. Valleys are usually V-shaped, with very little level bottom land. Equally small acreages of level land are found on the ridges. Differences in elevation between bottom land and ridgetops usually hover around the 500-foot mark. This rugged surface is the dominant landscape feature in most places. In certain localities in the Appalachian Highlands, a similar topography would deter use of the land for agricultural production. When the soils of the Kentucky Hills are considered, they are little more encouraging. The parent material from which the soils developed is usually derived from sandstone and shale which, as a rule, are not highly productive. Nor is soil development uniform. The early settlers along the streams and creeks learned from experience and observation that the soils of the northern and east-

ern sides of the ridges were deeper and reached farther up the slope than did soils on the opposite sides. This results from greater insolation on slopes with southern and western exposures. In winter, repeated thawing and freezing of the soils on these slopes promotes erosion. The moisture-holding capacity of the resulting thin soil is reduced until it is too low to produce crops in summer. An unusual land use pattern is the result. Only eastern and northern slopes are cleared and cultivated. The southern and western slopes are left in forest. Temperature and moisture conditions are favorable to all crops that grow in this latitude. The tract of land shown lies about 5 miles west of Jackson in Breathitt County. Farming is largely of the subsistence type. Many farmers work part time in forests and mines.

# Bluegrass Region of Kentucky

DN—1446

PLATE 32.—In Colonial times, a few settlers advanced as far as the Bluegrass Region of Kentucky. Considered from the geologic viewpoint, the Bluegrass Region is neither a basin nor a plain but a truncated dome, which has produced a rolling plain, fringed by a more dissected belt, and all surrounded by knobs and hilly country. All the land is well-drained; some has suffered from erosion. The principal soils are rather productive silt loams, which developed from limestone. In contrast to the forested surroundings, the settlers found in the region a parklike arrangement of native vegetation. Large openings in the hardwood forest were grown over with grasses, sedges, and canebrakes. Although the region was named for bluegrass, bluegrass is not indigenous to the region, having been introduced by settlers from the East. It grew well on the limestone soil and proved to be a prolific producer of seed and pasture. Grass seed became an article of trade with other frontier settlements, and in time the grass became known as "Kentucky Bluegrass." Grass seed has remained a cash crop of some importance ever since. The Bluegrass Region is the outstanding agricultural region of Kentucky. Most of the land is cleared and used for pasture and crops. Fence rows along the fields and pasture boundaries are a characteristic landscape feature, as may be noted in the tract shown, which lies 3 miles south of Paris in Bourbon County. A moderate humid climate with a frost-free season of 180 to 190 days and a mean annual precipitation of more than 40 inches would be favorable for the field crops that grow at this latitude. But as the soil is particularly adapted to grasses, the largest acreage is used for pasture. In the farm economy, livestock and its products are nearly as important as cash crops. Cattle, sheep, hogs, and thoroughbred horses play their part. Corn, small grains, and hay are the chief crops grown for use on the farm. Burley tobacco is the principal cash crop.

135

# Karst Lands of Kentucky

DN-144.7

PLATE 33.—The Karst Lands of Kentucky, of which the southern portion is better known as the Penny-royal Plain, form an irregular crescent around the western coal measures. All Karst lands are underlain by a soluble limestone. As the horizon of the land is nearly level, much of the precipitation is absorbed by the soil, from which it percolates through the rocks. Through the solvent action of the slowly moving water in the rock, the channels and caverns formed consti-tute a subterranean drainage system. Depressions formed over the inlets of the underground drainage system have produced the spattered sinkhole design that can be seen in the tract shown, which lies 2 miles west of Sonora in Hardin County. These sinkholes frequently impede cultivation of the land. They re-main wet longer than the adjacent uplands; some retain water for some time. The soils developed from limestone are usually silt or clay loams and erode rather easily. Erosion is most active around the rims of the sinkholes from which the soil is washed into the depressions. A certain regularity in the layout of the fields, as shown, indicates that the land was di-vided for the settlers. However, this is not a char-acteristic of the Kentucky Karst Lands as a whole. The climate conforms to the interior position and ele-vation of the region, and with a frost-free season averaging 190 days, it has the general characteristics of the lower Ohio slope in Kentucky. Precipitation, which averages around 46 to 48 inches annually, is higher than in the Bluegrass Region. Farming is largely centered on livestock, mainly cattle, with some dairying and hogs. Much of the land is used for pasture. Corn, some small grains, and alfalfa and lespedeza for hay are the principal field crops grown for use on the farms. Burley tobacco is the leading cash crop.

# Western Coal Measures of Kentucky

DN-1448

**PLATE 34.**—The Western Coal Measures of Kentucky are a composite of hills and plains in which the major branches of the drainage system indicate the distributional arrangement of the plains. Flat alluvial valley bottoms, which are more than 4 miles wide in places, separate the hills and rolling upland areas. Some of the hills rise more than 200 feet above the valley flats; the rolling areas have much lower elevations. The prevailing soils of the upland are silt loams, which developed from the disintegrated material of shale and sandstone with interbedded limestone in places. They are of moderate fertility. On the sloping upland, these fine-textured soils erode easily if not protected. Sheet and gully erosion have damaged considerable areas. Soil conservation practices are needed on the hills, and conversely, drainage improvements are needed on the flats below when they are used for crops. The tract shown, which lies 2 miles southwest of Ashbyburg at the northern end of Hopkins County illustrates land use on hills and bottoms. The hills in the northern part of the tract rise only about 100 feet above the lowland; but they are badly eroded. Much of the once cultivated land is reverting to brush and pasture. Reclamation of the lowlands is progressing from the foot of the hills to the creek channel, but a good many square miles are still wet and in forest. Although the growing season averages 190 days and the mean annual precipitation is 46 inches, most of the land is now used for pasture. Cattle, hogs, some sheep, and poultry are raised, and dairying is a sideline. Some tobacco is grown as a cash crop.

137

# Upper Ohio Hills

DN-1449

PLATE 35.—The hilly country that flanks both sides of the Upper Ohio River is sometimes referred to as the Upper Ohio Hills. This hilly belt lies outside the glaciated area and thus has been exposed to erosion much longer than the bordering drift plains to the north. The sustained carving action of water has produced a well-dissected and rather rugged land relief. In places, the hills rise 300 feet above the creek bottoms. The locality shown lies about 4 miles southeast of Stewart in Athens County, Ohio. This portion of Ohio was part of the "Ohio Company's Purchase" of 1889. It was later divided into townships 6 miles square, but the national system of subdivision was not followed strictly. The settlers cleared and cultivated considerably more land than is presently used for crops. Fifty years ago the acreage of cropland was approximately twice what it is now, a reduction caused mainly by the roughness of the land. The soils, which developed for the most part from weathered material of sandstone and shale, are fine-textured and erode easily. Sheet erosion has damaged some of the land and probably contributed to the reduction in crop acreage. Precipitation, which averages 40 to 42 inches for the year, is higher than on the plains to the north, and the average growing season of 170 to 180 days is slightly longer. As may be noted, the rectangular land divisions are marked by hedges, but cropland, pasture, and woodland are more or less adjusted to the land relief. Dairying and the livestock industry are the chief uses made of the land. About half the land is used for pasture; approximately one-eighth is used for cultivated crops, and the steeper slopes are left in woods. Small apple orchards are found on some farms.

# Drift Plain of Northeastern Ohio

DN-1450

PLATE 36.—In northeastern Ohio along the upland divide, much of the land is level or slightly undulating to gently rolling and drainage is not yet fully developed. The St. Lawrence drainage system is on one side and the drainage system of the Ohio River on the other. This part of Ohio was overrun by the glaciers of the Wisconsin period. It is covered by a mantle of glacial till, which is composed mainly of the ground-up material derived from shale and sandstone. The soils developed from the till are predominantly of the heavier types and are deficient in humus and acid. In texture, they range from loam to clay loam and the subsoil is a heavy plastic clay. Heavy soils with deficient surface and internal drainage are necessarily difficult to cultivate. Much of the land has been cleared, but only about a fourth of it is now used for crops. More land is used for pasture than for crops. Climatically, the area would be suited to diversified farming. The frost-free season averages 140 to 150 days, and precipitation averages 38 to 40 inches annually and is well distributed seasonally. Agriculture is centered on dairying and animal husbandry, mainly cattle and poultry. Corn, wheat, oats, and hay are the chief crops, but vegetables and Irish potatoes are grown for nearby markets. The tract shown lies in the northwestern part of Trumbull County about 2 miles southeast of North Bloomfield. This section of Ohio was first claimed by Connecticut; it was known as the Connecticut Western Reserve. In 1800, it was ceded to the Federal Government and subdivided into rectangular tracts. However, the townships are only 5 miles square, and, as shown, they are not sectionalized.

139

# Western Ohio Drift Plain

DN-1451

PLATE 37.—The surface of the western Ohio drift plain is undulating to smoothly rolling and slightly hummocky in places. A fairly deep deposit of glacial till provided the parent material from which the soils developed. Most of the soils range from silt loam to silt clay loam. They are acid in the surface horizon but the calcareous substratum is even heavier than the surface soil. Internal drainage of the soils in their natural state, therefore, is frequently deficient. Much of this nearly level land was cleared and used for crops, but crops were sensitive to wet spells that affected yields. To overcome this difficulty, tile drains were laid over much of this level country. Now most of the northwestern part of Ohio is organized into drainage enterprises. Precipitation averages from 34 to 38 inches annually, of which slightly more than half falls during the warm season. The mean length of the frost-free period ranges from 150 to 180 days. Summers are rather warm. The photograph was taken from the vicinity of Degraff in Logan County. A part of the city is shown. As may be seen, the land is divided into rectangular divisions, which are similar to the land divisions of the public domain, in that they consist of sectionalized townships 6 miles square. The difference lies in the numerations and direction. Ranges run from west to east instead of north to south; numeration of townships and sections differ also. This departure from the norm started in a purchase project on the Ohio River; it was extended between the Miami and Little Miami Rivers north into what is now Logan County. Most of the land is now used for farming; only a few woodlots and openly wooded pasture tracts are reminders of the former hardwood forest cover. Western Ohio is considered a part of the Corn Belt. Corn is the leading crop, but wheat, oats, soybeans, and leguminous hay are also important. Good proportions of these crops are sold. Next to cropland, pastureland is most extensive. The main sources of farm income, however, are sales of dairy products and livestock.

# Southern Michigan Upland

DN-1452

PLATE 38.—In southern Michigan, landforms are the product of glaciation. They consist of an irregular array of slightly rolling till plains, and strongly rolling moraines with interspersed depressions and broad wet bottoms along the sluggish rivers and creeks. Differences in elevation between the high and low points vary within 200 feet, but they are usually much less. Very little land can be classified as too rough for cultivation. A much greater acreage requires drainage. The upland soils are mainly the medium-textured sandy loams or loams. The substratum is frequently calcareous. Muck and peat are extensive lowland types. The usual growing season is more than 150 days. The annual precipitation of approximately 30 to 32 inches is lower than farther south, but the greater part falls during the warm season. The tract shown lies in the southwest corner of Jackson County. It is a rolling till plain, in which the arrangement of the cultural features is dominated by the rectangular division of the land. Fields, pastures, and woodlots are bounded by sectional division lines. The smaller square fields and pastures, which are frequently enclosed by hedgerows, contain 10 acres. The embankment that bends around the road intersection in which the village of Pulaski is located is an abandoned railroad tract. Agriculture is of the intensive Corn Belt type. Corn is the main crop but wheat, alfalfa, and clover are included in the rotation system. Vegetables and Irish potatoes are grown for market. On the whole, farming is organized around dairying and livestock. Dairy products, livestock, and poultry with its products are the chief sources of farm income.

# Fruit Belt of Michigan

DN-1453

PLATE 39.—The belt of country that stretches along the eastern shore of Lake Michigan from the southern boundary of the State to Grand Traverse Bay in the north is usually referred to as the Fruit Belt of Michigan. Land use here has been adjusted to temperature and soils. The surface is a composite of morainic hills, rolling drift plains, smooth glacial lakebeds, sand dunes, and interspersed depressions. The soils of the uplands range from sand to clay. In the lowlands, they are usually of the organic type. The climate is modified by the waters of Lake Michigan. The prevailing westerly air currents coming from the lake moderate the temperature, particularly in spring when they hold temperatures down during the day and prevent frosts at night. This delays blossoming until the danger of late frost is over. Fall frosts are retarded in the same way. The frost-free season ranges from 150 days in the north to 180 days in the south. The annual average precipitation of 30 to 32 inches is well distributed seasonally. The Fruit Belt tract shown lies in the midwestern part of Allegan County. Hutchins Lake is in the upper right-hand corner. Morainic hilly upland till plain and glacial lakebed make up the morphological background of the locality. How topography and soils affect land use may be seen in the photograph. Orchards and vineyards are confined to the rolling uplands where mineral soils prevail. Truck crops are confined largely to the muck soils of the drained lakebed south of the lake. Farming is diversified. There are many apple, peach, pear, and cherry orchards, and small fruits are grown also. Cabbage, celery, cauliflower, and cucumbers are the main vegetables produced for market. Dairy, poultry, and livestock farming are also important.

# Glacial Lake Plain, Saginaw Basin, Michigan

DN-1454

PLATE 40.—Glacial lakebeds occupy a considerable area in the Northern States. As a rule, their surfaces are smooth and almost level. They are sometimes divided by old beach ridges or waterlaid moraines, a few feet high, into upper and lower plains. Washed glacial till or, more often, waterlaid deposits formed the parent material from which the soils developed. The prevalent soil types are usually medium to heavy textured and very fertile. However, for agricultural use, drainage improvements are needed in many places. Most of this land is used rather intensively for crop production. The wetter land is used for pasture and woodlots. The photograph represents a tract in the Saginaw Basin in Bay County, above the lowest beach-line west of Linwood. The lowest land on the eastern margin lies about 3 miles west of Linwood on the shore of Saginaw Bay. It is approximately 20 feet above the water level of Lake Huron. Within the area shown, the land rises another 25 feet westward. The climate of the bay area is comparable to that of southern Michigan. The frost-free period averages 140 to 150 days, and the precipitation averages 30 inches annually. Agriculture is diversified and includes a number of specialties. The greater part of the farm income is derived from crops but livestock is a close second. The principal field crops are corn, wheat, oats, barley, and alfalfa. Of the crop specialties grown for the market, dry beans come first, followed by Irish potatoes, sugar beets grown for production of sugar, and vegetables. Among the livestock enterprises dairying predominates, but sales of livestock and of poultry and poultry products contribute a good share to the farm economy of the basin.

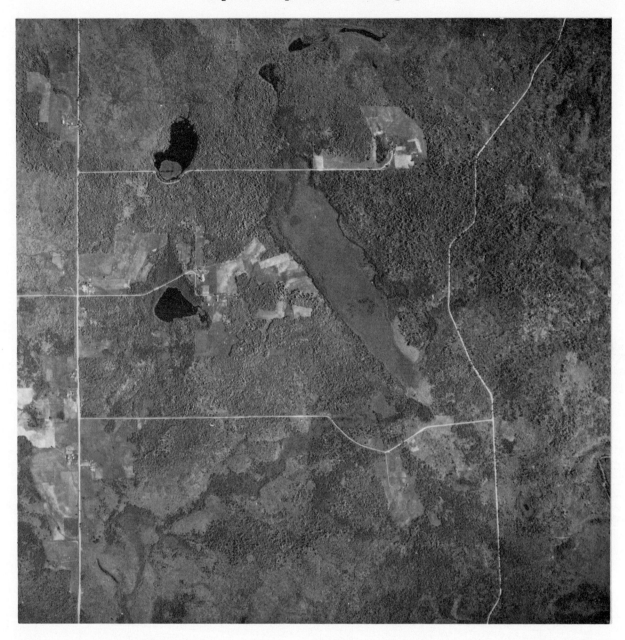

DN-1455

PLATE 41.—In the Northern Peninsula of Michigan and the adjacent counties of Wisconsin, much of the land is either rough and rugged or swampy or wet. Only a small part of the land has been cleared and improved for agricultural production. Farms are more or less clustered along the main lines of transportation, but in the intervening locations, they are few and scattered. Of the landforms, the mountains and knolls are of preglacial origin, although many of the morphological details, such as the moraine and drift deposits or drumlin formations, are of glacial origin. Lakes are more numerous on the Wisconsin side than on the Michigan peninsula, and wet land is more extensive in the eastern than in the western half of the peninsula. A similar distinction is evident in the soils. Sands are more prevalent in the eastern part and the medium to heavy-textured types are more in evidence in the west-ern part. In addition to the northern climate, the often rocky and stony soils are a drawback to agricultural use of the land. Temperature gradients from the lakeshore to the interior are rather steep. On the lakeshore, the average length of the frost-free season is around 140 days; inland it may range from 80 to 90 days. The annual precipitation is approximately 30 inches. Much of this falls as snow, which may cover the ground for 3 months or more. The scattered location of farms is illustrated by the tract shown, which lies 2 miles north of Paulding in the southeast corner of Ontonagon County. Most of the land is cutover; some is cleared and used for crops and pasture. General farming prevails. Dairy products and livestock are the main sources of farm income. Mining camps and lumber mills provide the market. Hay, oats, and potatoes are the main crops.

# Central Plains of Indiana

DN-1456

PLATE 42.—The Central Plains of Indiana are an extension of the drift plains of western Ohio. The action of water has not modified greatly the surface configuration left by the retreating ice sheets. Near the larger watercourses, the land is more rolling. Low bluffs, 20 to 50 feet high, may define the alluvial valley floors. The interstream portions of the plain are usually only undulating or slightly rolling. The depressions frequently require drainage improvements for use as cropland and extensive areas have been so improved. Soil distinctions frequently coincide with the better and poorly drained areas. Glacial till provided the material from which the soils have developed. Over large areas, this consists of a surface layer of loess-like texture. Silt loams are the prevailing soil types on the better drained land. In the depressions, the soil is usually a silt clay loam. As the better drained land dries out more readily, it gives the surface a billowy appearance. Corn Belt climate characterizes the area. Summers are warm; the frost-free period averages 160 to 170 days; and precipitation is around 38 inches annually, of which 60 percent falls during the warm season. A section of the undulating plain south of Rossville in Clinton County is shown. Cropland and pasture are dominant land uses, but many farms have woodlots. Sales of livestock, mainly cattle and hogs, are the main sources of farm income. To these are added dairy and poultry products. The main crops are corn, wheat, oats, soybeans, and leguminous hay, of which a large part is used on the farms but a good share also reaches the market. Property lines, location of roads, and field operations are controlled largely by the rectangular division. Indiana was the first State in which the official system of land division was used for almost the entire State, so that any section can be identified with a few symbols.

145

# Knobstone Escarpment in Southern Indiana

DN-1457

PLATE 43.—In southern Indiana, the limit of glaciation shows a remarkable indentation. The recession of the glacial boundary is about 90 miles deep. It outlines the Knobstone country, which extends in a north to south direction. The Knobstone Ridge is an outstanding topographic feature of southern Indiana. Actually, it is an elevated westward tilted plain, bounded on the east by a steep escarpment. Along the Ohio River, the hills rise to 500 feet or more from the river bottom. Farther north, in the portion of the escarpment shown, which lies about 4 miles north of New Albany in Floyd County, the difference in elevation between the rim of the escarpment and the plain below is 450 feet. Both glaciated and unglaciated country appear in the photograph. The unglaciated plain above the escarpment is deeply dissected and the steeper slopes are left in woods. The rolling plain below was overrun by the glacier of the Illinoian period, which affected the soil development. In the Knobstone country, the parent material of the soil is derived from sandstone and shale, while in the plain it is old glacial till. There are also slight differences in climate, which have not been recorded effectively. Precipitation is around 42 inches annually in the plains and averages up to 4 inches higher in part of the Knobstone country. The frost-free season averages 190 days in the low country and almost 10 days less on the high land. Additional distinction is the land division. The Knobstone country was public domain and is divided into townships and sections. The plains portion is part of "Clark's Military Grant;" it is divided into 500-acre tracts with orientation of the lines derived from the Ohio River. The physical background accounts for the differences in land use and farming in the 2 areas. The acreage used for cropland in the plains is much larger than that so used in the Knobstoneland. Livestock is the chief item in the farm economy in both sections, but dairying is more prominent in the plains. Sales of crops are high in both areas, but fruit is more important in the hills and tobacco more so in the plains.

# Illinoian Drift Plain of Southern Illinois

DN-1458

PLATE 44.—Except for the rugged Ozark spur, southern Illinois lies at the southern limit of glaciation; it was covered with ice during the Illinoian glaciation but was not invaded by the ice sheets of the Wisconsin period. Smooth plains with a gently rolling surface resulted. The area is traversed by broad alluvial flats, which range up to 2 miles wide. These flats usually lie less than 100 feet below the general level of the plain in which the sluggish meandering streams provide insufficient drainage for the land. As in central Illinois, the parent material from which the soils developed is mainly derived from the mantle of loess that covers the glacial till. Soil development took place under forest cover. Consequently, the high humus content and the dark color of the prairie soils farther north is missing. The prevailing soils are the heavier types, usually silt loams with a heavy clay substratum. Southern Illinois is slightly warmer than the central part of the State. Summers are warm and the frost-free period averages 180 to 190 days. Also, the annual average precipitation of 40 to 44 inches is somewhat higher than in central Illinois. The tract shown lies in the north-central part of Franklin County. Meander bends of the Big Muddy River appear in the wooded alluvial bottom. Rolling land borders the river bottom, and farther back the land is almost level. As may be observed, erosion is active on the rolling land. The upland is used for cropland and pasture. Forest is confined mainly to alluvial flats, which would require drainage improvements for agricultural use. A few woodlots are scattered over the farming areas. Livestock and its products, particularly hogs, cattle, poultry, eggs, and dairy products, are the main sources of farm income, although a good share of the field crops, chief of which are corn, wheat, soybeans, and hay, also reaches the market.

147

# Central Prairie of Illinois

DN-1459

PLATE 45.—The central prairies of Illinois were covered by ice sheets in the pre-Wisconsin and Wisconsin periods of glaciation. The surface characteristics of the morainic and drift plains are derived from glaciation, but they have been modified along the rivers and larger creeks where the land is more dissected and rolling. Nevertheless, the outstanding characteristic of the area is that of a plain. Glacial deposits of varying thicknesses were left by the ice, although most of the soils developed from loess, which covers all of central Illinois and constitutes the parent material of the prairie soils. Silt loams are the prevailing types on the better drained land, and clay loams are more often found in the shallow depressions. The soils, which developed under grass cover, have a high humus content and are very fertile. Although these prairie soils are nearly black, they do not belong to the black-earth group, as the calcareous subsoil horizon is missing. Woodland is confined to the steeper slopes near the water channels where the soils are lighter in color.

The groves near the farmsteads were planted. Although the climate of the Central Illinois plains is humid, precipitation is not as high as it is farther east. Normally, it is from 32 to 38 inches annually; however, the largest proportion falls during the warm season. Summers are warm, and the frost-free period averages from 160 to 180 days. The tract shown lies at the northern end of McLean County. This is true Corn Belt country. Most of the land is used for crops, and field operations are mechanized. Straightening the courses of the meandering creeks has improved drainage and produced greater regularity in the shape of the bordering fields, thus facilitating field operations. This region produces cash grain. Corn is the leading crop, but oats and soybeans are also important. Livestock is a close second to cash grain in the farm economy, with hogs in the lead and cattle second. Poultry contributes its share to the farm income. Most of the farms contain at least 160 acres, land values are high, and many farms are operated by tenants.

# Dairy Region of Southeastern Wisconsin

DN-1460

PLATE 46.—In southeastern Wisconsin, glaciation has produced a diversity of surface forms. These forms have affected land use in its quantitative development and also in the distributional arrangement of settlement and the land use pattern. Strong terminal moraines with hills and rocky soils, smooth, slightly rolling drift plains with soils ranging from sandy or gravelly loam to clay loam, and wet lowlands with peat and muck soils are assembled irregularly. The many lakes are an attractive feature of the rural landscape. The climate is considered humid but the annual average precipitation is only 30 inches, of which around two-thirds falls during the warm season. The summers are fairly warm, and the frost-free period averages around 160 days. Although the land is divided into sections and townships, roads are freqently deflected from rectangular land-division lines by wet lands, lakes, and hills.

This in turn has affected the location of farms and fields. The tract of land shown lies north of Dousman in the western part of Waukesha County. The dry land is level to slightly rolling, but extensive wet lands are responsible for the irregularities in the settlement and land use patterns. Much of the wet land has been improved by drainage and clearing and is now used for hay and pasture. Although this area lies outside the Corn Belt, corn is the leading crop. It is followed by leguminous hay and oats. Most of the field crops are used on the farms. Only a small proportion is sold. The farm economy is centered on livestock, and dairying is the principal industry. This is one of the best-known dairy regions in the United States. Milk is the main source of farm income. Livestock sold and poultry and its products are next in importance. Vegetables are grown to some extent for the market.

# Drumlin Field in South-central Wisconsin

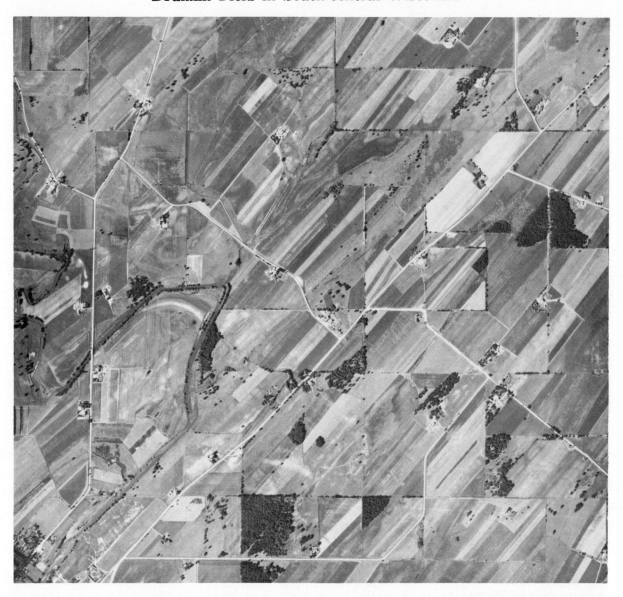

DN-1414

PLATE 47.—In south-central Wisconsin, particularly the eastern half of Dane County and in Dodge and Jefferson Counties, glaciation has produced a peculiar landform, called drumlins. Drumlins are elongated hillocks, usually composed of till, and infrequently of rock and gravel, which may be a mile or more long, a quarter of a mile wide, and perhaps 50 to 100 feet high. The major axes of the drumlins indicate the flow direction of the ice sheets that formed the drumlins. In this instance, when the Green Bay glacier reached the end of the Winnebago Basin on its southward journey, it started to spread out, as indicated by the direction of the drumlins. In the south-central part of Dodge County, the drumlins lie in almost true north to south direction. but toward the west they gradually veer and finally are alined in a southwest to northeast direction. How this radial swing in direction of drumlins has affected land use is illustrated. The section of the drumlin field shown lies on the western boundary of Dodge County, and the outskirts of Columbus may be seen in the lower left-hand corner of the photograph.

Originally, the drumlin field of Wisconsin was openly wooded with interspersed prairies. The intervening lowland was wet, and even swampy and marshy in places. The soils of the drumlins range from sandy loams to silt loams. Peat and muck are frequently found in the depressions. Climatically, the drumlin field does not differ much from the rest of southeastern Wisconsin. The frost-free period averages around 150 days and precipitation about 32 inches, most of which falls during the growing season. Land use, as developed on the drumlins, is controlled by two factors. Farm boundaries are controlled by the rectangular land divisions, oriented north to south and east to west, but for the most part, farmsteads and field operations follow the directions of the drumlins. Most of the land has been cleared, and much of the wet land has been drained, so that cropland and pasture are the dominant landscape features. Dairying is the principal type of farming. Corn, oats, and leguminous hay are grown largely for use on the farm. Green peas are a cash crop. Livestock and poultry are also important.

150

# Military Ridge of the Driftless Area, Southwestern Wisconsin

PLATE 48.—The Driftless Area comprises the rougher, more dissected part of southwestern Wisconsin with small extensions into northwestern Illinois and southeastern Minnesota. On the glacial map, the area stands out as an island in the glaciated region, although glaciologists point out that as the bordering ice sheets were of various ages, it was never an island surrounded by ice (*49*). Differences in elevation between the larger valleys and the higher ridges or upland plains are usually only about 500 feet; nevertheless, the valleys are steeply incised and thus much of the land is too rugged for cultivation. The southern section, which is separated from the northern section by the Wisconsin River, has its own drainage system, of which Military Ridge is the divide. The soils on the upland are largely derived from loess. The climate of the Driftless Area is humid, and although the mean annual precipitation is not heavy, two-thirds of it falls during the growing season. The area is higher than the land to the east and the west. The difference is also recorded in the temperature; the mean length of the frost-free period is reduced to 150 days. The Military Ridge, of which a tract near Edmund is used to illustrate the setting, is more of a plain. Originally, it was a prairie branching out on the spurs. The slopes were wooded, and the steeper slopes along the creeks are still kept in woods. To conserve the soil on the more rolling land, conservation practices are now followed extensively. Usually, the southern end of the Driftless Area is included in the Corn Belt. Corn is the leading crop, followed by oats and alfalfa. Considered from the land use viewpoint, more land is used for pasture than for crops. Thus, livestock is the dominant interest of the farmers. Hogs, cattle, and milk provide most of the farm income. Only a small proportion of the field crops is sold.

# Sandy Outwash Plain, Northern Wisconsin

DN-1418

PLATE 49.—Within the cutover region of the Lake States are a number of good-sized areas in which poor soils and rough topography form the chief impediments to agricultural use of the land. Wisconsin has its share of these areas. Plains of this type are located in the central, northern, and northwestern parts of the State. These sandy lands usually are rolling, and in the aggregate, the intervening wet depressions may occupy as much ground as the dry land. The dryland soils are prevailingly light in texture. They are either sands or sandy loams with a light-textured substratum, frequently rocky and stony, while the soils in the depressions are peat and muck. In the northern area, the climate is an added drawback to agricultural use of the land. Summers are comparatively cool and short and the frost-free period averages from 100 to 120 days. Precipitation is normally around 28 inches for the year, but because most of it falls during the warm season, it is sufficient. Settlement in these areas is sparse and scattered. In itself, this has its economic and social disadvantages. Improvement and maintenance of roads and transportation of children to school over long distances are often difficult and costly. Service costs frequently exceed the fiscal resources of counties or districts. To avoid an expansion of civic obligations, many counties have adopted rural zoning ordinances that make settlement or resettlement of abandoned farms unlawful. The most northerly of these plains extends as a belt from Minnesota along the St. Croix River to the Bayfield Peninsula. The area shown lies in the southwestern corner of Douglas County. It illustrates the prevailing situation in the plain. Not much land is cleared and cultivated. Farming is mainly of the self-sufficing type and many farmers also do nonfarm work.

# Red Lake Swamp, Northern Minnesota

DN-1462

PLATE 50.—Swamps dominate the landscape in much of northern Minnesota. In the aggregate, they total more than 5,000 square miles. To a large extent, they are concentrated on the old glacial lakebeds, of which Lake Agassiz is the largest. Swamps occupy the eastern extension of this lakebed, where the expansive flats form the drainage divide between the waters tributary to the Rainy River on the east and the Red River on the west. The southern boundary of this more or less coherent swamp district is formed by the high beachline of Lake Agassiz, which passes just south of Red Lake in an east-west direction. In this area, well-drained land with mineral soil comprises only a small percentage of the total. Most of it is in narrow strips along the natural drainage channels. Some islands above the general level of the swamps must be included. The soil of the swamps is peat. In its natural state, most of the swampland was wooded. Floating bogs or muskegs covered with sedges, rushes, and dwarf trees were found in the swamps. The watertable of these swamps has been lowered considerably through drainage operations. Drainage canals enter them in many places, and as the surface slopes are frequently only 2 to 3 feet per mile, the ditches often follow section lines. Large areas of this drained peat have been ignited by forest fires and have burned out. The precipitation, which is low for a humid climate, averages around 22 inches annually, although three-fourths of it falls during the warm season. Summer temperatures are cool and the frost-free season is around 110 days. A settlement near the northern shore of Upper Red Lake is shown. Ditch-bank grades that have been converted into roads make such interior locations accessible. Not much land is cleared and used for crops. Farming in areas of this kind is a pioneering enterprise.

153

# Glacial Lake Plain, Northwestern Minnesota

DN-1463

PLATE 51.—The waters of the Valley of the Red River of the North did not always flow toward the Arctic into Hudson Bay. During the glacial period, glaciers blocked the northern end, damming up the waters that collected in the valley into an immense lake that discharged its overflow to the south into the Minnesota and Mississippi Rivers and through them into the Gulf of Mexico. Lake Agassiz, as this former lake is now called, was rather shallow and the lakebed is now a distinct feature of the landscape. Beachlines indicate the different stages of the lake and separate the lower from the upper levels. The bottom land along the Red River is nearly level. Before the settlers arrived, it was predominantly open prairie. Natural tree growth, mainly oaks, is confined to the banks of the sluggish streams that meander through the lowlands. The soils, which are dark and very productive, contain much humus. In the lower portions, they are usually clay that becomes lighter in texture toward the beach where the soils may be sandy loams. Northwestern Minnesota is drier than any other part of the State. Annual precipitation in the Red River Valley ranges from 20 to 22 inches, although from 16 to 18 inches fall during the summer. The mean length of the frost-free season ranges from 110 to 120 days. The tract shown lies on Buffalo River, near Georgetown in Clay County. Drainage over much of this lowland has been improved through ditching. Agriculture is mainly of the cash-grain type. Farms are large, and fields of 160 acres are not uncommon. Oats, barley, and wheat are the chief crops, and production is mechanized. Flax is grown mainly as a seed crop, and the fibers furnish the raw material from which cigarette paper is manufactured. On the lighter soils, farming is more diversified. As protection against the wind, the farms that border the river have their farmsteads in the shelter of the tree belt, while on the open plain, farmsteads are in planted tree shelters.

# Prairie-forest Transition Belt, South-central Minnesota

DN—1464

PLATE 52.—In south-central Minnesota lies a zone that marks transition in more than one respect. One of the transitions is from prairie to forest; the other is from the smoother plain to a more diversified surface configuration associated with terminal moraines, outwash plains, lacustrine beds, and till plains. All of these landforms have resulted from glaciation, which has also affected the soils to a considerable extent. This area lies near the fringe of the Corn Belt, which means that the summers are comparatively warm. The frost-free season averages around 140 days. The annual mean precipitation ranges from 24 to 26 inches, and the larger part falls during the warm season. Some of the surface characteristics mentioned above may be detected in the cultural landscape as recorded by aerial photography. The tract shown lies in Meeker County, 2 miles east of Forest City. It includes a number of these surface features. The smooth stretch of land south of the Crow River, most of which is cultivated, is part of a glacial lakebed that was originally prairie. The soils are heavy. The belt north of the river is part of the lakebed but has lighter textured soil and was forested. Immediately to the north of this lakebed is a rolling till plain with some woodlots and wet spots, which becomes more rolling and choppy toward the northeast until it approaches the characteristics of a strong terminal moraine. The agriculture of the area is diversified. Corn is the chief crop, but oats, barley, alfalfa, and flaxseed are also important. Some of the crops are sold but the major proportion is used on the farms. The farm income is derived largely from animal husbandry, with dairying, hogs, poultry products, and cattle important.

# Dissected Plain, Southeastern Minnesota

DN-1465

PLATE 53.—Southeastern Minnesota and the adjoining counties of Iowa have a rather hilly topography. The district is located within the glaciated regions, but this part was not overrun by the ice sheets of the Wisconsin period. On the whole, the area consists of a rolling upland, deeply incised by the creeks and rivers that drain it. Differences in elevation between the valley floors and the upland exceed 500 feet only along the Mississippi bluffs: Upstream on the tributaries, the differences are smaller. Although the land is divided into sections and townships, the land use pattern is mainly controlled by the relief features. Loess covers much of the more hilly section, where it provided the parent material from which the soils developed, while the old and leached glacial till provided the parent material for the loess-free areas. The upland soils are predominantly silt loams, rich in humus and dark in color. The prairies that originally extended over the rolling upland account for the dark soils. The lighter colored soils are confined to the wooded areas on the valley slopes. The valleys are warmer than the upland plains. The frost-free period in the Mississippi bottoms is around 160 days; on the rolling plains farther back it averages 140 days. The annual average precipitation is approximately 30 inches. The tract shown lies in the southeastern part of Winona County near the boundary. Most of the land is in farms, but only the valley bottoms and the rolling uplands are used for crops and pasture. The steeper portions of the valley slopes are left in woods, which occupy about a third of the area. Farming is concerned primarily with livestock. Cattle, hogs, dairying, and poultry and its products provide most of the farm income. Crops, of which corn, oats, and hay lead, are grown mainly for use on the farm.

# Prairie Land, North-central Iowa and Southern Minnesota

DN-1466

PLATE 54.—The plains of north-central Iowa and southern Minnesota were overrun by the ice sheets of the Wisconsin glaciation. They emerged from the glacial period with a slightly rolling surface, which has been modified greatly since. Much of the land consists of shallow depressions, in which natural drainage is poor. Consequently, its use for cultivated crops was formerly at the risk of crop failure. Most of the land is now included in drainage districts. With the straightening and deepening of drainage channels, as shown, and the tiling of wet places, most of the land can now be used for crops. Before settlement, the land of this region was open prairie. The soils developed from calcareous till under grass cover. As a result, they have a high humus content, which makes them dark gray or almost black, but as they do not have the accumulated lime horizon in the substratum, they do not belong to the chernozem group. Except for the soils on the outwash plains, the prevailing types range from loams to silt clay loams. The climate is of the midcontinental type with warm summers and not really severe winters. The growing season averages around 150 days. The annual average precipitation is 30 inches, of which more than 20 inches falls during the warm season. The land is highly productive and is used largely for crops. The tract shown lies about 5 miles south of Britt in Hancock County. The principal crop is corn, followed by oats, soybeans, and tame hay. Only minor portions of the crops reach the market. Livestock is the main item in the farm economy. Hogs lead, but cattle, poultry and its products, and dairy products are also important. The tree groves or shelterbelts planted on the northern and western sides of the farmsteads as protection against the northwesterly winds are characteristic of these otherwise treeless plains.

# Loess Plain, Western Iowa

DN-1467

PLATE 55.—In western Iowa, the physical background, especially in regard to lay of the land and character of soils, has meant adjustments in land use, which in spatial order and composition differ from those in other parts of the State. Although the area is within the glaciated region, the glacial drift deposits belong to the older period. They were later covered by a mantle of loess, from which the soils developed. The upland is tilted toward the Missouri River. As a result of the erosion and stream action of the greatly ramified tributaries of the Missouri, it represents a rolling to strongly rolling plain with rough spots in places. The rounded ridgetops were originally prairies while woodland occupied the lower slopes and creek bottoms. As this part of the Missouri slope lies near the western fringe of the humid zone, precipitation is moderate. The annual average ranges from 26 to 30 inches, but two-thirds of this falls during the growing season of approximately 160 days. Dark silt loams, which are fertile but easily eroded, are the predominant upland soils. That erosion is taking its toll, especially at the upper draws of the creeks, may be recognized in the tract shown, which lies on the Missouri slope 4 miles southeast of Logan near Hard Scratch in Harrison County. Much of the land is used for crops, and fields and operations are adjusted to the rectangular division lines. Following these lines on strongly rolling land entails difficulties. To ease the grades, roads are deflected, and on the steeper slopes near the creeks, fields are more irregular. More land is left in pasture, upon which woodland frequently encroaches. Agriculture is diversified. Corn is the leading crop, followed by oats, wheat, and alfalfa. A good share of the crops reaches the market but the main income of the farmers is derived from livestock, chiefly hogs, cattle, and dairy products.

# Loess Hills, Southern Iowa

DN-1468

PLATE 56.—The physical environment of southern Iowa differs in more than one respect from that of the northern part of the State, and the use made of the land reflects these differences. The glacial till deposits in southern Iowa and northern Missouri belong to the pre-Wisconsin period; thus they are much older than the deposits in northern Iowa. The glacial till itself is covered by a mantle of loess, the parent material from which most of the soils developed. Streams have dissected the former plain, leaving remnants in the form of flats along the divides. A strongly rolling to hilly topography characterizes much of the area. Most of the soils are silt loams in texture, but they are not uniform in other respects. On the divide flats, where the soils developed under grass cover, they are almost black and have a heavy plastic subsoil. Artificial drainage of flat fields is necessary to obtain the best yields from crops. The soils on the slopes, which de- veloped under tree cover, are gray or brown. Fre- quently, they have excessive surface drainage and erode easily. The annual average precipitation of 34 to 36 inches is slightly higher than that in the rest of the State. The growing season of 160 to 170 days is somewhat longer. The land use pattern has its own distinctions. As may be noted in the tract shown, which lies in the southeast corner of Monroe County, some of the steeper slopes have never been cleared. Pastures and cropland are dominant uses of the land, but a good share is in woods; in fact, trees and brush encroach on the pastures. Corn, leguminous hay, soy- beans, and oats are the more important crops, but only a small part reaches the market. The farm in- come is derived mainly from animal husbandry, in which cattle leads. Hogs and some sheep are raised also.

# Ozark Border, East-central Missouri

DN-1469

PLATE 57.—In the main, the Ozark Highland of Missouri and Arkansas is a well-dissected plateau with a strongly rolling surface. Occasional hills and ridges, meandering streams with sharply incised valleys, and some remnants of the former plain, break the distributional regularities of the terrain forms. In Missouri, the underlying stratified geologic formations are mainly limestone with igneous rocks protruding in the center. Originally, the Ozark Plateau was largely covered by a heavy deciduous forest. Silt loams, the prevailing soil types that developed from the disintegrated rock material, are gray or grayish-brown and are rocky in many places. Elevations on the Missouri Ozark Dome surface vary from approximately 900 to 1,800 feet. This part of the plateau is higher than the country to the east and the west. As a rule, summers are not oppressively hot nor are winters severely cold. The frost-free season averages from 170 to 190 days, and the annual precipitation increases from an average of 40 inches in the north to 50 inches in the south. The tract shown lies about 3 miles southeast of Washington on the Missouri River in Franklin County. Although the tract is on the Ozark Border on less rigorous terrain, the difficulties of cultivating the land are apparent. Erosion is active on the sloping land, and soil-conservation practices are needed in much of the Ozarks. Land ownership is controlled by the rectangular system of land division, but roads, fields, and cultural practices are frequently adjusted to the lay of the land. The acreage of cropland decreased considerably during the last half century, while the acreage of pasture increased. Corn is the main crop, followed by wheat, lespedeza, and clover, all of which are grown primarily for use on the farm. Livestock and livestock products are the chief sources of farm income.

# Ozark Center, Missouri

DN-1417

PLATE 58.—Near the eastern end of the Ozarks, where the intrusive granites form knobs and mountains, the surface is rugged. This area is also the highest part of the Ozarks on the Missouri side. No climatic records are available from the higher levels, but even those from the valley stations indicate that the climate is cooler than in the surrounding country. The average length of the frost-free period is 170 days. Precipitation, which averages from 42 to 46 inches, differs from that of adjacent areas. Most mountain slopes are rough and stony, and forestry is the best use that can be made of the land. A number of purchase units of the national forest are located in the area. The State parks in these mountains are an indication of their recreational value. Settlement and agricultural use of the land are confined to the scattered basins and the alluvial floors of the valleys. How settlement in these narrow valleys has penetrated the wilderness is illustrated in the tract shown, which lies at the fork of Carver Creek, about 3 miles northwest of Sabula in Iron County. Farming in these mountains is largely self-sufficing and livestock is the main source of the meager farm income. Many farmers work part time off the farm.

# Bottom Land and Bordering Upland of the Missouri River, Missouri

DN–1470

PLATE 59.—Missouri is divided by the Missouri River into two dissimilar parts. The northern division lies almost entirely within the glaciated region of the pre-Wisconsin period. It is a dissected rolling plain, hilly at the fringes, which frequently rises from the river bottoms 100 feet or more within a short distance. Originally, the smoother, slightly rolling drainage divides were prairies, and the more rolling valley slopes were wooded. Certain soil distinctions have resulted. The upland soils are mainly silt loams developed from loess and to some extent from underlying drift deposits. The distinctions derived from the vegetative cover are expressed mainly in humus content and color. Because of their high humus content, the grass soils are dark. Conversely, the woodland soils are light. There are no pronounced climatic distinctions between lowland and upland. The frost-free period averages 180 to 190 days, and precipitation normally ranges from 36 to 40 inches annually. Erosion is rather active on the sloping land. Because of the difficulties of cultivating the sloping land, the acreage of cropland has decreased during the last few decades and the acreage in pasture has increased. Some of the pasture has been invaded by brush and trees, as may be noted in the tract shown, which lies west of Camden in Ray County. The bottom fields of the tract are about 20 feet above the normal water level of the river. To prevent flooding, the upland creeks have been channeled from the points at which they enter the bottoms. Much of the upland is in pasture. All well-drained bottom land is in crops. Corn is the main crop in both areas but wheat is important in the bottom lands, while oats are included as a rotation crop on the uplands. The type of farming is adjusted to these conditions. Farming on bottom land is based on cash crops, and that on upland on livestock, particularly hogs and cattle.

# Rolling Prairie, Eastern Kansas

DN—1471

PLATE 60.—The smoothly rolling country that extends from eastern Kansas to the Missouri Ozarks usually is included in the eastern humid portion of the Central Plains. However, these plains lie near the western fringe of the humid zone, and precipitation may depart considerably from the annual averages of 36 to 40 inches. Normally, the growing season is close to 190 days. Limestone and close-grained sandstone are the prevailing rock formations that provided the disintegrated mineral base from which the soils in the southern part of the area developed. Loess furnished the parent material of the soils at the northern end. In its natural state, the area was prairie. Along the watercourses were belts of woodland, which are still in evidence. The soils are chiefly silt loams with a high organic matter content, dark and very produc-

tive. Much of the land is used for crops, as may be noted in the tract shown, which lies near Edgerton in Johnson County. Arrangement of farms and fields follows the rectangular land divisions. As a rule, square sections bounded by roads are divided into quarter-section farms of 160 acres. The area still is considered to be part of the Corn Belt and corn is the chief crop. Farming, however, is more diversified than in the Corn Belt proper, probably because of the proximity of Kansas City. Other important field crops are wheat and alfalfa. Vegetables and horticultural specialties also contribute to the farm income. Although good proportions of the crops are sold, the chief source of farm income is livestock, mainly animals sold, but sales of dairy and poultry products are important also.

# Flint Hills, Kansas

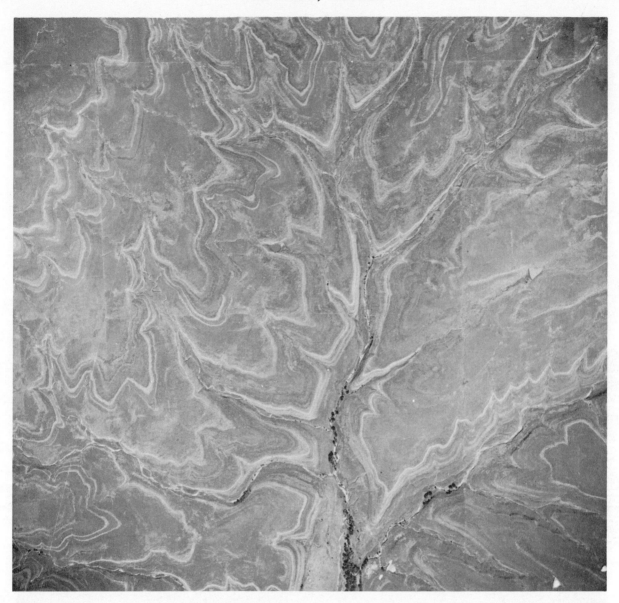

DN-1472

PLATE 61.—The Flint Hills in eastern Kansas appear from the distance as a swell in the plains longitudinally interposed between the Arkansas and Kansas Rivers. As a landform, the Flint Hills are not an imposing feature of the landscape. In most instances, the difference in elevation between the hills and the plains to the east and west is not more than 300 to 400 feet. The case is different when land use is considered. In contrast to the plains, where most of the land is used for cultivated crops, the Flint Hills proper are used only for pasture. The reason for this restriction is found in neither climate nor land relief, but in the soil. Interbedded shale and limestone are the underlying rock formations from which erosion has carved the hills. Of the two, the cherty limestone is more resistant to weathering than shale, and, as a result, the soils developed from the accumulated material are rocky and shallow, and thus unsuited to cultivation. However, they support a luxuriant growth of nutritious grasses. The Flint Hills are on the western border of the humid region. As they extend for approximately 200 miles in a north to south direction, the length of the frost-free season normally ranges from 180 to 200 days. Annual precipitation averages from 32 to 38 inches, most of which falls during the growing season. Draws in the upper reaches of the hills, about 6 miles north of Grenola in Elk County, are shown. The land is sectionalized like the plains country but the dividing lines are only faintly discernible. To conserve water, dams have been built across creeks to form ponds and provide water for cattle. Cattle raising and fattening are the best use that can be made of this land. Of particular interest are the contours produced by outcropping limestone ledges. Although these outcrop lines may not conform strictly to the contour definition of passing through points of equal elevation, they do reveal the surface morphology of the hills. Nature has here provided an example on which the form characteristics of contours are clearly exposed and can be studied.

# Great Bend Plain, Central Kansas

DN-1473

PLATE 62.—Land use capability on the plains of central Kansas is determined largely by climate and to a lesser extent by land relief and soil. Some tracts are excluded from arable use because of broken surfaces or stony or sandy soils, but these are not the predominant land types. The prevailing land relief is rolling to strongly rolling in places. Soils developed from the disintegrated bedrock material, which may be derived from shale, limestone, or sandstone. In the northern part of the area, the parent material was loess, but all upland soils developed under grass cover. As a result, the latter contain much organic matter, which makes them dark. In texture the soils are mainly silt loams. Central Kansas lies in the subhumid belt. The frost-free season normally ranges from 170 to 200 days, and the average annual precipitation is 25 to 30 inches. Because of the hot summers and the high transpiration ratio, this is not sufficient for diversified farming. Hard winter wheat is the principal crop. It is grown on a large acreage with mechanized operations on large fields. Wheat is grown on the same land year after year. An upland tract west of Great Bend in Barton County is shown. As may be noted, the fields frequently contain 160 acres or more. Many farmers have planted shelterbelts to protect the farmsteads from wind; some shelterbelts also are planted along roads or across fields. Winter wheat is the chief cash crop in this region; livestock, mainly cattle, is a secondary source of farm income.

# High Plains, Western Kansas

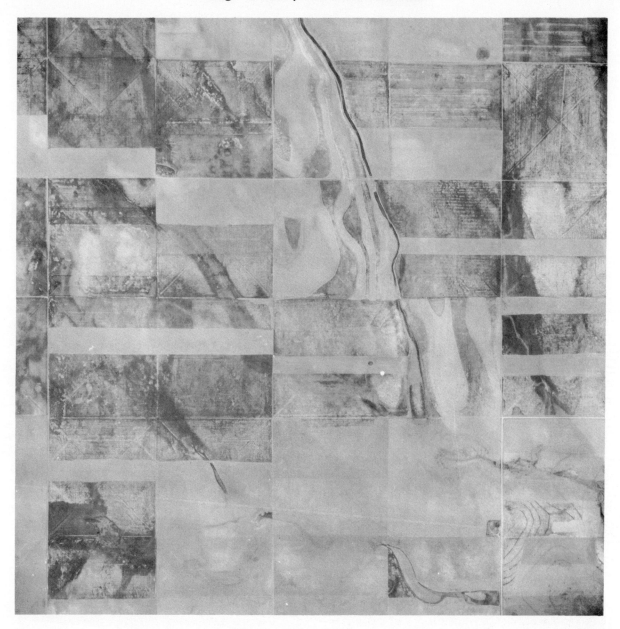

DN–1474

PLATE 63.—On the High Plains of western Kansas, physical conditions impose severe handicaps to agricultural use of the land. Climate alone injects a considerable element of risk into crop production. The area lies in the semiarid region. It has a growing season of 160 to 180 days, and the average annual precipitation ranges from 15 to 20 inches. Most of the precipitation falls during the warm season, but when considered in relation to the dry winds and the high daytime temperatures, it is not a true measure of available moisture. Moreover, like most averages, it is not a reliable indicator of what may be expected. Recurring variations in which a number of humid years are followed by some dry years, which result in crop failures, are not uncommon. Erosion from water and wind is a constant hazard to conservation of the soil. As a rule, moisture supplied by precipitation is insufficient to grow a crop on the same land every year. Dry-farming methods, in which land lies fallow for a year to conserve soil moisture and stripcropping is done to prevent wind erosion, are commonly followed. Wind erosion can be severe during protracted dry spells on unprotected land, as may be observed in the picture on the fallow land. The tract shown lies in Greeley County, Kans., near the State boundary. For a long time, grazing was the prevailing land use of the region. Since the advent of mechanized farm operations, and a favorable price level for wheat, much of the sod has been broken for crop production. Production of grain is now more remunerative than stock farming, although the annual average yield of wheat for 1926-48 was only 8.2 bushels for Greeley County. In this region, farmsteads are few and far apart. Grain farming of this type is done largely by "suitcase" farmers who live in town. Some sites of former farmsteads may be seen in the photograph.

# Loess Plain, Eastern Nebraska

DN-1475

PLATE 64.—Eastern Nebraska is part of the area known as the Corn Belt. Physiographically, it is an imperfectly dissected plain, gently rolling with some depressions on the broad divides, and severely rolling, with some rough and broken tracts on the slopes along the drainage channels. It lies in a transition zone. Rainfall decreases from the humid belt along the Missouri River westward so that most of the area is in the subhumid zone. The annual precipitation averages from 25 to 30 inches with two-thirds of it falling during the warm season. Usually the growing season lasts from around 160 to 170 days. Before the arrival of the settlers, the country was grassland. Narrow belts of hardwood were to be found along the drainage channels, and remnants of these belts still exist. As a result of the unequal distribution of pre-cipitation over the seasons, these upper drainage channels do not carry water throughout the year. Most of the upland soils are silt loams developed from the loess that covers the area. They are dark colored and have the calcareous subhorizon characteristic of the chernozems. Erosion is active over much of eastern Nebraska. The tract shown is on rolling land in Thayer County between Chester and Hebron. The track of an abandoned railroad that formerly connected these two places is recorded in the photograph. Roads usually follow the land-division lines; each mile-square section is bounded by a road. Farming is diversified. Corn is the main crop, followed by wheat, oats, and hay. Cash crops and livestock are of approximately equal importance in the farm economy of the region.

# High Plains, Western Nebraska

DN-1415

PLATE 65.—Western Nebraska reaches into the semi-arid high plains, where climate restricts land use possibilities on the best land to either cropland or grazing. When it is not broken by sharply incised water channels or valleys, the surface is a slightly rolling plain or tableland. The annual average precipitation ranges from 15 to 20 inches. This average, however, is derived from records in which the upper and lower extremes are far apart. Consequently, it **contains** an element of uncertainty. Precipitation may vary greatly from year to year. The frost-free period usually lasts from 140 to 150 days. Summers are hot, and the evaporation–transpiration ratio is correspondingly high. Winters are cold, and strong winds frequently sweep the plains. Soils vary in texture from fine sandy loams to silt loams, and the subsoil horizon is calcareous. As these soils developed under short grass cover, they do not have the high organic-matter content of the chernozems or the prairie soils farther east. Brush and scattered tree growth are confined to the breaks where ground moisture conditions are somewhat more favorable. Much of the land is used to grow grains, chiefly hard winter wheat, with dry farming methods. The tract shown lies in the western part of Banner County and touches the rim of Scotts Bluff Basin to the north. Dry-farming methods are combined with stripcropping to prevent wind erosion. As may be observed, strips of land 350 to 660 feet wide, perpendicular to the prevailing wind direction, are alternately cultivated or left fallow. They give the area its characteristic land use pattern. The average annual yield of wheat per acre in Banner County for 1926-48 was 14.8 bushels.

# Sand Hills, Nebraska

DN-1416

PLATE 66.—The Sand Hills of Nebraska are a unique terrain feature both morphologically and in extent. The Sand Hills occupy an area of 19,000 square miles, of which 18,000 square miles are in Nebraska. The remaining 1,000 square miles are in South Dakota. Roughly a fourth of Nebraska is taken up by the Sand Hills. No semblance of order is apparent in the arrangement of the hills over much of the area, although in some parts, particularly in the center and along the eastern border, a nearly east-west orientation of ridges and valleys is noticeable. The Sand Hills are frequently referred to as sand dunes, but this is not always fitting. Although they are the product of wind action on the disintegrated material of the local Tertiary formation, some of the larger ones still contain cores of the old formation. Wind has moved, sifted, and redeposited the loose material in the form of hills and ridges up to 100 feet high in the western sector decreasing to swells on the eastern spurs. The soils of the hills are loose sand, but those in the depressions are chiefly loamy sand and, infrequently, sandy loam. The vegetative cover consists of tall native grasses, which protect the sand from blowing and provide a means of using the land. Normally, precipitation ranges from 18 to 22 inches a year; the frost-free season runs around 140 to 150 days. Little or no surface runoff occurs in the Sand Hills. Precipitation readily infiltrates the sand and is transmitted to the ground water. In many of the depressions, lakes are formed on the ground-water level. Almost the only use that can be made of the land is pasture; very little is used for cultivated crops. Wild hay is cut in the depressions; it is the main crop of the region and is used as feed for cattle during the winter. Cattle ranches are large and thinly scattered. The tract shown, which includes a ranch and some small lakes, lies in the heart of the Sand Hills, in Sheridan County.

# Glacial Till Plain, Southeastern South Dakota

DN-1476

PLATE 67.—The part of South Dakota that lies east of the Missouri River is within the region that was invaded by the glaciers of the Wisconsin period. The landforms left by the glaciers have not been greatly modified. The surface consists of a slightly rolling plain, which terminates at the Missouri River bluffs in the west and south. The James River and its tributary creeks that drain the area have cut only shallow channels. Many small depressions and lakes are scattered over the plain, but the morainic belts in the southern half have no strongly expressed relief features. The climate of eastern South Dakota is not uniform throughout, and this necessitated adjustments in type of farming. The southern part, where the frost-free season lasts normally up to 150 days and precipitation averages 24 and more inches annually, three-fourths of which falls during the growing season, is part of the Corn Belt. Farther north and west, where the normal annual precipitation falls to 18 inches and the growing season gets shorter and the temperatures cooler, farming is of the Wheat Belt type. Most of the soils developed from glacial till under grass cover and subhumid conditions. Consequently, they belong to the chernozem group and are mainly of the medium-textured types. Much of the land is used for crops. The tract shown is in Davison County, south of the road that connects Mitchell with Mt. Vernon. Farms and fields are large, and operations are mechanized. Planted shelterbelts for wind protection may be recognized near some of the farmsteads and in places along the roads. Farming is diversified, and although this is the northwestern fringe of the Corn Belt, corn is still the main crop. Other important crops are barley, oats, wheat, and tame and wild hay. Some of the crops are sold but most are used on the farms; livestock is the principal cash product.

170

# Great Plain, Western South Dakota

DN–1477

PLATE 68.—Aside from the Black Hills uplift, western South Dakota represents an extensive plain adjoining the glaciated region. It has been exposed to geologic erosion for a long time, and as a result, it is badly dissected by drainage channels. The valley floors of the major streams and their tributaries, at the most, are not more than a few hundred feet below the general level of the plain, but they are flanked by a belt of rough land, which frequently approaches Bad Land conditions. Most of South Dakota west of the Missouri River is semiarid. Annual precipitation ranges from 15 to 22 inches, of which about three-fourths falls during the warm season. Normally, the frost-free period lasts from 130 to 150 days. Soils have developed from the weathered material of the underlying sedimentary formations of shale, sandstone, and cherty limestone. They range in texture from sand to clay with the heavier types predominating. Short grasses are the prevailing vegetation cover; tree growth is confined to the banks of the streams and the Black Hills. Nonmigratory grazing is the most extensive use of the land, as only a relatively small part of the smooth upland is used for cultivated crops. Outside the irrigated areas, small grains, mainly wheat but some oats, barley, rye, and seed flax, are grown with dry-farming methods. The photograph illustrates the situation along the northern tributaries of the Belle Fourche River in the center of Meade County. The raising of livestock, mainly cattle, is the principal farm enterprise; production of crops is secondary.

# Strong Moraine, Northeastern South Dakota

DN-1478

PLATE 69.—Northeastern South Dakota has several physical features that are not shared by other sections of the State. Taken as a whole, it is still a wide, open plain, varied only by landforms associated with glaciation. Near the northern boundary of the State, the James River passes through the almost level bed of the extinct glacial Lake Dakota. Morainic belts flank the basin on both sides; they rise gently not more than a few hundred feet above the general level of the basin floor. The morainic belt to the east, however, has a stronger relief expression than the western belt. It consists of a chaotic assembly of knolls, ridges, lakes, and depressions, which reduce the crop-use capability of the land. Precipitation, which averages from 18 to 22 inches annually, is not quite as high as in the southern part of the State, nor are summer temperatures. The frost-free period, which normally lasts from 130 to 140 days is not quite so long. The well-drained soils of the area, whether they have glacial till or lacustrine deposits as parent material, developed under grass cover and fall into the chernozem group. The proportion of land that can be used for crops is greatly reduced in the belts of strong morainic topography, as illustrated. The tract shown lies in the Sisseton Indian Reservation, about 4 miles west of Veblen. Most of the land is in pasture. Fields are scattered, and they are neither as large nor as regular in shape as those on the smoother land. The wooded belts along the streams, which originated in the morainic belt, are an outstanding feature of the landscape. Farming is diversified. Some corn is grown, but small grains, particularly wheat and oats, are the leading crops. Livestock and cash grains are the main sources of farm income.

# Beach Ridges of Lake Agassiz, Red River Valley, North Dakota

DN-1479

PLATE 70.—The eastern tier of counties in North Dakota, or at least a large proportion of the land they contain, lies in the Red River Valley. During the glacial period, this valley was the lake that is now referred to as Lake Agassiz. When agricultural products of the different sections of the State are compared, the Red River Valley ranks among the highest and most reliable producers, which indicates that physical conditions are favorable to farming. The lay of the land over most of the basin is almost level. Exceptions are the beach ridges, which mark the different stages of the lake water level. Usually, these ridges are not more than 20 to 30 feet high and 1 to 3 miles apart. They divide the basin into a lower bed and terraces. The slopes of the beach ridges are gentle and do not prevent cultivation. Soil distinctions correspond largely to these divisions. On the lower valley floor, the soil is a heavy black clay loam. Between the beach ridges, the soil is a black loam, whereas the belt between the upper beach ridge and the shoreline of the lake has a black sandy loam. The beach ridges themselves are sandy loam with gravel. Precipitation averages only 20 to 22 inches annually, but as approximately two-thirds of this falls during the warm season, it is usually adequate for the crops grown in this latitude. The frost-free period is comparatively short, and usually lasts around 110 or 120 days. Winters are cold. Much of the land is used for crops; farms and fields are large and operations are mechanized. A beach-ridge sector 4 miles north of Arvilla in Grand Forks County is shown. Field operations along the ridges are deflected in the direction of the ridges. Windbreaks are commonly found near the homesteads and some appear along the borders of the fields. Farming is centered on cash crops. Wheat, oats, barley, flaxseed, and potatoes are the principal crops for market, but livestock contributes to the farm economy to some extent.

# Drift Plain with Kettleholes, Northeastern North Dakota

DN-1480

PLATE 71.—Except for the southwestern part, all of North Dakota lies within the glaciated region, but the signs of glaciation are more in evidence north and east of the Missouri River than south of it. The Missouri Plateau that borders the river to the north is fringed by a strong terminal moraine, and much of the land is too rough for cultivation. Terminal moraine belts also traverse the drift plains farther north, but the rough morainic landforms are not the only obstacles to arable use of the land. In places sparingly, but in others densely, drift plains are spattered with depressions and sloughs, which frequently contain water or are wet ground but which cannot be drained readily to permit cultivation. These depressions, or kettleholes, usually resulted from the melting of ice blocks that were imbedded in the drift, or they are excavations made by the rushing water from the ice sheets. Cli-

mate imposes its own restriction on the crops that can be grown. Precipitation averages only 14 to 16 inches annually, and the frost-free season is approximately 110 to 120 days. How cropping can be restricted by these depressions is illustrated in the tract shown, which lies 4 miles south of Munich in Cavalier County. By means of a grid estimate, it was found that in the 4 square miles in the center, 11 percent of the land area was taken up by the depressions, but that their irregular distribution interfered with field operations to the extent that an additional 18 percent of the dry land has not been cultivated. Productive brown sand and silt loams are the predominating upland soils. Agriculture is centered on cash crops, but livestock is also important. Wheat, barley, oats, flaxseed, and wild hay are the more important crops. Most of the wild hay is cut in the wet depressions.

# Bad Lands Along the Little Missouri River, North Dakota

DN-1481

PLATE 72.—Southwestern North Dakota has practically no landforms that can be attributed to the action of glaciers. The thin layers of till on some of the smooth plains and the occasional boulders south of and adjacent to the Missouri River indicate that at one time the continental ice sheet crossed the river for a short distance. However, the principal surface features are the result of weathering and erosion. The underlying stratified deposits of silt, sand, and clay, with interbedded lignite coal seams, have retained a gently rolling surface on the broad divides but are badly dissected along the drainageways. The soils developed from the weathered material of these formations are brown, medium to heavy textured. With sufficient moisture, they are quite productive. Precipitation, however, averages annually from 14 to 16 inches, and most of this falls during the warm season. The frost-free period, which normally lasts from 120 to 130 days, is favorable for all the small grains. Because of the physiographic setting, a large acreage of the smoother land is used with dry-farming methods to grow cash crops, mainly wheat, while the rougher land is grazed. Bad Lands, as the roughest portions are called, are rather extensive in this end of the State. According to a reconnaissance survey, they comprise more than 3,600 square miles. The most extensive areas are located along the Little Missouri, of which a tract in Slope County is shown. Intermittent tributary creeks have cut ravines into the geologic formations and have dissected the land minutely. The walls of the ravines are steep and largely barren, although some cottonwoods grow along the creeks. In places, hay is cut on the broader bottom of the river but ranches are widely spaced, as the Bad Lands themselves have only a low grazing value.

# Missouri-Yellowstone Plain, Eastern Montana

DN-1482

PLATE 73.—On the plains of eastern Montana, outside the glaciated region, a large expanse of country must be considered as lying on or near the border of tillable land use. Much of this land is badly dissected by sharply incised channels. The ravines are frequently so numerous and so closely spaced that they do not leave smooth tracts large enough to accommodate fields for mechanized operations. Even the less dissected part of the plain has a rolling, somewhat choppy, surface. It is not favorable to the long straight-lined field operations customary in this part of the country, where stripcropping is followed to prevent wind erosion. The principal drawback of the region, however, is the climate. The average annual precipitation is around 15 to 16 inches. This is low in itself, but it also has considerable plus and minus departures. Summers are mild and not very long; the frost-free period normally lasts from 3 to 4 months.

Winters are likely to be severe. An economic factor is involved in the cultural use of the land. High market prices for wheat, the chief crop grown with dry-farming methods, tend to encourage expansion of crop acreage, which has increased considerably in the last few decades. As an example, from 1939 to 1949, the acreage of cropland harvested increased in McCone County by more than 130,000 acres, or 130 percent, although the 1926-48 average yield of wheat per acre for the county was only 8.9 bushels. The upland tract shown lies about 6 miles southeast of Weldon in the center of McCone County. It illustrates the physiographic background and certain fields that are of recent origin. As may be noted, there is room for additional expansion. With the land used as it is now, livestock and cash crops are almost equally important in the economy of the area.

# Triangle Area, North-central Montana

DN-1483

PLATE 74.—North-central Montana has a diversity of landscape features. The horizon of the plain is pierced by isolated mountains or is interrupted by valleys and basins. The northern part is in the glaciated region and has landforms not found in the southern part. The climate is more spotty, particularly so far as precipitation is concerned. The annual average is less than 12 inches in some places and more than 18 inches in other places. Summers are moderately warm, with a frost-free season of approximately 120 days, but winters are cold. The Judith Basin receives the greater amount of precipitation so that crops can be grown there without resorting to dry-farming methods. Elsewhere dry-farming methods are followed for production of grain. In such a diversified region, it is therefore not possible to select a small tract and present it as a typical sample of the land use pattern of the whole region. The tract shown here is on glaciated land and lies in Chouteau County, 3 miles west of Big Sandy. The average annual precipitation in these environs is only 12 to 13 inches, so that dry-farming methods must be followed to grow small grains, mainly wheat, as a cash crop. The 1926-48 average yield of wheat for this county was 14.8 bushels per acre. Field patterns on the smooth tableland and the rolling valley land differ noticeably, however. Alternate stripcropping is prevalent on the smooth upland to prevent wind erosion. Some of the strips are a mile long but only 140 feet wide. Shorter and wider strips or compact fields are the order in the valley, which is the preglacial bed of the Missouri River. The Great Northern now follows this old bed from Virgelle on the Missouri to Havre and down the Milk River to its junction with the Missouri River. Although much of the land can be used only for grazing, cash grains dominate the farm economy.

# Continental Divide Along the Idaho-Montana Boundary

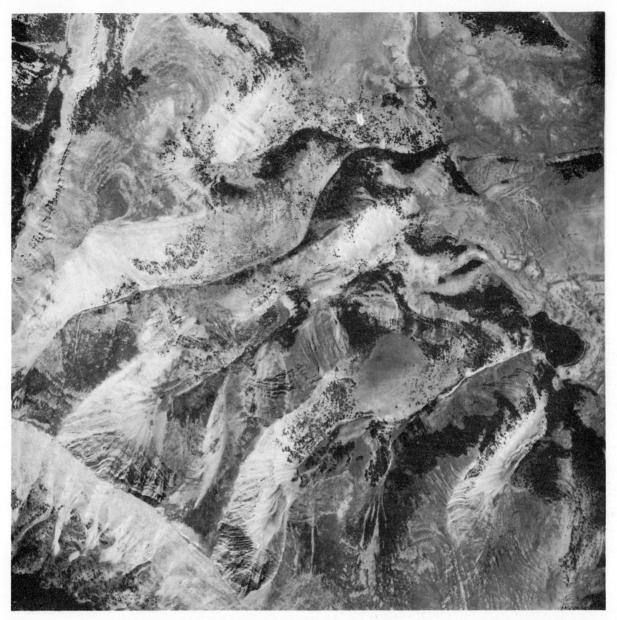

DN-1484

**PLATE 75.**—Western Montana is mountainous throughout. Ranges of the northern Rockies traverse the area from the southern boundary northward into Canada, but they are not everywhere so closely spaced as to occupy the entire area. Wide, open valleys and basins are interspersed. The mountains are not as high as in some other parts of the Rockies. The valleys themselves are high, especially at the headwaters of the Missouri, where they range in elevation from 4,000 to 6,000 feet. As a result the frost-free season averages only 40 days a year on some of the higher levels. Precipitation varies considerably with location and elevation. Annual averages range from 10 to 40 inches. Thus, the land use potentiality, especially the tillable use, is necessarily restricted. In the open valleys, the lower slopes are used for grazing during the cooler seasons. During the summer, livestock, mainly cattle and sheep, are grazed in the mountains, large proportions of which are in national forests. On some irrigated land on the lower levels and benches in the valleys, small grains, potatoes and sugar beets are grown. The main crop, however, is hay, both wild and tame, which is needed for winter feeding. Livestock is the principal source of farm income. The ruggedness of some of the country may be seen in the tract shown, which represents a section of the Continental Divide on the Montana–Idaho State boundary. The sharp crested range that runs through the southwest corner of the tract is the Continental Divide. Dolomite and limestone are the rock formations of this part of the Beaverhead Mountains, which rise here to more than 9,000 feet at the crest. Although it is considered forest, the tree growth is comparatively sparse and is confined largely to eastern and northern exposures. Nutritious grasses provide the summer range on the accessible mountain meadows and slopes.

178

# Big Horn Basin, Wyoming

DN-1485

PLATE 76.—The Big Horn Basin in Wyoming is almost entirely surrounded by mountains. Drainage is provided by the Big Horn River, which enters the basin through the Wind River Canyon in the south and leaves it through the Big Horn Canyon in the north. Because of this all-round sheltered position, precipitation is lower here than in any other part of Wyoming. In some of the lower elevations, the annual average precipitation is less than 5 inches, although for the basin as a whole, it ranges from 5 to 10 inches. For the same reason, summers are longer and warmer; the frost-free season normally lasts from 120 to 140 days, or about 20 days longer than elsewhere in the State. Because of the low precipitation, crops cannot be grown without irrigation. With grazing as the only possible use of most of the land, agriculture is centered on animal husbandry, particularly cattle and sheep, even though large irrigation projects are located in the basin. The center of the basin is largely hills and ridges, but there are also basins and benches on which the water has been diverted for irrigation. Small grains and hay in addition to potatoes and sugar beets are the main crops grown on the irrigated land. In the outer belt of the basin, cropping is confined to the bottoms of the larger creeks. The outer belt consists of a series of ridges and mesas produced by the inwardly tilted stratified formations with clifflike slopes that face the mountains. The section shown lies about 4 miles northwest of Thermopolis, where Owl Creek passes through the belt. Hayfields and a number of ranches are located in the creek bottom. Sagebrush plus some grass is the dominant vegetation on the sharp crested ridges, some of which have tree growth on the upper levels and northeastern exposures.

179

# High Plains, Wyoming

DN-1486

PLATE 77.—On the High Plains, production of grain with dry-farming methods extends from Nebraska into the three Piedmont counties in southeastern Wyoming. Farther north on a few of the higher and smoother spots of the plains, grain farming is attempted. In the interior basins of Wyoming, crop production is confined entirely to irrigated land. The crop is usually harvested hay, which is needed as winter fodder. This is arid range country. The annual precipitation usually does not exceed 10 to 15 inches. To utilize the scanty water supply most effectively, water management has become a ranch practice. Except for those that have their sources in the mountains, creeks carry water only intermittently. To retain some of the water for livestock the creeks are dammed up in many places.

Also, flush water is frequently diverted from creeks by means of ditches. The tract of land shown lies in Converse County near the junction of LaBonte Creek with the North Platte River. The creek has a half-mile-wide bottom and trees grow along its banks. A ranch with hayland and fields is located on the bottom. LaBonte Creek, which has its source in the Laramie Range, is perennial. Sand Creek, 2 miles to the east, has its source in the plain. Most of the year, it is only a dry sandy draw. Prairie grasses and sagebrush predominate in the native vegetation. Cattle trails traverse the plain but the braided field road in the southwest corner is part of the Old Oregon Trail. The almost straight lines across the country are pipelines that may carry either gas or oil.

# Mountain Crossing, Southwestern Wyoming

DN-1487

PLATE 78.—The mountains of the West imposed formidable obstacles to the westward movement of the pioneers. Not until the low points in the mountain chains had been found could settlers from the East occupy the western basins. Wyoming contains a number of basins connected by comparatively low crossings through which the wagon caravans of the settlers moved. One of these, the mountain saddle that separates the Green River Basin from the Great Basin of the West, was a concentration point for the roads along which the early pioneers moved westward. Brigham Young and the Mormon pioneers went through here in 1847 on their way to Utah. Many of the Forty-niners passed this way to Oregon and California, and later the Pony Express used this low ridge as a crossing place. Its central location makes this mountain saddle one of the principal gateways between the East and the West. The first of the East–West rail connections—the Union Pacific—to run through it, was opened in 1869. The approach to the saddle in the mountains, which to the north are known as the Bear River Divide, and to the south are spurs of the Uinta Mountains, is provided by two valleys, one from the east and the other from the west. These valleys are used by the railroad, and at their head they are connected by a short tunnel. The western approach to the tunnel is shown. The highest rail point, 7,217 feet, is at Altamont, the tunnel's western portal. Land use in this rugged country is confined almost entirely to seasonal grazing. Winters are cold and precipitation is low, although it varies considerably with elevation. A few miles to the northwest, in Evanston, the annual average is around 14 inches. In the basins east and west of Evanston, it is much less. The native vegetation of the lower levels consists mainly of sagebrush and some grasses. Grasses are more common on the higher levels. Aspen appear on the ridges and fringe the coniferous forests of the mountains.

# Northern Colorado Irrigation District

DN-1488

PLATE 79.—The Colorado Piedmonts are in the rain shadow of the Rockies, where western winds prevail during the colder season. During the warm season, only the dehumidified air currents from the Gulf reach them. Deficiency of moisture was the main drawback to more intensive use of the alluvial basins at the foot of the mountains. To improve the situation, irrigation systems have been built, mainly in the basins and on the terraces of the larger rivers. One of the largest areas developed through irrigation is the Northern Colorado Irrigation District, of which the more compact portion is confined to the basin north of Denver. Irrigation was developed with the runoff from the eastern slopes of the Rockies, where heavy snowfall during the winter stores and releases water for use in the valleys during the summer. With the increasing water needs of Denver and the chronic shortage of irrigation water on the lower levels, an additional supply of water was needed. It was obtained through transmountain diversion from the other side of the Continental Divide. The Moffat Tunnel brings additional water from the western slope of the Rockies to Denver, and the Big Thompson Tunnel farther north brings more irrigation water to the district. With the normal annual precipitation ranging from 12 to 16 inches and the frost-free season from 140 to 160 days, dry farming is feasible. Actually, dry and irrigated farming are sometimes carried on adjoining tracts, as shown. This tract is east of Niwot and north of Gun Barrel Hill in Boulder County. It is in the Northern Irrigation District, where low hills form islands in the basin. Here, dry farming on the smooth hill slopes ends at the upper irrigation ditch. As Denver provides a market, farming is diversified. Small grains as a cash crop are the main products of dry farming. On the irrigated land, livestock, dairy products, and poultry and its products are the main items in the farm economy. Among the important crops are barley, corn, wheat, and alfalfa and other hay, but dry field beans, Irish potatoes, sugar beets, vegetables for sale, and nursery products also add considerably to the farm income.

# South Platte-Arkansas Divide, High Plains of Colorado

DN-1489

PLATE 80.—On the High Plains of Colorado, land is not used for cultivated crops to the same extent as is done farther east. Along the eastern boundary of the State, cash-grain farming, mainly wheat produced with dry-farming methods, is about as dominant as it is in western Kansas. Westward, however, fields become more scattered, and in many places they are absent altogether. The land is used predominantly for grazing, primarily as a result of the terrain. Rivers and creeks, most of which have flowing water only intermittently, have dissected the land, leaving only remnants of the former plain or tableland. Precipitation on the divides of the rivers that traverse the High Plains hovers around 16 to 18 inches annually. This is somewhat higher than on the lower lands. Inversely, the growing season is slightly shorter. The frost-free period is around 140 days in the center of the High Plains. Although the country is prairie, trees appear on the escarpments and the rough land on the headwaters of streams. The tract of land shown is on the South Platte–Arkansas divide in El Paso County, north of Rattlesnake Butte. All this area is above 7,000 feet in elevation. A belt of trees on the low escarpment delimits the tableland. Most of the land is used for grazing, and fields are confined to the smoother ground. Soils developed mainly from sedimentary formations of the Tertiary age; they fall into the brown prairie group. Crops are grown largely as feed for livestock. Corn is a leading crop, but wheat, sorghum, barley, and hay are grown also. Dry beans are grown for the market. The major proportion of the farm income, however, comes from the sale of livestock and dairy products.

# Eastern Section of San Luis Valley, Colorado

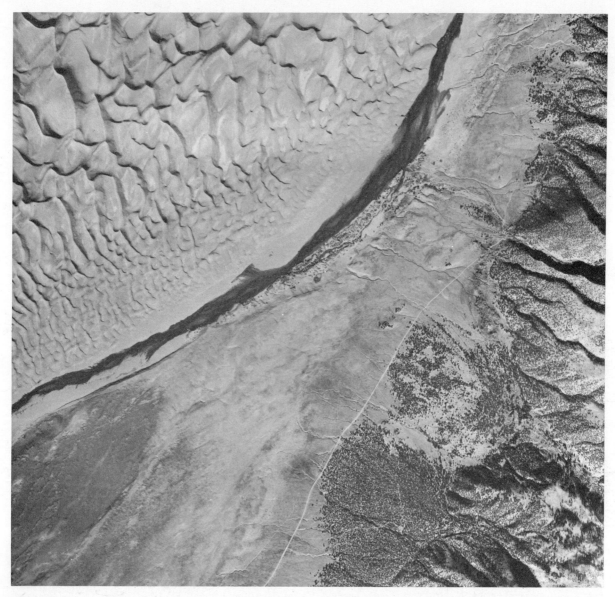

PLATE 81.—In the Central Rockies of Colorado are a number of basins, usually called parks, of which the San Luis Valley in the south is the largest. It contains more than 3,000 square miles of slightly rolling country. As it is surrounded by mountains, little precipitation reaches the valley floor. For a large part of the valley, the average annual precipitation is less than 8 inches, too little to grow crops without irrigation. Much of the valley has been reclaimed through irrigation by using the waters of the Rio Grande, which has its source in the San Juan Mountains to the west. The valley lies at an elevation of more than 7,500 feet, which shortens the frost-free season to around 100 days. Crops grown under these conditions are mainly feed crops, but Irish potatoes and vegetables are important cash-crop specialties. Not much water is available for irrigation from the Sangre de Cristo Range to the east. On the eastern side of the valley, only a few spots are irrigated. The rest is arid grazing land or, as in the case of the Great Sand Dunes, it has no productive use. Much of the mountain land and the arid land in the valley is in State and Federal ownership. The tract shown is at the northern boundary of Alamosa County; it includes the foot of the mountain and part of the sand dunes. North of this point, the drifting sand is stopped by the mountains. Although the sand dunes have no productive use, they have recreational value and are now included in the National Monuments. As in other places, the sand dunes act as catchment areas of precipitation and as a water reservoir which feeds the springs at the encampment place below the dunes. Forestry and grazing are the use potentialities of the mountains that are included in national forest. Scanty grazing is provided by the land on the lower levels. The lower limit of tree growth is well defined; it follows the talus slope of the mountains at an elevation of 8,100 to 8,200 feet. Alluvial fan formation and disappearance of the intermittent streams when they reach the valley floor are additional features.

# Grand Valley Irrigation Project, Western Colorado

DN-1491

PLATE 82.—Western Colorado is so mountainous that for one mountain county (San Juan) no farms were reported in the latest census. Most of the high mountain areas are included in national forests, and forestry and summer grazing are the principal land use. Cattle ranches are scattered along creeks and rivers in the valleys, where the livestock range during the cold season. To a considerable extent, irrigation is tied in with the livestock industry, but on the larger projects, crop specialties are grown. This is true in the valleys as well as on the plateaus. On the Mesa Verde in southwestern Colorado, where dryland and irrigated farming are closely connected, dry beans are a main crop. Farming is more diversified in some of the irrigated valleys. The tract shown lies between Grand Junction and Clifton in the Grand Valley Project in Mesa County. From the many small fields, it is apparent that the land is used intensely. Not only are many different field crops grown but deciduous fruit orchards are an outstanding feature of the landscape. Operators of commercial orchards must consider location with regard to unseasonal frosts. On this project, air drainage through the mouth of Hogback Canyon is better at the upper end, and most of the orchards are in this section. The elevation of the project is around 4,500 feet, somewhat lower than projects in other valleys. This has prolonged the frost-free season to 180 days as an average and permits more intensive use of the land. In addition to corn, small grains and alfalfa, sugar beets, dry field beans, potatoes, and vegetables are grown. Of the orchard fruits, peaches predominate but other tree fruits and grapes are also represented. In the orchard section, farms are small but with the more general type of farming their size increases. For the region as a whole, the major part of the farm income is derived from livestock and its products.

DN-1492

PLATE 83.—Land use on the high plateaus in southern Utah is severely restricted when crop production is considered. For the most part, the land is mountainous, rough, and stony. Precipitation is not as high as it is in the northern mountains. Usually it averages only 10 to 12 inches for the year. Exceptions occur in small areas, as in the vicinity of Orderville, where the average is 15 inches. Because of the low rainfall, forest vegetation over much of the area is not in closed stands. On the plateaus, woodland has a more park-like composition. The area is primarily range country with a few spots of irrigated land or dryland fields scattered over the region. With this as the resource base, the area is sparsely populated, and only occasionally have small towns grown up in the valleys. One of these spots, the surroundings of Orderville in Kane County, is shown. Orderville lies at an elevation of nearly 5,500 feet, but parts of the mountains to the north rise to more than 10,000 feet. Most of the mountain and plateau land is in public ownership and is used for grazing. The more or less open woodland on the plateaus to the south can be grazed almost the year round, but on the higher mountains and plateaus to the north, grazing is restricted to the warmer season. Farmers raise mainly cattle and sheep. In the valleys, some irrigation is practiced to produce hay, mainly alfalfa. Although it is not particularly an agricultural area, the area is rich in natural attractions and is a well-known summer vacation ground. Several national parks and monuments are located in this part of Utah.

# Wasatch Front near Logan, Utah

DN—1493

PLATE 84.—Utah may be roughly divided into two sections; one from which a certain amount of water is available, and the other in which the demand for water exceeds the local supply. The first can be identified with the mountains and plateaus in the east. The second is the part that belongs to the Great Intermountain Basins and Ridges to the west. Precipitation in the mountains, expressed in annual averages, is as high as 30 inches. In the basins, it is as low as 6 inches. A similar difference exists in the length of the growing season. In the mountains, the normal length of the frost-free period may be as short as 60 days. In some parts of the basin, it is as long as 180 days. Along the contact line of these two regions, which is usually referred to as the Wasatch Front, the changes are most marked. It is here that the larger settlements and irrigation projects are located. Because of their concentrated needs for water for domestic use, most of the cities in the area have grown up at the foot of the mountains where an adequate water supply is available. Logan is an example. As may be observed, the water of Logan River is used as soon as it leaves the gorge. An irrigation ditch branches off in the gorge. All the more intensively used land lies below the irrigation ditches, which follow the mountain base. The agricultural college is on the higher level just outside the gorge, and the city and irrigated land are below. Above the ditches, some benchland is cultivated but most of the land, including the mountainsides, is grazed. Tree growth is rather sparse on the lower slopes of the mountains; it becomes denser with the increase in elevation and the northern exposure. Similar settings are repeated all along the Wasatch Front. Agriculture receives its orientation from livestock; dairying and poultry raising are important. Small grains, sugar beets, fruits, and vegetables are grown as cash crops.

# Bear River Migratory Bird Refuge, Utah

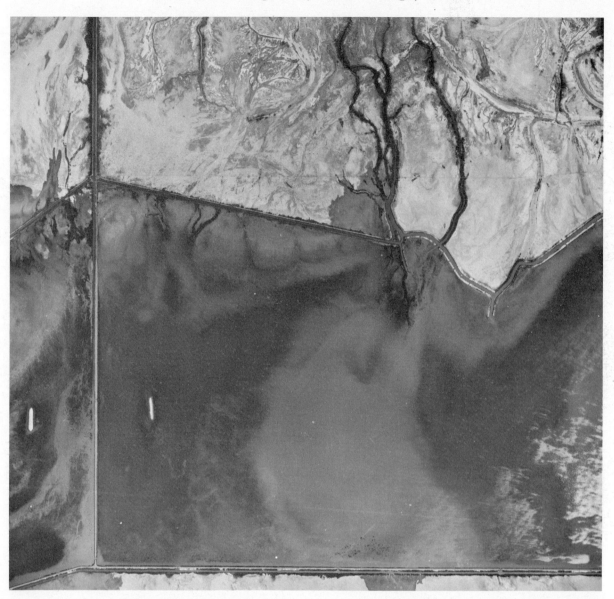

DN—1494

PLATE 85.—Changes in the natural environment began with man's appearance on the scene. Usually, they are made for his benefit. Man's activities, however, are so far-reaching in their reactions that they may change biological conditions. This is true especially in urban and industrialized areas, but it happens also in rural districts. One of the rural instances is illustrated. The name, Great Salt Lake, was truly descriptive when the settlers first used it, but with Bear River Bay a part of the lake, the name is less accurate now. With construction of the South Pacific railroad embankment across the lake in 1902 and 1903, the waters of the bay were separated from the waters of the lake. The bay received a continuous supply of fresh water from Bear River; it discharged the salt water into the lake through the opening in the embankment. Within a short time, the salt content of the bay water and the alkalinity of the flats along the shore were lowered to the extent that marsh vegetation, which was originally confined to the Bear River

Delta, spread along the northern shore of the Bay. Migratory waterfowl in great numbers had made Bear River a resting place in their long flights. But upstream diversion of the water introduced diseases which, in addition to the hunting of the birds for market, reduced the flocks by hundreds of thousands annually. In 1928, to conserve and protect waterfowl, the Congress established the Bear River Migratory Bird Refuge by setting aside 65,000 acres of land and water at the delta shore. But as the water level of the lake fluctuated as much as 16 feet and a reduced inflow readmitted the salt water of the lake into the bay, stabilization of the water level was necessary. To do this, about 26,000 acres around the delta were diked to produce shallow basins which retained the water of the river. The flocks of the flyways have again increased by 1½ to 2 million birds a year. Ducks, geese, herons, swans, pelicans, and ibis make the refuge their stopping or nesting place.

# Open Rangeland, Eastern Nevada

PLATE 86.—Most of the State of Nevada lies in the arid region. Only a few of the higher mountains receive an annual average precipitation of more than 15 inches. By far the larger part of Nevada receives less than 10 inches. Of the rivers and creeks, only those that have their headwaters in the higher mountains contain water the year round. The others are dry for long periods at a time. Under these conditions, arable land use is reduced to places where water can be diverted for irrigation. For the rest of the State, land use depends on the use that can be made of the natural vegetation, and this is mainly grazing. On the lower levels, the natural vegetation consists largely of sagebrush with a sparse admixture of grasses. Open stands of arid woodland, pinyon and juniper, with a larger proportion of grasses in the sagebrush cover, appear on the higher levels. The tract shown lies in the northeast corner of White Pine County. The draws are dry, and stock water is impounded on the larger run. On the knobs and ridges a scattering of arid woodland appears. Faint livestock trails traverse the open range. Compared with eastern pasture, the carrying capacity is low and frequently seasonal, which makes the land unsuited to individual homesteading. Most of the land is publicly owned and is used with permits for grazing. As for its use potentiality, it is the undisputed domain of cattle, sheep, and coyotes.

DN-1496

PLATE 87.—In Nevada, crop production is confined mainly to irrigated land, and it occupies only a comparatively small acreage of the total land area. That so little land is irrigated is primarily a result of water scarcity. The Humboldt and Carson Rivers are the larger ones but even they do not carry enough water to irrigate all the land along the valley and basin floors that might be reached. Both rivers converge on Carson Sink in the western part of the State. This is the part of Nevada that contains the lowest, driest, and warmest spots in the basin. Average annual precipitation is less than 5 inches over much of the basin floor, and the frost-free season runs normally from 130 to 160 days. The evaporation rate is high. Alkali accumulations in low places make the soil unfit for crop production. A sample of irrigated valley land, in Carson Valley, 5 miles north of Minden in Douglas County, is shown. Of the approximately 115 square miles of valley floor in Carson Valley, only 29 square miles are irrigated cropland; 51 square miles are irrigated pasture, which is mainly only wild grass pasture. Although no detailed study has been made, indications are that the salinity of the soil is one of the factors that prevent expansion of arable land use in this locality. Agriculture here is concerned mainly with the raising of cattle and sheep for the market. Dairy and poultry products also contribute to the farm income. The principal crops are alfalfa and clover hay, followed by small grains as feed crops.

# Lake Walcott Dam, Snake River, Idaho

DN—1497

PLATE 88.—From the point at which the Snake River enters the plain down its nearly 300-mile-long course to the junction with the Boise River, its waters are used in places either for irrigation or for the generation of hydropower. Along almost its entire course through the plain, the Snake River flows in a canyon that ranges in depth from 150 feet near the American Falls to 500 feet at the lower end of the plain. The climate of the plain is arid. The average annual precipitation ranges from 8 to 12 inches, and the frost-free season lasts around 140 days. Irrigation is essential for crop production. Wherever the waters of the Snake River are used for irrigation in the plain, they must first be lifted above the rim of the canyon. This is done in several places by means of dams. Lake Walcott is used as an illustration. Canals on both sides of the river convey the water by gravity from the lake formed behind the dam to the benches below.

Aside from functioning as a reservoir of irrigation water, the lake has been set aside as a national wildlife refuge. The number of farms on irrigated land and the size of the fields are indications that the land is used intensively by greatly diversified farming enterprises. Rectangular land-division lines define landownership, but both large and small fields may be adjusted to these divisions or may have irregular shapes to conform to the contour of the land and the water-supply system. Among the crops grown are specialties such as Irish potatoes, sugar beets, and dry beans, but alfalfa and small grains are also grown. Livestock enterprises supplement the crops. A considerable quantity of feed is grown and used in these areas. Dairying is connected with many farms and winter feeding of range cattle and sheep, in which beet tops provide a share of the feed, is a significant segment of the farm industry in the irrigated areas.

# Snake River Plain, Southern Idaho

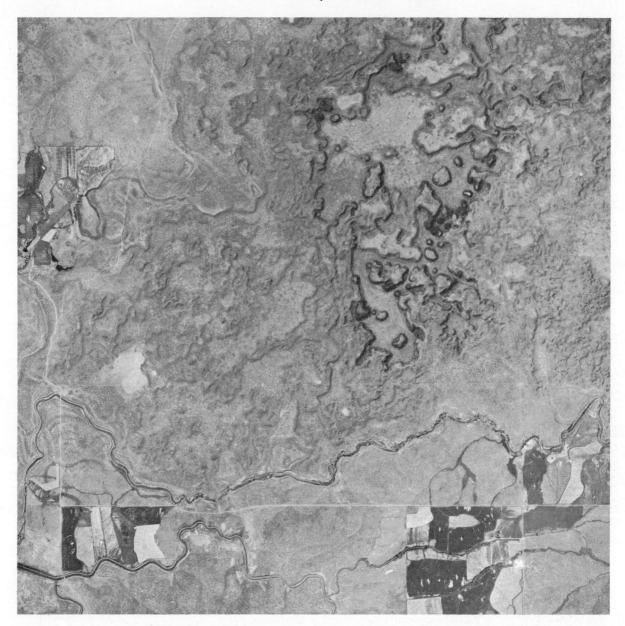

DN-1498

PLATE 89.—The Snake River Plain in southern Idaho is one of the largest plains west of the Rockies. In all, it covers more than 16,000 square miles. Aside from some isolated crater cones and low hills at the foot of the mountains, no outstanding surface features break the undulating horizon. These general impressions, however, must be modified when the local details of landforms are considered. A large part of the area is rough, rocky, and broken, characteristics that can be identified with the kind of land the Spanish settlers farther south called "malpais"—bad country. In both instances, this is the result of lava flows. The rough basaltic rock has not yet sufficiently weathered and disintegrated to produce a smooth surface with an adequate soil cover. It is only the pockets in these lava sheets that have smooth surfaces and soil deep enough for arable use of the land. Aridity also prevents use of the land for crops. Precipitation averages no more than 8 to 12 inches annually and crop production calls for irrigation. This rough land can be used only for grazing, and even this is not possible everywhere. The pockets in which water is available harbor the farms, which are usually stock farms. Hay is grown to provide fodder for the winter. The tract shown lies about 3 miles northeast of Burmah in the northern part of Lincoln County. The canal shown in the photograph carries water from Big Wood River across the divide to an irrigation project on Little Wood River.

# Upland Benches, Eastern Snake River Valley, Idaho

DN–1499

PLATE 90.—On the eastern end of the Snake River Valley and the divide of the Great Intermountain Basin, which extends from eastern Idaho into northern Utah, are extensive upland benches or tablelands that are used for dryland farming. The benches resulted mainly from basaltic lava flows, but the soils developed from the loess that covers them. Light brown silt loams, some of which are calcareous even in the surface layer, prevail. The surface is slightly to strongly rolling and is sharply incised by creeks. Precipitation averages annually from 14 to 16 inches, and crops are produced by dry-farming methods. The land is treeless, except in the creek bottoms, where cottonwood, willow, and poplars grow in a narrow belt along the watercourses, or on the breaks or mountains, where scanty growths of pines and junipers are found. Sagebrush with some bunchgrass is the native vegetation of the benchland. The tract shown lies at the confluence of Willow and Meadow Creeks in Bonneville County. Here, the canyon-like valley of Meadow Creek is from 300 to 400 feet deep. Although most of the upland is used for crops, few farms are located on the benches. More often, farms are located in the creek bottoms, where they are more sheltered and where water is readily available. Winter and spring wheat are the leading cash crops but barley and oats are also grown. Field operations are mechanized, and large fields are the rule. The customary practice is to crop the land every other year, allowing it to lie fallow between. For the 1926–48 period, the average annual yield of wheat per acre for Bonneville County was 24.4 bushels.

# Nez Perce Prairie, Northern Idaho

DN-1500

PLATE 91.—In northern Idaho, farming is mainly dryland farming. It is carried on for the most part in a belt at the foot of the mountains adjoining the Palouse country to the west. This belt has a southward extension on the tableland of the Clearwater River bend, but the extension cannot be considered true Palouse country. It consists of a high plain at an elevation of approximately 3,000 feet. The plain is deeply incised by river canyons, and in contrast to the greatly dissected and strongly rolling to hilly Palouse country, the surface is smooth and only slightly rolling. The soils of the two areas also differ. A mantle of loess, from which the soils developed, covers the tableland; but over some stretches it is thin and the subsoil developed from the weathered material of the underlying basaltic rock. The soils of these prairies are silt or silty clay loams, dark in color but leached.

Only on the western edge of this region have the soils acquired one of the Palouse soil characteristics—a calcareous subhorizon. Precipitation is higher than in the Palouse country to the west. It is sufficient to prevent accumulation of calcium in the lower soil horizon. The annual average is around 20 inches, of which most falls during the cool season. Usually, the frost-free season lasts 140 days or more. The tract shown is on the Nez Perce Prairie in the environs of Craigmont in Lewis County. Mechanized cash-grain farming, mainly wheat and barley, predominates, although dry field peas are also grown on a commercial scale. Summer fallow is not practiced to the same extent as on the lower land farther west. Livestock and livestock products play a minor part in the farm economy of the area.

194

# Blue Mountain Plateau, Washington

DN-1501

PLATE 92.—South of the Snake River, in Washington, a tilted plateau skirts the Blue Mountains. With reference to land use, it may be considered a southward extension of the Palouse country. This plateau is so deeply dissected by creeks that in places the walls of the gulches occupy as much space in the areal composition of the landscape as do the smooth remnants of the plateau itself. In this region, land relief greatly affects land use. Precipitation on these plateaus, especially on the higher levels at the foot of the mountains, is higher than it is north of the Snake River. Annual averages range from 20 to 30 inches, and the frost-free season may last from 140 to 180 days. The plateau section shown lies 5 miles by air southwest of Asotin in Asotin County. The difference in elevation between the Asotin Creek, which touches the northern margin of the photograph, and the point at which the Cloverland Road in its winding ascent from the valley gains the plateau level and straightens out is more than 1,000 feet. The absolute elevation at this point is more than 2,000 feet; from there it rises gradually to the south and west. Up to an elevation of 4,000 feet, these plateaus are treeless. Only in the gulches does tree growth start at a lower level; some trees fringe the watercourses. Land use is divided between grazing and dry farming. On the smooth plateaus, which have a silt loam soil developed from loess, small grains, mainly wheat and barley, are produced by dry-farming methods. Summer fallow is practiced extensively. The rougher land can be used only for grazing. A combination of cash-grain farming and livestock production provides the foundation for the farm economy of the areas. The land is divided into townships and sections, but only on the plateau is land use adjusted to these divisions.

195

DN-1502

PLATE 93.—The Columbia Plateau has been called the "Granary of the West." Commercial production of grain, mainly wheat, as the prevailing type of farming indicates the dominant use of the land. Land use, however, is not uniform throughout the region, mainly because of the variations in terrain, soils, and climate. There are tracts of smooth highland but large stretches of land are strongly rolling to hilly and are traversed by broad and braided channels of scabland in which the soil is thin and rocky. This land can be used only for grazing. Upland soils are mainly loams and silt loams developed from loess, which at one time covered the entire plateau. During the Wisconsin period of glaciation, ice sheets advanced to the northern border of the region where rushing streams of water from the melting ice cut the scabland channels. Erosion also has greatly dissected the eastern belt of the plateau and has produced the strongly rolling to hilly surface of what is known as the Palouse country. The name is taken from the Palouse River, which traverses the belt. Climatically, the Columbia Plateau forms a transition zone that ranges from semiarid in the lowlands to subhumid in the highlands. The average annual precipitation is from 8 to 10 inches, and the frost-free period lasts from 120 to 160 days. Dry-farming methods are practiced. Usually the land lies fallow every other year. As a rule, this is not combined with stripcropping, as may be noted in the Palouse land shown, which lies on Pine Creek near the southern boundary of Spokane County. Contoured stripcropping would no doubt be effective in checking soil erosion but it is not in universal use. The slopes are fairly steep—in the area shown, the slope gradient is nearly 400 feet per mile—and are incised and ridged. This makes adjustment to contoured stripcropping more difficult. The farm economy is dominated by cash crops, and livestock is secondary. Winter wheat is the leading crop, followed by spring wheat, rye, oats, and dry field peas.

# Eastern Slope of Cascade Mountains, Washington

DN-1503

PLATE 94.—The Cascades are forest-clad mountains but from the viewpoint of land use, forestry in these mountains is a one-sided industry. The term "one-sided" is used here in its literal sense. Commercial forests are largely confined to the western side or slopes, while the eastern slopes have more open stands, usually of timber that is unmerchantable either because of small size, poor quality, or insufficient volume per areal unit. Only more or less disconnected sites on the eastern slopes of the Cascades can be classified as producing commercial stands. This difference is due to climatic conditions. On the western side, precipitation is heavy and supports a dense forest stand. The eastern side is in the rain shadow of the moisture-carrying westerly winds. Precipitation is comparatively light; it decreases from about 70 inches along the divide to 20 inches at the foot of the mountains in terms of annual averages. The heavier stands of timber are therefore confined largely to the northern and eastern exposures, where the evapotranspiration ratio is low. The spur of the Cascades shown provides a setting of this kind. It is about 12 miles east of the divide, and, if the landlines were surveyed, it would fall in T37N, R20E. The crest of the spur has an elevation of around 8,000 feet, which is close to the upper limit of tree growth in this latitude. Tree stands are mainly open so that grasses are also able to grow. Summer grazing is the chief economic use made of this land. Grazing is not possible on the western slopes where the dense canopy of coniferous trees eliminates forage plants.

# Logging Operations, Anderson Mountain, Washington

DN-1504

PLATE 95.—For a long time, western Washington was the chief lumber-producing State of the West. Even now, the regional economy is tied up with the products of the forest to a large extent, and indications are that this relationship is not likely to change profoundly in the future. The reason for this supposition is supplied by the natural environment itself. From the divide of the Cascade Mountains down to the shore of the Pacific, most of the land must be classed as hilly and rough or mountainous, and consequently not suited to arable farming. As it is exposed to the moisture-carrying winds from the Pacific, precipitation ranges on the average from 20 to 100 or more inches annually. The summers are long and moderately warm. On the lower levels, the frost-free season usually lasts 200 days or more; and the winters are mild. Under these conditions, the land is able to produce a dense stand of commercial forest. The denseness of the timber stand may be observed in the virgin forest tract north of the cutover land shown. The photograph illustrates logging operations on the eastern slope of Anderson Mountain in Skagit County and shows some farms in the Samish River Valley. The logging road zigzags up the mountain. It starts at an elevation of 200 feet in the valley and ends at 2,500 feet, the highest central loading point on the crest of the mountain. As the converging skid tracts indicate, under favorable conditions, the logs are pulled as far as a third of a mile to the central loading point. Farming in this area is diversified. Many of the farms are small and are of the noncommercial type. Dairy and poultry farms are prevalent, although vegetables, tree fruits, and berries are also grown on a commercial scale.

# Rolling Foothills, Willamette Valley, Oregon

DN-1505

PLATE 96.—Within the Willamette Valley in Oregon are hills and mountains with eminences that sometimes rise 1,000 feet or more above the valley floor. These hills take up a good part of the valley; they have prevented development of the geometric regularity in the land use pattern so often found in plains. Not all the land is suitable for crops because of the rough, steep slopes with their attendant danger of erosion. As a whole, the climate of the valley is favorable for intensive use of the land. Annual precipitation averages from 35 to 70 inches, but it is not equally distributed over the seasons. Precipitation is heavy in winter, but during July and August less than an inch a month may fall in the lower places. The frost-free season of 180 to 200 days is long enough for all temperate crops.

Farming is diversified, especially in the more rolling country. The area shown lies at the foot of the Chehalem Mountains in Washington County. Dairy, poultry farms, fruit, and nut farms, among others, are found here. Some small grains and leguminous hay are grown, and red clover, vetch, dry field peas, fescue, and other seeds are produced also. Among the deciduous tree fruits, peaches, prunes, and cherries lead, but nuts, particularly walnuts and filberts, are also grown extensively. In addition to orchard crops, strawberries, blackberries, raspberries, grapes, and vegetables are grown commercially. The farm income of this region is about equally derived from livestock and its products, and crops grown for the market.

# Level Floor, Willamette Valley, Oregon

DN–1506

PLATE 97.—At the southern end of the Willamette Valley, the floor spreads out to an almost level plain, 20 or more miles wide in places. This wide alluvial terrace is bordered by the rolling slopes of the foot-hills, which also extend into the valleys that penetrate the Coastal Range and Cascade Mountains. Differences in climate are not pronounced enough to change the land-use capability of the rolling country as compared with the flat valley bottom. Summers are long; the frost-free period normally lasts around 200 days. Annual precipitation averages from 35 to 40 inches over the lower parts of the valley, but it is not evenly distributed among the seasons. Dry summers and wet winters are characteristic of the entire valley. No such broad statement can be made as to the character of the soil. Because of physiographic and soil distinc-tions, there are marked differences in the use of the land between the rolling margin and the flat center of the valley. A more diversified type of farming, which includes orchards, is practiced on the rolling margin, while livestock farming is centered on the alluvial bottoms, where some crops are grown also. The soils of the level center are mainly heavy tex-tured. Together with the inadequate surface drainage, this impairs internal drainage and makes cultivation difficult. Much of this level land was originally open country covered with grasses, perhaps more of the savanna or park vegetation type than prairie. Trees are scattered over much of the pasture and fields. The area shown lies in the center of the valley, about 2 miles west of Shedd in Linn County. Surface drainage has been improved in places by straightening out the drainage channels. In the flat part of the valley, agri-culture is centered largely on livestock farming. Dairy and poultry products, in addition to the animals sold on the market, provide the main share of the farm income. There are also crop specialties of importance. One of them is seed production, with ryegrass seed as the outstanding representative. Another is mint grown for its oil content.

# Jordan Valley, Southeastern Oregon

DN-1507

PLATE 98.—Southeastern Oregon is part of the Snake River drainage basin, but it shares the physical characteristics of the Great Intermountain Basin. The chief drawback to more intensive use of the land is the climate. Precipitation averages from 8 to 12 inches annually, and although elevations in the basins usually range only from 4,000 to 5,000 feet, the frost-free season is comparatively short. On the higher plateaus and ridges, frost may occur in any month of the year. Under these conditions, grazing, the only use made of the land, depends on the natural vegetation, which is largely of the sagebrush type. A desert shrub vegetation with a sprinkling of grasses has at best only a low carrying capacity, and the grazing is only seasonal. During the winter, livestock usually are kept near the ranch and supplied with additional feed. Ranches are located where rights to the use of water have been acquired, and where the water can be used for livestock and for irrigation. Most of the land in the open-range country is in public ownership. It has been organized into grazing districts in which grazing is regulated through the permit system. The site location of a ranch headquarters is represented in the photograph. The small village is Jordan Valley on Jordan Creek, a mile west of the Idaho boundary. Ranches are sparingly spaced along the valley bottom and the water of the creek is diverted in a number of places for irrigation. Hay, both wild and tame, is the principal crop harvested in this range country.

# Coast Ranges, Northern California

PLATE 99.—The northern part of the Coast Ranges in California differs in some respects from the central and southern parts. No wide-open valleys separate the mountains. Hilly and mountainous land is the dominant feature of the landscape. Climate provides another distinction. Seasonal variations in temperature are moderate. The summers are not dry and hot nor are the winters cold. The growing season is long. Normally, it lasts from 120 days near the crest of the mountains to 260 days at the coast. Precipitation over much of the area is high; it ranges from 60 to 100 inches as the annual average. A heavy coniferous forest, the well-known redwoods of northern California, is supported by it. How large the mature redwood trees are, and how dense the forest stand is, may be perceived from the appearance of the virgin forest cover in the photograph. The area shown lies about 20 miles inland from the coast, on the Eel River, with the village of Homes on the river terrace. The settlement and land use patterns may be seen. Clearings and settlements are confined to nearly level spots in the hills and on the river terraces. The cost of clearing the land of these large stumps is almost prohibitive. Frequently, the cost of removing the stump is considerably more than the cost of the land itself. Most farms are not of the commercial type; they produce only for home consumption. Dairying on a commercial scale is confined mainly to coastal areas. Forestry will no doubt remain the prevalent use of the land, as the redwoods produce desirable lumber. Some redwood tracts are included in the Humbolt Redwoods State Park.

# Chaparral, Lower Sacramento Valley Slope of Trinity Mountain, California

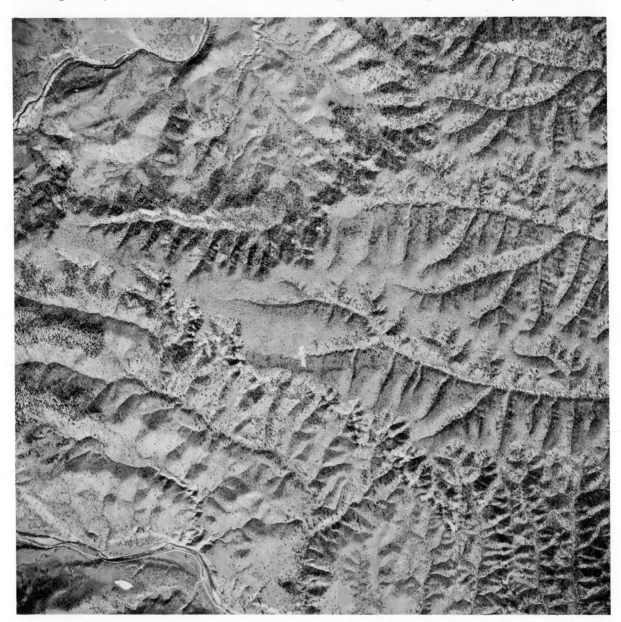

DN-1509

PLATE 100.—California has a woodland belt that represents a transition from grassland to forest and is usually referred to as chaparral. The belt surrounds the plains of the Central Valley and spreads out over the hills of the Coastal Range in southern California. Chaparral, or the brushfield belt, occupies in the aggregate a considerable acreage which, in round figures, approximates 20 million acres, or 20 percent of the total land area of the State. Chaparral may be divided into a number of types according to density and composition of shrub, tree, herb, and grass cover. The chaparral shown is of the open woodland type which prevails on the lower slopes of the Sacramento Valley. Live oaks, grass, and sagebrush make up the usual plant cover. The site shown lies on Beegum Creek Fork, which forms the northern boundary of Tehama County, halfway from the Sacramento River to the Trinity Mountain divide. The locality is around 1,500 feet high, some 2,000 feet below the forest boundary on this side of the mountains. No weather station is located nearby, although by interpolation, the annual mean precipitation would be near 25 inches, of which only 4 inches fall during the warm season. As may be seen, the land is badly dissected, and grazing is the only use that can be made of it. Cattle and sheep are able to use the range the year round, although few ranches are located in the area. A large proportion of the livestock is transferred to the valley for winter feeding.

# Ricefields, Sacramento Valley, California

DN-1510

PLATE 101.—A favorable combination of physical factors in the natural environment, mechanized operations, and economic opportunity, permitted the conversion of large tracts of California land, which formerly were used only for grazing or for production of barley and wheat by the dry-farming method, to flooded ricefields. Most of the basin floors along the Sacramento River were transformed in this way. Climatically, the Interior Valley of California provides the high summer temperatures and the long growing season, approximately 240 days, needed by rice. Precipitation averages annually from 15 to 20 inches, of which only 2 to 4 inches fall during the warm season. Land used for production of rice is flat; frequently the slope gradient is not more than 3 to 5 feet per mile. The soils of this area have developed under grass cover, are dark gray to black, and heavy textured with an adobe subsoil. Water for irrigation is obtainable upstream from the Sacramento River; it is distributed chiefly by gravity through a system of canals. Power equipment is used to prepare fields for rice culture. Fields are large, as shown in the tract pictured, which lies in the Colusa Basin on Sycamore Slough, 6 miles south of Grimes. For rice culture, the fields are usually subdivided, provided with irrigation and drainage ditches, and levees to hold the water on the fields. The riceland is ploughed and the seedbed is prepared while the land is dry. Rice seeding in California is now done mainly by planes over the submerged fields. Seed rice is soaked for a day or two so that it will sink immediately when broadcast over the water. The ricefields remain submerged until harvesttime approaches. Then the land must be drained to dry it out and make it firm enough to support the tractor-drawn combines that harvest the grain. Yields average around 4,300 pounds of paddy rice per acre, and 8 man-hours of labor are required per acre. Riceland is rotated with wheat or barley, or it is left fallow and used as pasture. In contrast to other farming areas, few or no farmsteads are located in the ricefields of California. Rice growing has ceased to be a family occupation but has become more of an engineering enterprise.

# Delta of the Sacramento and San Joaquin Rivers, California

DN-1511

PLATE 102.—The delta at the junction of the Sacramento and San Joaquin Rivers is a distinct geographic unit when physiography, soils, and land use are considered. Physiographically, the area consists of numerous islands formed by the sloughs that meander through this lowland. Originally, most of the land was tule-marsh. Over most of the area, the land surface lies close to the mean sea level. The natural levees usually are a few feet above, while the center of the island may be a few feet below, mean sea level. The land was subject to flooding or was submerged most of the time. Soils developed under these conditions are composed of mineral alluvium and much organic matter. The preponderance of either mineral or organic material in the soil largely determines the use potentiality of the land when it is reclaimed. Reclamation was necessarily a separate project for each island. Levees had to be built to protect it from overflow, and drainage had to be installed to relieve it from surplus water. All the larger islands are now reclaimed. Twitchell Island on the San Joaquin is shown. Surface soils on this island are silty clay loams with an organic substratum; muck is confined to the lower areas. Much of the land on these islands is used intensively. The growing season is long, but the rainfall averages only 15 to 20 inches annually. Of this, 2 inches fall during the warm season, so that irrigation is essential. The principal products are vegetables, which include asparagus, celery, beans, Irish and sweet potatoes, and onions. Sugar beets are also grown as a cash crop. Corn, grain sorghum, small grains, and hay are grown also, and some land is used for pasture.

# Lowland on the San Joaquin River, California

DN–1512

PLATE 103.—Irrigation has increased the productivity of the soil on much of the land in the San Joaquin Valley but, paradoxical as it may seem, it has also decreased productivity over an extensive acreage. Seepage water from irrigated land on the higher levels of the valley raises the water table in the trough from which it rises by capillarity to the surface and evaporates. Groundwater of arid regions usually contains more salts in solution than does groundwater of humid regions. In the process of evaporation, these salts remain in the soil, where they accumulate. With sufficient concentration, they become toxic to plants. In popular parlance, the accumulations of salts in the soil are usually referred to as alkali, although they are not all of the same chemical composition. Considerable damage has been caused by alkaline accumulations on irrigated land in arid countries. In California alone, several hundred thousand acres of formerly productive land have been reduced to grazing use only because of the alkali accumulation. Most of this land is in the San Joaquin Valley. Different reclamation methods have been developed, depending on kind of alkali and soil, but all require improved drainage. Much of the land can be reclaimed where adequate drainage can be established and sufficient water is available to dissolve the alkali and remove it through leaching. Some alkali land has been reclaimed in this way. One of these reclamation projects on the San Joaquin River on the Sanjon de Santa Rita Grant in Merced County is shown. Drainage canals have been built, old drains have been straightened or deepened, and many ditches have been installed. The first plantings usually are of the more salt-tolerant crops, such as barley or alfalfa.

# Eastern Side of San Joaquin Valley, California

DN—1513

PLATE 104.—Agricultural development in the eastern San Joaquin Valley is much more impressive than in the western part of the valley. The greater development in the eastern valley was made possible by water management. Temperatures are favorable for many subtropical and warm temperate crops and fruits. The growing season is around 280 days; summers are warm and winters are mild. But precipitation, which averages from 10 to 15 inches annually, is too low to permit intensified and diversified land use and to support a dense population. With the use of the water supplied by the heavy precipitation on the western slope of the Sierra Nevada, the natural obstacle of water shortage has largely been surmounted for the eastern side of the valley. The land is now closely settled. The larger towns all lie east of the San Joaquin River, and the land is divided into small farms, usually 20 to 40 acres in size. Land use is intensive. The tract shown lies north of Sanger in Fresno County. This locality marks the approximate northern limit of commercial citrus fruit orchards in the valley. Nevertheless, farming to the north specializes largely in production of fruits and field crops suited to the warm temperate climate. Vineyards are extensive; they produce raisins, and table and wine grapes. Figs, olives, peaches, and plums are grown also. Cotton is an important field crop. Interspersed are dairy, poultry, and truck farms. Although this is not a complete picture of farm activities in the eastern half of the San Joaquin Valley, it indicates the diversity of land use for farming purposes. The major part of the farm income is derived from fruits and crops, and the smaller part from animal husbandry. Through the more intensified use of the land, farm production has increased in recent years to a point at which California counties lead in value of farm products in the United States. This distinction formerly belonged to Pennsylvania counties.

# Western Side of the San Joaquin Valley, California

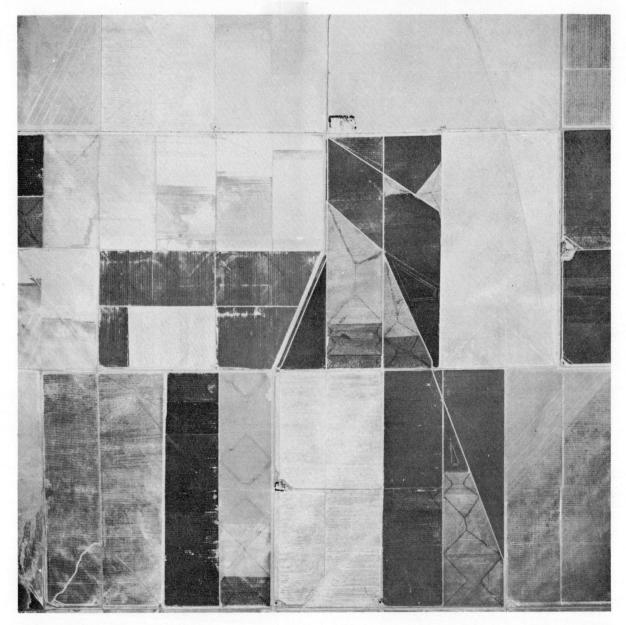

DN-1514

PLATE 105.—The climate of the San Joaquin Valley is such that most of the land cannot be used for intensive crop production without irrigation. Precipitation averages only 10 to 15 inches annually. Irrigation with the waters of the Sierra Nevada began nearly a century ago, and it has expanded continuously. But, until recent years, irrigation was confined almost entirely to the eastern side of the San Joaquin Valley as there is little runoff from the coastal range, and the Sierra does not furnish enough water to expand irrigation to the western side of the valley. With the development of the Central Valley project, water from the Sacramento River for the western side of the San Joaquin Valley will become available through pumping from the lower to the higher levels of the valley floor. Rice is already grown in the area. In the meantime, dry farming is carried on in areas outside the irrigation installations. Barley and wheat especially are still grown to a considerable extent with dry-farming methods. The land is cropped every other year, and the large-scale operations are fully mechanized. Fields of 320 acres are not rare as may be observed in the tract shown, which lies about 10 miles west of Helm on the western side of the San Joaquin Valley in Fresno County. The large fields and sparse settlement on the western side of the valley provide a strong contrast in land use patterns when compared with the eastern side of the valley in Fresno County, as illustrated in Plate 104.

# Corona Basin, Southern California

DN–1515

PLATE 106.—The coastal ranges in Southern California are rather openly spaced with broad valleys and basins interspersed. It was mainly in these valleys and basins that the early Spanish settlers located their claims and received their grants of land. The Spanish nomenclature of landscape features is reminiscent of these events. The climate is characteristic of mediterranean climates. Temperatures are mild in winter and not too hot in summer. The frost-free season usually lasts from 200 to 280 days. Precipitation, in terms of annual averages, ranges from 15 to 20 inches; only a few of the higher spots in the coastal ranges are within the 30- to 40-inch limit, but in these areas only a few inches fall during the warm season. In most places, precipitation alone is inadequate for intensive use of the land. Management of the meager water resources to supply water for irrigation and urban needs is essential. Land use varies greatly with locality, and farming is often specialized. Dairy, poultry, truck, fruit, and nut farms are represented. A fruit-growing district at the foot of the Santa Ana Mountains, south of Corona, where good air drainage favors the fruit-growing industry, is shown. This tract of land lies within a Spanish Grant, and thus it is not divided into square townships and sections. Orchards are located on a gentle slope that rises from 700 to 1,500 feet within 3½ miles. The mountains are included in national forests. The runoff from the mountains is used to irrigate the orchards, in which ditches, roads, and plantings follow the contour. Walnuts, almonds, olives, oranges, lemons, grapefruits, grapes, peaches, apricots, apples, and cherries are grown in this part of the coastal range. Vegetables, berries, cotton, small grains, and alfalfa are found on the lower level valley plains. Fruits and nuts, however, are the principal cash crops.

# Imperial Valley, California

DN-1516

PLATE 107.—The Colorado River is the oldest and most successful hydraulic engineer we have in this country. For millions of years, it has been at work sculpturing the upper reaches of its basin and excavating the Grand Canyon. At the same time that it was wearing down the rocks upstream, it was transporting the spoils of its labor hundreds of miles downstream to build a broad dam across the Gulf of California. The part of the gulf that was cut off from the main body dried out in time to the level of the Salton Sea, some 240 feet below sea level, leaving a desert depression. Not until man diverted a part of the Colorado water back into the basin and used it for irrigation, was the regime of the desert broken. In this way, the Imperial Valley, as it is now called, was converted into a garden spot with an almost year-long growing season. The high summer temperatures have been tempered somewhat by irrigation. The smooth surface of the gently sloping basin floor permits location of laterals along the rectangular land-division lines. These named or numbered laterals, which are usually a half mile apart, distribute the water from the main canal near sea-level elevation over the valley. The square 160-acre quarter-sections are frequently individual fields as they appear in the tract shown, which lies north of Calipatria. Truck farming is the principal enterprise. Lettuce, cantaloupes, melons, green peas, and tomatoes are the main off-season products. The second most important crop is flax, which is grown primarily as a seed crop. Some grapefruit and dates are grown as are alfalfa, sugar beets, small grains, and hay. Crops provide the larger part of the $75 million gross farm income reported by the census for 1949, although animals and animal products contribute a good share. As a farming area, the Imperial Valley is unique in that most of the cultivated land is from zero to 225 feet below sea level.

# Phoenix Basin, Arizona

DN–1517

PLATE 108.—The lower end of the Gila and Salt River Valleys in Arizona is a vast desert plain studded with disconnected mountains and ridges. Most of the time, the tributaries of these rivers are only dry arroyos or river wash, as the climate of the region is characteristic of the southwestern desert. Precipitation ranges from 3 to 10 inches when expressed in annual averages, although it may be concentrated into a few downpours occasioned by thunderstorms. Temperatures are high, and the frost-free season lasts from 240 days to almost year long on the lower levels near the Colorado River. Under these conditions, land use depends more on the water available than on anything else. In the desert country, grazing is possible, provided springs, wells, or tanks supply the water needed for livestock. Population concentrations and irrigated agriculture have used the waters of the rivers since Indian days. With the increase in population and the expansion in crop production, it became necessary to regulate the supply of water. Storage reservoirs were built on both rivers in the mountains, and now the area supports a diversified agriculture. A tract of irrigated land on the Agua Fria River west of Phoenix is shown. The Agua Fria River is only a dry wash. Irrigation water is brought into the area by canals from the Salt River. Crops of subtropical and temperate climates are grown; they include cotton, vegetables, sugar beets, potatoes, soybeans, barley, flaxseed, alfalfa, hay, and seeds. The fruits—mainly grapes, oranges, grapefruit, and dates —are largely subtropical. Livestock and its products, particularly dairying, are also well represented in the farm economy, but crops are the principal cash products.

# Canyon de Chelly, Arizona

DN-1518

PLATE 109.—Much of the highland in the 4-State corner, which is frequently identified as the Colorado Plateaus, is Navajo country and is included in Indian reservations. Most of the Navajo country has an elevation of more than 5,000 feet, but some of the higher points rise to more than 9,000 feet. Because of the elevation, the climate is rather cool but fairly dry. The annual average precipitation ranges from 8 to 14 inches and is rather evenly distributed over the seasons. The frost-free season averages from 140 to 200 days. Land use in this part of the country is not only an adjustment to natural conditions but is guided by centuries of custom and tradition. Archaeologists tell us that some of the present villages were occupied centuries before white men arrived in America. Other sites were occupied during the first centuries of our era, but a protracted drought forced the people to move. The cliff dwellings in the Canyon de Chelly (a corruption of Navajo, meaning "in the rocks") are in that class. According to one authority (55), these sites were occupied as early as the middle of the fourth century A. D. (111). The canyon has been established as a national monument. A section that contains Monument Rock is shown. Most of the plateau land is used for grazing. Vegetation consists of the sagebrush type in the lower valleys, short grass on the plains, pinon-juniper on the upper levels and mesas, and yellow pine in the mountains. Pine timber in the mountains grows to commercial size but is usually inaccessible to market. The upland vegetation in the photograph is of the pinon-juniper type. Crops are grown on irrigated or subirrigated patches on the creeks. Indian corn, vegetables, wheat, barley, alfalfa, and dry beans are the chief crops. The main income is derived from livestock and its products, which include horses, cattle, sheep, hogs, poultry, and goats.

# Rio Grande Valley, Northern New Mexico

DN-1519

PLATE 110.—Irrigated agriculture on the upper Rio Grande in New Mexico had its beginnings before white men arrived at the scene. When the Spanish began to explore and to colonize the region in the middle of the 16th century, they found that the Indians had built community ditches that diverted the water from streams to irrigate the land. Since then the irrigation systems have been enlarged and improved, but the historical connection of land use with the colonizers is still noticeable in the land use pattern. North-central New Mexico contains many medium-sized and large Spanish land grants, located mainly on streams, which mark the area in which the Spanish-speaking population is concentrated. These grants were not ordinarily subdivided into townships and sections. Consequently, land-division lines do not conform to the rectangular order. Furthermore, the old custom of dividing the land among the children on the death of the parents has been followed. As a result, most of the farms contain less than 20 acres. Elevations along the Upper Rio Grande are above 5,000 feet, and the frost-free season usually lasts from 140 to 180 days. Because of the low precipitation—10 inches in the valleys, rising to 20 inches or more in the mountains—crop production in this part of New Mexico is confined largely to irrigated land; the dry land is used for grazing. A tract on the Rio Grande above the town of Bernalillo is shown. It contains both dry upland and irrigated bottom land. Irrigated farming of the villagers is mainly on a self-sufficing level or is a part-time occupation. Very few crop products are sold. The greater part of the farm income is derived from sales of livestock products.

# Llano Estacado Rim, New Mexico

DN-1520

PLATE 111.—As a rule, regional land use areas are not delimited by nature. A distinct boundary that indicates the end of one association of land uses and the beginning of another is usually lacking. Ordinarily, there is a transition zone in which one dominant use gives way to another. One of the exceptions is the Llano Estacado, which is well-defined in all directions, except the south, by a low escarpment. In most places, the escarpment is not more than 200 to 300 feet high. It serves as a morphological boundary and defines land use as well. The segment of the escarpment shown is on the northwest corner of the tableland in the southwest corner of Quay County. This is the highest point of the Llano Estacado; it is almost 5,000 feet above sea level. The average annual precipita-tion is around 16 inches, and the frost-free season averages 180 days. The surface of the tableland is smooth and has many of the shallow saucerlike depressions that are characteristic of this highland. This corner of the tableland is outside the pump-irrigation district. Crop production must rely on dry-farming methods. Wheat is the leading crop, but sorghums for grain, broomcorn, cotton, beans, and other crops are grown also. Farm income is now derived mainly from crops, but cattle and sheep together are a close second. West of the escarpment, the land is more dissected and receives less precipitation so that fields are widely scattered. Most of this land is used for grazing.

# Johnson Mesa, New Mexico

DN-1521

PLATE 112.—The range in elevation under which cultivated crops are produced varies considerably in different parts of the world. Frequently, it is a matter of latitudinal climate. Near the equator, crops can be grown at considerable elevations. Near the Arctic Circle, they must be grown near sea level. Within this latitudinal span, the lower limits are found in depressions below sea level, where well-drained soils and water are available. The upper limit depends on location. With increasing altitude, the Arctic climate is approached vertically, and is reached in midlatitude at variable elevations. Moreover, land level enough for cultivation usually is confined to valleys or basins and, in some instances, to plateaus. In the United States, crops are grown in a variety of high places. In North Park, Colo., some crops are grown near the 8,000-foot level, but above that the crop usually consists only of wild hay. On the Mesa Verde,

beans, the chief crop, are grown at elevations of from 6,500 to 7,500 feet. From the evidence we have, it appears that the highest points in the United States that produced cultivated crops are the mesas in north-central New Mexico, especially Johnson Mesa, of which a part is shown. Some of these fields are above the 8,200-foot level. Although no climatological records are available for the mesa proper, from the records of nearby stations and from local information, it appears that precipitation is slightly higher on the mesas than on the plains below. On the mesas, it reaches at least 20 inches as an annual average. Inversely, temperatures are lower; the frost-free season approximates 110 days. The soils are fertile clay loams of the grassland type. Winter and spring wheat, oats, and barley are the chief crops grown. Some small grains and timothy are grown for hay.

# Rim of Cimarron Breaks, Oklahoma

DN-1522

PLATE 113.—The Panhandle of Oklahoma extends well into the western high plains, where land use is divided on a physiographic-soil basis between dry farming and grazing. Average precipitation in these 3 counties decreases from 22 inches in the eastern county to 18 in the western county. As it is distributed over the year and concentrated in downpours that have great erosive power, this is not a great deal of moisture. The frost-free season averages from 175 to 190 days. Much of the surface is still intact as a smooth slightly eastward sloping plain, but the rivers and their tributaries have excavated broad ravines and have dissected the surface in places. How the tributary creeks of the Cimarron River work their way back into the upland is illustrated. The rim sec- tion of the 10- to 12-mile-wide Cimarron Valley shown is about 7 miles northeast of Boise City. The soils of this part of the plain are chiefly calcareous, dark-colored fine sandy loams or silt loams. When exposed to the strong winds of the plains, they are subject to blowing. As may be noticed in the photo- graph, the fields on the upland extend to the rim of the breaks. Below the rim, the land is more dis- sected and is used for pasture. Large-scale mechan- ized grain farming prevails on the upland. Hard win- ter wheat is the leading crop, but sorghum and barley are also grown for the market. Summer fallow is practiced to some extent, but it is not general. Live- stock contributes a large share to the regional farm economy.

DN-1523

PLATE 114.—The central plains of Oklahoma are mainly rolling on the upland divides, but steeply rolling to rough in the belts that border the watercourses. Rivers and the larger creeks have flood plains that are sometimes more than a mile wide. Some parts of these plains are protected from overflow by levees or creeks, which have been straightened to improve drainage. The region lies in a transition zone from the subhumid to the semiarid. Precipitation averages from 25 to 30 inches annually. Heavy downpours take their toll of the land through erosion. Strong winds are an additional hazard to the land. To break the force of the wind in many places, windbreaks are planted across the fields. Temperatures are warm in summer and moderate in winter. The frost-free period averages from 200 to 230 days. Originally, the rolling upland was prairie while more or less open woodland, composed partly of mesquite, covered the steeper slopes, of which some tracts are still in evidence. Soils, which developed from the weathered material of sandstone and shale, have a substratum that is mainly calcareous. They are dark colored, fine sandy to silt loams. Adjustment of land use to these conditions has produced a diversified agriculture. Much of the land is used for crop production with soil conservation practices, but the rougher land is left in woods and pasture. The land use pattern is illustrated by the tract shown, which lies on Willow Creek, 8 miles north of Fort Cobb in Caddo County. Cotton, corn, sorghum, wheat, and peanuts are grown for the market and produce the major part of the farm income. Income from livestock, mainly animals sold and dairying, ranks second.

217

# Cove in Ouachita Mountains, Oklahoma

DN-1524

PLATE 115.—Land use in eastern Oklahoma is controlled largely by land-relief features. A number of counties in this part of Oklahoma are mountain counties. Physiographically, those north of the Arkansas River belong to the Ozark Plateau and those south of the river to the Ouachita Mountains. Of the two, the Ouachita Mountains extend farther into Oklahoma. Structurally, they are distinct from the Ozarks in that they consist of a series of long mountain ridges with interspersed valleys. Ridges and valleys provide the natural background for the spatial arrangement and the relative proportions of field and forest in the regional land use pattern. By far the largest proportion of the Ouachita Mountain land is in forest. Farming usually is strung along the valleys. A sample of this arrangement is shown. The tract lies on North Boggy Creek, 3 miles west of Limestone Gap, Atoka County. The concentration of fields marks the oval end of a valley surrounded by low ridges. This tract is on the western spurs of the Ouachita Mountains bordering the coalfields of eastern Oklahoma. This part of the State is in the humid region. Annual precipitation averages 40 or more inches and the frost-free season lasts for more than 200 days. Thus a variety of crops can be grown. Accordingly, agriculture is diversified in the direction of crops and livestock. Many of the farms are small part-time enterprises operated near the self-sufficing level. No great surpluses are produced for market. Peanuts and some cotton are the principal cash crops. The larger part of the farm income is derived from livestock and its products.

# Northern End of Texas Black Prairie

DN-1525

PLATE 116.—In its northern extremities, the Texas Black Prairie is not the compact body of smoothly rolling plain that it is in the center. Tributaries of the Red River have worked their way into the upland, dissecting the plain into lobes separated by broad shallow valleys. Differences in elevation between upland and valley bottoms usually do not exceed 100 to 200 feet. The valley slopes are mainly gentle enough for cultivation, but erosion has cut back into the smooth prairie surface, washing the silt into the bottoms. The alluvial bottom lands built up by the creeks are often more than a mile wide and must be drained before they can be used as cropland. The upland soils belong to the rendzina group; they have developed from highly calcareous marls or chalks under a grass vegetation, and are dark or nearly black. Although they are heavy-textured clays, they are crumbly. These soils are very productive. This part of Texas lies on the western border of the humid region. Rainfall is close to 40 inches as an annual average and is fairly well distributed over the seasons. Temperatures are relatively high, and the frost-free period lasts approximately 240 days. The edge of the Texas Black Prairie is illustrated in the tract shown, which lies immediately north of Leonard in the southwest corner of Fannin County. Active erosion at the heads of the creeks may be seen in the photograph. Here, cotton is still king among the crops. Farms are mainly small to medium-sized. They are arranged in a rectangular block pattern but follow no definite system of land division. Aside from cotton and peanuts, corn and other field crops are grown to some extent. Much of the land is used for pasture. Livestock and its products contribute significantly to the farm economy.

219

# Limestone Plains, North-central Texas

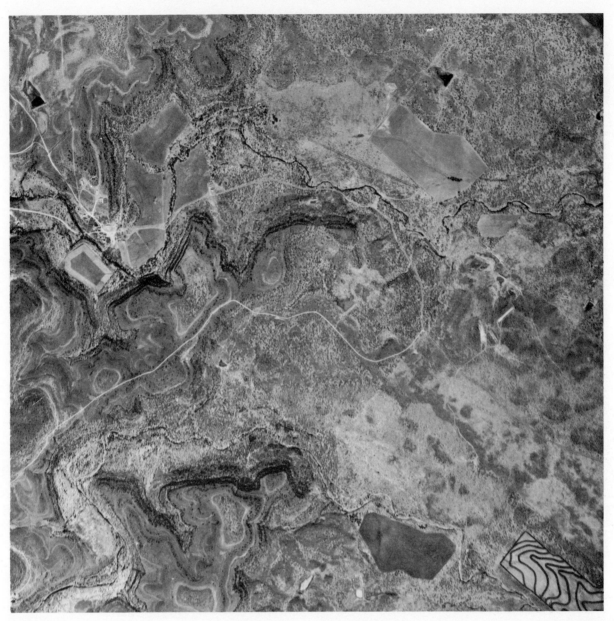

DN-1526

PLATE 117.—In north-central Texas, a belt known as Limestone Plains, extends in an almost north–south direction from the Red to the Colorado River. The central part of this belt is not so much a plain as a succession of benches that rise westward in well-defined steps from 100 to 200 feet in elevation. The surface, therefore, is largely one of smoothly rolling benchland and dissected hilly escarpments. Climatically, the area falls within the subhumid zone near the semiarid limits. Of the approximately 24 to 26 inches of annual average precipitation, more than half falls with considerable irregularity during the warm season. Normally, the frost-free period lasts more than 220 days. Neither lay of the land nor climate account, therefore, for the limited use of the land for crops. The restraining factor over much of the upper benches are the soils. Dark-colored silty clays or clay loams predominate but they are of the rocky or stony types so that cultivation is difficult or precluded. Grazing is the prevailing land use with some crop fields near the ranches as illustrated. The ranch shown is 8 miles north of Albany on Foyle Creek, Shackelford County. As is true of most of the rangelands in the Southwest, the virgin grassland has been depleted and is now heavily infested with brush. Overgrazing, and the consequent destruction of the native grass cover, are usually regarded as the cause of the brush invasion, which in this area consists mainly of mesquite. A heavy brush cover necessarily reduces greatly the grazing capacity of the range. Eradication of brush and restoration of the productivity of the range are costly whether mechanical or chemical techniques are used. As shown, some good-sized tracts have been cleared of brush.

# Rough Land in the Plains, Texas

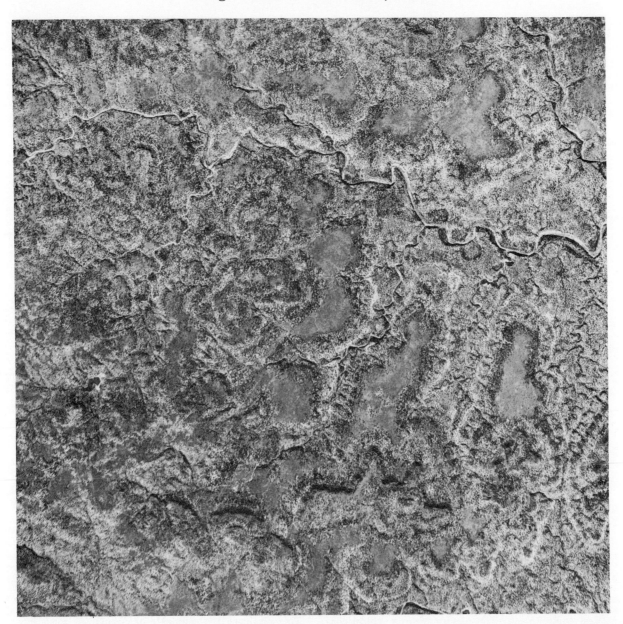

DN-1527

PLATE 118.—Extensive areas of north-central Texas are included in the plains as they have no outstanding relief features that might earn them another designation. Although elevations vary very little, these areas are so badly dissected that most of them are rough. The soil of the eroded surface usually is a heavy clay, which is often rocky and stony. This rough land frequently forms belts along the rivers, but large areas are found also on the headwaters of creeks. Because of its roughness, arable use of such land is not feasible. Small level interspersed spots on interstream divides are isolated and are inaccessible to wheeled travel. Summers are warm; winters are mild; and precipitation normally averages around 25 inches annually. As these rough areas are almost devoid of settlement, no road system has been developed. The only use that can be made of the land is grazing, but its value is low even for grazing, as the natural vegetation has a comparatively low carrying capacity. Scrubby cedars, mesquite bushes, and hackberry along streams with a more or less scanty admixture of grasses is the characteristic plant association. Grazing of such land is usually managed from large livestock ranches. As the winters are mild, grazing is year-long, and the livestock require little care. The tract shown lies approximately 6 miles west of Pease River on Canal Creek in Foard County. As may be observed, it is a wilderness; there is no dwelling within square miles of land and no road enters the area.

221

# Llano Estacado, Texas

DN-1528

PLATE 119A.—Land use on the Llano Estacado has changed greatly in recent years owing to the introduction of pump irrigation. These changes are illustrated on the two aerial photographs taken of the same area with a time lapse of 12 years. The photograph above was taken early in November 1941, when land use still was closely adjusted to the conditions of the natural environment. The picture records typical conditions over much of the north-central plateau. There, the surface of the Llano Estacado is marked with numerous shallow, saucerlike depressions, irregularly distributed. These, with the square sections into which the land is divided, controlled cultural operations. The average precipitation is low; it decreases from 21 inches on the lower eastern side of the plateau to 16 inches on the higher western end; and the frost-free season usually lasts from 180 to 210 days. Semiarid conditions made dry farming methods necessary. To hold the scanty precipitation on the land, field operations followed the contour of the shallow depressions. This produced the segments of circular patterns interspersed with straight-line fields on the level ground. As it happened, this picture was taken after a number of days of heavy rains which converted the lowest points of the depression into temporary lakes.

222

# Llano Estacado, Texas

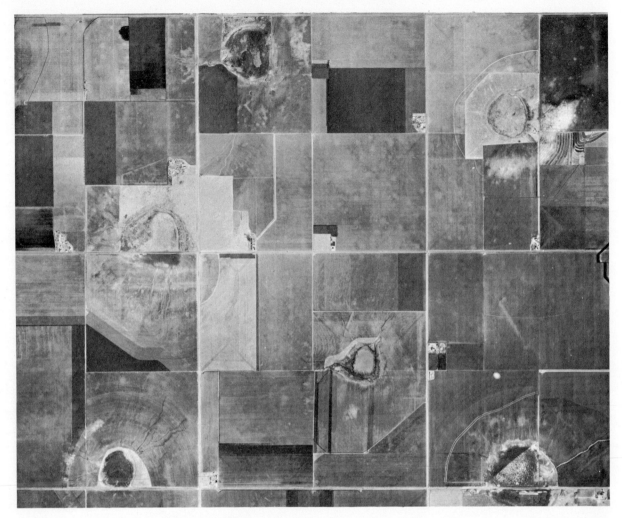

DN-1529

PLATE 119B.—The locality represented in this photograph is the same as the one shown on the preceding page. It lies on the Lamb-Castro County boundary 6 miles west of State Highway No. 51. The major difference between this and the opposite photograph is that this photograph was taken in the spring of 1953, nearly 12 years later than the other. During these intervening years, the installation of pump irrigation changed not only the land use pattern but the agricultural economy of the region.

In this instance, irrigation is mainly supplemental to precipitation, because precipitation is irregular in both time of occurrence and quantity. This climatic diversity even happens to be recorded in the pictures. What appears to be lakes in the earlier photograph are dry bottoms in the later one. With the application of well water for irrigation, the hazards of prolonged dry spells have been largely eliminated. Although this has permitted production of a greater variety of crops, in the main, the same crops are grown but their relative importance has changed. Cotton, in particular, has increased its dominance in both acreage and value over other crops. Another notable change is that contour cultivation has given way to straight-line operations in most instances.

# Tahoka Lake, Texas

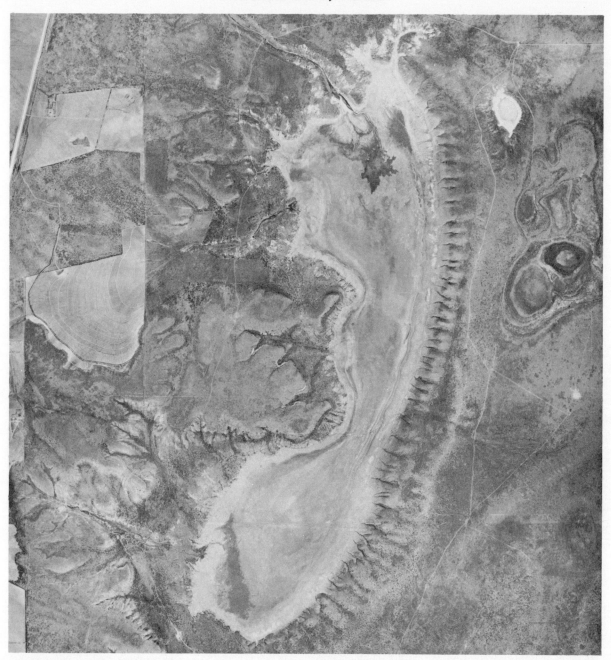

DN-1530

PLATE 120.—Landforms on the Llano Estacado comprise a unique assortment of sandhills and depressions. Both affect land use, but they did not arise from action of the same forces. The origin of the hundreds of shallow, round depressions scattered over the High Plains are variously explained. They are thought of as sinkholes produced by the dissolving action of water on the underlying limestone and chaliche. Neither of these formations is encountered over the plateau in sufficient thickness to account for all these depressions. Subsidence of the surface deposits over collapsed caverns in the pre-quaternary rock formations is a second explanation. Both processes may be involved, but neither can account for the sand dunes on the east side of the playas. The dunes are built of sand and silt scooped by the wind out of the playa bottoms. That powerful winds swept over the Llano Estacado during pleistocene time is evident from the two traverse dune belts and the accumulations of sand below the western escarpment. The playas, of which there are a number, are the larger of the depressions. Playas consist of intermittent lakes that receive the runoff of their surroundings. When dry, they are saline lake bottoms. Tahoka Lake in Linn County, Texas, is shown. The land that surrounds the playas can be used only for grazing; the playas themselves are barren. As may be seen in the photograph, the playa dunes are deteriorating. Erosion has cut runnels that dissect the dunes. As an example of ridges built of material blown out of depressions, these dunes have their analogy in the spoilfields of sand on the eastern side of the Carolina Bays.

# Concho Basin, Texas

DN-1531

PLATE 121.—Among the many distinct geographic units in Texas are basins, of which the Lipon Flats or Concho Basin is perhaps the best known. Physiographically, the basin belongs to the plains country of west-central Texas. The approximately 700-square-mile basin is traversed by the Concho River with San Angelo at the western end. Over most of the basin, the surface is smoothly rolling, and there are few obstructions to cultural use of the land. Equally favorable for crop production are the soils, which are dominantly silty clay loams. They are calcareous in surface and subsoil and are well supplied with humus, which gives them their dark brown to black color. The drawbacks to arable farming arise from the climate of the area. Temperatures are high in summer and mild in winter; the frost-free season averages around 220 days. Precipitation is comparatively low. The annual average is from 18 to 20 inches, and most of it falls during the warm season. To obtain the full benefit of local precipitation, any runoff that collects in the drainage channels is commonly diverted back to the land through ditches. Some pump irrigation is also applied in places. The prevalent land use pattern is illustrated. Farms lying some 12 miles east of San Angelo are shown. To conserve moisture and prevent erosion, most of the fields are cultivated on the contour. Cotton is the principal cash crop. Sorghum, oats, and other crops are also grown to some extent. Much of the land is used for pasture. Livestock and livestock products are also an important part of the farm economy.

225

# Farming Frontier, Semiarid Western Coastal Plain, Texas

DN-1532

PLATE 122.—Climate is the chief physical factor that affects agriculture. Immense land areas are excluded from arable land use because of the deficiencies of climate. Climatic hazards are found almost everywhere. These hazards increase in severity and frequency, mainly in the direction of diminished temperature and precipitation until a limit is reached beyond which use of the land for crops becomes uneconomic. No definite line can be drawn to indicate the climatic limit to which cultivated crops can be grown because variables that cannot be stabilized are involved. Climate is subject to cyclic variations; economic conditions change; mechanization has changed cultural practices; plant breeders produce crop varieties better adapted to withstand deficiencies of climate; and proper management of water can ameliorate precipitation deficiencies, although management in turn, is subject to physical and economic limitations. At any one time, the boundary that indicates the limit of arable crop production toward the arid side is a jagged line with protruding points and exclaved areas. It is in these advanced positions that local water resources are frequently tapped and used for irrigation to supplement the scanty and uncertain precipitation. The environment of Cometa, 12 miles west of Crystal City in Zavala County, is shown. This is an outpost on the climatic frontier and part of the land is irrigated. The annual average precipitation of the area is around 20 inches, and most of it falls during the warm season. Temperatures are high; the frost-free season runs from 270 to 280 days. Most of the land is used for grazing; and livestock and its products provide the major part of the farm income. Crops grown for market, however, are important also. Cotton and vegetables, grown largely under irrigation, are the chief cash crops. As may be noted, some of the cropland is reverting to brush.

226

# Balcones Escarpment and Southern Black Prairie, Texas

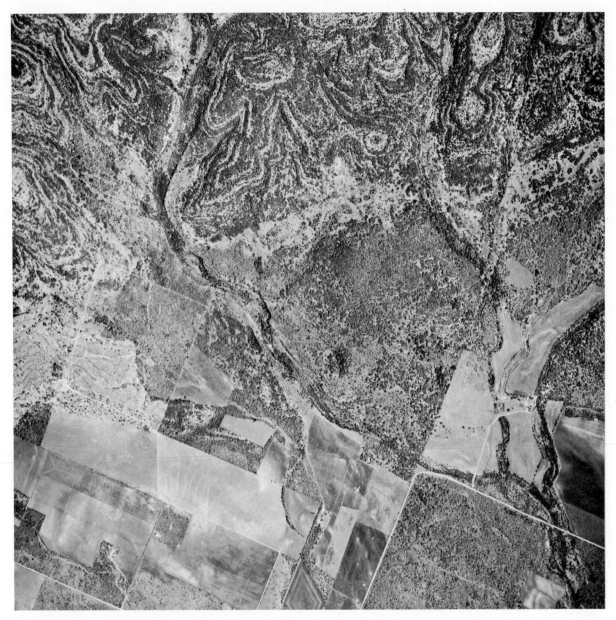

DN—1533

PLATE 123.—The Black Prairie of Texas is a well-known physiographic regional unit, but when land use is considered, it is not equally satisfactory as a unit. The acreages of land used for crops vary markedly between the northern and southern sections. The Colorado River serves as the dividing line. The distinction between the two sections is mainly of climatic origin and was brought about largely by diminished rainfall. Temperatures are comparatively high, and the growing season, with 260 or more frost-free days, is long. The average annual precipitation of 20 to 32 inches, however, is barely enough to grow a crop. Irrigation is resorted to by many for more intensive use of the land. Not all the smooth land is cleared and used for crops, as is apparent in the part of the Black Prairie shown. The tract shown lies about 15 miles northwest of San Antonio. It takes in part of the Balcones Escarpment and the Black Prairie belt. The Balcones Escarpment, which rises to 500 feet or more from the plain, forms the mountainous edge of the Edwards Plateau. Limestone with interbedded sandstone and shale are the outcropping rock formations of the deeply dissected escarpment, on which the woodland vegetation—mainly juniper, live oak, mimosa, and other shrubs—has established itself along the ledges, forming a natural contoured planting. Except in some valley bottoms, the rugged surface with its shallow, rocky soil can be used only for grazing. Cattle and sheep are grazed on the more open and less rugged ground, and Angora goats range through the hills in great numbers. The mohair produced in the United States is obtained mainly from these goats. On the southern Black Prairie, corn, sorghum, oats, cotton, flaxseed, and peanuts are grown, and vegetables are produced under irrigation. Much of the land is used for grazing; livestock is an important part of the farm economy.

# Lower Rio Grande Valley, Texas

DN-1534

PLATE 124.—The Texas side of the Lower Rio Grande Valley is one of the most intensified and diversified farming areas of the United States. Such an intensive use of land would not be possible under natural conditions. Precipitation averages from 20 to 24 inches annually, and average temperatures range from around 60 degrees in January to around 85 degrees in July. The frost-free season usually runs for more than 300 days. Irrigation, for which the Rio Grande provides the water, is essential to arable use of the land. Supply, conservation, and use of the waters of the Rio Grande are regulated through agreement between the United States and Mexico, the two countries concerned. Irrigation is not confined to the delta or flood plain of the river; it extends to parts of the adjacent plain to which the water is lifted by pumps. The plains section shown lies 5 miles southeast of Edinburg in Hidalgo County. The slightly undulating plain is a few feet higher than the alluvial bottom. It is free from overflow, whereas parts of the lowlands along the river are flooded occasionally. The soils in the lower alluvial delta are heavy light-colored clays, while the soils of the plain are prevailingly dark brown calcareous clay loams. Most of the farms are small or medium-sized, and their operators specialize in a diversity of products. Cotton, citrus fruit, especially grapefruit, and vegetables are grown extensively for the market. Livestock and livestock products, particularly dairying, also contribute to the farm economy of the area.

# Sand Plain, Southern Texas

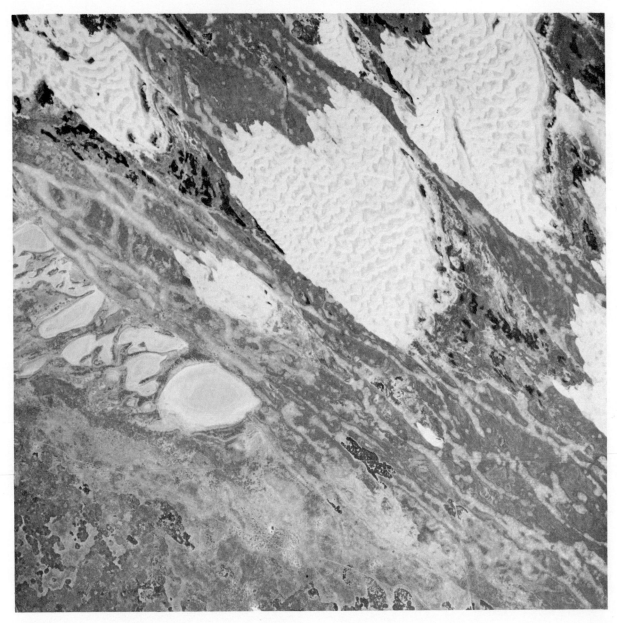

DN-1535

PLATE 125.—On the southern end of the Gulf Coastal Plain in Texas, between Baffins Bay and the Rio Grande delta, a stretch of sandy country extends inland for nearly 100 miles. In areal spread, this sandy plain comprises some 4,000 square miles, which is large enough to be considered of regional proportion. Aside from the gradual rise inland of the plain, variations from the general level are localized. In reality, the plain is a composite of flats, billowy patches, mounds, ridges and sand dunes, interspersed with shallow depressions. Mounds and ridges rise to 50 feet and more above the level of the plain. No drainage channels traverse the plain. All the rain that falls—some 20 to 25 inches—is absorbed by the fine porous sand that covers the plain. Many of the depressions contain water at times and thus form intermittent lakes. Originally, the Sand Plain was prairie with mottes and groves of live oaks scattered over the grassland, but is has been invaded by mesquite and is now largely brushland. The tract shown lies 8 miles inland from the Laguna Madre shore and 11 miles south of Baffins Bay. Sand dunes have their drift orientation in a northwest direction; they are more numerous and extensive near the coast than farther inland. The best use that can be made of such land is grazing. Large ranches are operated in the area, and as the winters are mild the livestock, mainly cattle, can make year-round use of the range.

# Interior Coastal Prairie of Texas

DN-1536

PLATE 126.—The Interior Coastal Prairie of Texas is the smaller of the grassland belts, known as black prairies, that originally traversed the wooded part of the coastal plains. This prairie parallels the coast 100 miles inland between the Brazos and San Antonio Rivers. As on other black prairies, the soils are or were heavy black or clay loams with a high humus content developed from calcareous clay. The interior Coastal Prairie, however, has a more rolling surface than either the Gulf Coast Prairie or the Texas Black Prairie farther inland. Although average precipitation ranges from 30 to 40 inches annually, erosion is likely to be very damaging unless precautionary measures are taken in the cultural use of the land. The creeks that emerge from this prairie have little or no bottom land; they are still cutting and dissecting the surface. Settlement, division, and use of the land in the central part of this prairie are illustrated. The tract shown lies 2 miles northeast of Shiner in Lavaca County. To prevent erosion, most fields are contoured for the main crops, cotton and corn, which otherwise would induce erosion. The diversified farms are medium-sized. The long frost-free season of approximately 280 days is favorable for production of cotton, which is the outstanding cash crop of the region. Livestock and livestock products, poultry, and dairying combined, however, are a close second in the economy of the region and affect the use made of the land. A large acreage is used for grazing.

# Gulf Coast Prairie of Texas

DN—1537

PLATE 127.—The Gulf Coast Prairie of Texas is not uniform in its physical aspects nor is its inherent productivity everywhere fully developed and used for agricultural production. Much of the prairie is still in its natural state and can be used only for grazing. The interstream flats are extensive; the surface slopes are so slight that differences in elevation are frequently less than 5 feet per mile. Heavy soils retard internal drainage. Aside from the natural levees along the rivers and creeks, the soils are usually dark gray to black clays with calcareous nodules in the impervious clay subsoil. Small sandy mounds 2 to 3 feet high are more conspicuous in the eastern section of the Coastal Prairie, and depressions or "hog wallows" as they are called locally, are more numerous in the central part. The Gulf Coast Prairie gets progressively drier toward the west. Precipitation is around 52 inches annually at the mouth of the Sabine River and 26 inches at Baffins Bay, which may be considered as the semiarid-subhumid boundary. The frost-free season lasts from 280 to 340 days. Cotton, which was for some time the main crop of the Coastal Prairie region, has been almost entirely replaced by rice, production of which is expanding. In the drier western part of the prairie, cotton is still the principal crop and its production is expanding. The natural setting of a central prairie tract in Brazoria County, 5 miles north of East Columbia, is illustrated. The conversion of the Coastal Prairie to rice culture usually requires community organization, as a system of canals and ditches must be established to make water available for flooding the rice fields and draining the land to make mechanized field operations possible. Raw land is usually held in large tracts. Development of surface use is frequently complicated by oilfields, which introduce the question of oil occurrence and value as one of foremost concern.

# Central Section, Texas Black Prairie

DN—1410

PLATE 128.—The central division of the Texas Black Prairie is located on the western edge of the humid east. Therefore, its climate is more favorable to agriculture than the southern division. In terms of annual averages, precipitation ranges from 30 to 40 inches, which is distributed fairly evenly throughout the seasons. Temperatures are high in the summer—they average around 84 degrees in July—and mild in winter. The frost-free season normally lasts from 230 to 250 days. On the eastern side, the land is gently rolling. On the western side, it is even more rolling and erosion is more of a problem. Soils are predominantly fertile dark brown to black clay loams or clays, which developed from limestone, chalk, or marls under prairie vegetation. The rivers that traverse the prairie belt have cut channels up to 150 feet deep in these forma-

tions. Some, as the Brazos River, have broad terraces of alluvial soil, which are lighter in both texture and color than the upland soils. Most of the land in this division of the Texas Black Prairie has good physical qualities for cropping. It has provided the background for the concentrations of the farms and cropland in this part of Texas. The part of the prairie shown is the smoother black waxy prairie type, which is found south of Waco in McLennan County. Farms are mainly small to medium-sized. Cotton is the chief cash crop grown; it accounts for nearly half of the value of farm crops sold. Corn, oats, and other feed crops are also grown to some extent, as livestock and livestock products, especially dairy and poultry products, contribute a good share of the farm income.

# Forest Belt, Eastern Texas

DN-1409

PLATE 129.—In the forest belt of eastern Texas, land use has changed repeatedly since the arrival of the first settlers nearly a century and a half ago. Land was frequently obtained from the Spanish government in large tracts on which the settlers started a subsistence type of farming. Cotton, which was introduced after the War Between the States, became the cash crop that gave farming its present orientation. With the opening of the country through railroads and roads, lumbering spread. Most of the land has been cut over but lumbering is still a local industry. With the introduction of sustained forest-yield practices, it will no doubt increase in importance. The climate is favorable to cotton growing. Precipitation averages annually from 40 to 50 inches, and the frost-free season usually lasts from 230 to 260 days. Agriculture, based mainly on cotton, expanded on the cutover land. It reached its peak in the early years of this century.

Since then, agriculture has declined. During the last quarter-century, the acreage of harvested cropland in 32 counties in eastern Texas declined nearly 2 million acres, or 60 percent, as an overall average. Several things may have helped to bring about these changes. One stems from the land itself. As a rule, Coastal Plains soils are not highly productive inherently; they need heavy fertilization. Many of the farmers were tenants who did not follow soil-conserving practices. Also, industrial employment attracted farm labor. How this change has affected the land use pattern is illustrated in the photograph. The tract shown is on State Highway 31, 7 miles east of Tyler in Smith County. Formerly, most of the land in this locality was used as cropland. Now the greater part of it is reverting to woodland. In this county alone, cropland harvested was reduced in the last decade from 144,000 to 69,000 acres, or 52 percent.

# Boston Mountains, Arkansas

DN–1408

PLATE 130.—The Boston Mountains form the southern ramparts of the Ozark Plateau. Rising from the Arkansas Valley to elevations that approach or even exceed 2,500 feet, the Boston Mountains constitute the highest portion of the Ozarks themselves. The former plateau is here maturely dissected by steep-walled, V-shaped valleys carved into the formations of sandstone and shale. Little or no bottom land has been built up along the streams, and only small remnants of smooth land remain of the old plateau level. As the land is mountainous and rugged throughout the region, its cultural use is confined to scattered areas. The drainage divide in the vicinity of Boston in Madison County is shown. In contrast to most other mountain areas, fields and farms are located at the tops and crests of the mountains; farms in the valleys, with fields on the lower slopes of the mountains, are exceptions. The climate is humid; the annual average precipitation is close to 50 inches. Most of the land is in forest, and some of the old fields are reverting to woodland. Forestry is the best use for most of the land; a large acreage is included in the purchase area of the Ozark National Forest. Farming in these mountains is near the subsistence level. Livestock is the chief source of farm income. Corn and hay are the most important crops but little of either reaches the market. Some cotton fields are occasionally seen on the lower levels, but for the region as a whole, cotton is unimportant. Elevation has lifted the mountains out of the Cotton Belt by reducing the growing season to less than 200 days. The foot of the Boston Mountains just about defines the northern limit of the Cotton Belt in this part of the country.

# Northern Border, Ouachita Mountains, Arkansas

DN-1407

PLATE 131.—Land use over much of the Ouachita Mountain region in Arkansas is controlled by the outstanding mountain chains and over large areas by low ridges also. Frequently, the intervening broad valleys are composed of a succession of low narrow ridges which, because they are banded groups, are almost as effective in controlling arable use of the land as are the higher mountains. The higher chains of the Ouachita Mountains are in the southern part of this mountain region, which, in turn, is bordered along the Arkansas River by a belt of lower ridges. The land use pattern produced through consistent adjustment of use, particularly arable use, to the natural background provided by geologic, soil, and physiographic conditions reflects the influence of these environmental factors. As in most of the former public-domain territory, the land is divided into rectangular sections, townships, and ranges, but only fragmentary lines of the systems appear in the spatial order of the pattern. The ridges and valleys shown are part of the Petit Jean Valley in Logan county; they lie between Blue Mountain on the east and Magazine Mountain on the west. At the most, the ridge crests rise only around 200 feet above the valley floor. Roads and cultivated lands follow the trend of the ridges, but property lines are oriented north to south and east to west. As a result, few fields are rectangular. The soils are chiefly loams and silt loams and the ridge soils are usually stony. The frost-free season lasts around 220 days, and the average annual precipitation is close to 50 inches. Farming is diversified. Livestock provides the principal source of farm income. Much of the cleared land is used for pasture. Cotton is the principal cash crop, but corn leads in crop acreage.

# Flood Plains of the Mississippi, Arkansas

DN-1406

PLATE 132.—A number of Arkansas counties are located entirely or to a large extent in the flood plains of the Mississippi River and its larger tributaries. Under natural conditions, these broad lowland belts along the rivers were in constant danger of flooding and large acreages were usually wet or swampy. Only the lands on the natural levees built up by the rivers and the higher spots in the plains were settled and used to grow crops. Not until the land was protected from overflow by levees on the rivers and a drainage system installed could it be settled and converted to more productive use. Much of the alluvial soil is medium to heavy textured. When sufficiently drained, the soils are fertile, and within the prevailing growing season of 210 days or more a variety of crops can be produced. With the improvement in flood control and drainage, most of the land was converted into farms and is now used for crops. The tract of lowland shown lies 2 to 3 miles back of the river levees between Holt and Wilson in Mississippi County. A system of drainage canals, with a pumping station at their confluence to lift the water over a ground swell, has reclaimed the former semiswampy depressions for crop production. Agriculture in these bottom lands depends largely on cash crops. Approximately half the cropland is used for cotton, but soybeans, alfalfa, and corn are also grown. Livestock and its products occupy a relatively minor position in the farm economy of the area.

# Mississippi Silty Terraces, Arkansas

DN-1405

PLATE 133.—Rice culture in Arkansas is a relatively new development. The first commercial crop of rice was grown in 1904 on the terrace prairie near Carlisle, from which rice growing spread south, east, and north. Lay of land, soils, and climate have all contributed to a favorable natural environment for production of rice on the northern terraces. These terraces are located up to 40 and more feet above the river bottoms, have an undulating surface, and a silt loam soil with a heavy silty clay or clay subsoil. A warm season of 220 to 230 frost-free days and an average of nearly 50 inches of precipitation annually are favorable to rice production. Originally, some of the terrace land was prairie, and it was on the prairie that rice farming started. Much of the riceland now in operation had to be cleared of trees and stumps, and to hold water on the land, field levees had to be constructed. Water to flood the ricefields is usually obtained from wells and streams and lifted by pumps on the fields. Heavy pumping has lowered the water table. As a preventive measure, a good many reservoirs were constructed on the secondary streams to hold the water back and make it available to growers. Arkansas County soon took the lead in rice growing and has since retained it. A tract of riceland south of Almyra in Arkansas County is shown. The expansion of rice culture on such terraces as these has made Arkansas, with its annual production of around 9 million bags, a major rice-producing State. Agriculture, however, is diversified. Other important crops are cotton, lespedeza seed, soybeans, oats, and corn. Even livestock makes a notable contribution to the farm economy of the region.

237

DN-1404

PLATE 134.—The Coastal Plain of Arkansas south of the Ouachita Mountains may be divided conveniently into three major land types—the rolling upland, the nearly level terraces, and the broad alluvial river bottoms. Broadly speaking, surface relief, soils and drainage can be identified with these divisions. On the upland, the soils are mainly sandy loam with a heavier reddish subsoil and are well drained; on the terraces, the soils are chiefly gray silt loams with a heavy silty clay subsoil and are frequently inadequately drained. The alluvial soils range in texture from fine sand to clay, are dark gray or brown, and are poorly drained over much of the bottom land, but they are usually considered to be more productive than either terrace or upland soils. The climate in this part of Arkansas is humid and rather warm with an annual mean precipitation of around 50 inches and from 220 to 230 days without killing frost. Originally, all the land was covered with forest, which on the upland and terraces consisted mainly of short leaf and loblolly pine, and on the bottomland of mixed hardwoods. All of the land has been cut over but only a small part of it has been cleared and used for crops, as may be noted in the upland tract shown, which lies 6 miles northwest of Fordyce in Dallas County. Cotton is the main cash crop, and some additional farm income is derived from livestock. Farming as a labor-employing industry has had competition, especially from oil and gas fields, lumbering, and manufacturing, and it is now declining. The acreage of cropland harvested declined in 11 Coastal Plain counties by more than 40 percent during the last quarter-century. When used for crops, the land is not very productive without soil improvement, although it is good forest land and no doubt will be used to produce forest crops for some time to come.

# Mississippi Flood Plain of Louisiana

DN–1403

PLATE 135.—In Louisiana, a large part of the Mississippi flood plain remains to be reclaimed. Most of the forest in these bottom lands has been cut over, but only small areas of the forest lands have been cleared and converted to agricultural use. Drainage over much of these lands is still deficient, and arable use is of necessity selective. Actual differences in elevation between swells and troughs within the alluvial bottoms are not more than a few feet, but they prevent uniform drainage of the land. These swells and troughs are the byproducts of the river's labor in filling and building up the alluvial plain. The Mississippi River tends to meander, and, as a result, its channel has changed frequently. Old oxbow bends were filled up and new ones were formed. The natural levees built by the river on its banks are now the higher and drier swells that alternate with depressions. As a rule, the soils on these swells are fine sandy loams as compared with the clays of the lower land that lies behind them. Adjustment of clearings to these micro-relief features has produced the unique land use pattern of the lowlands. The crescent-shaped strips of fields and forests that are features of the pattern are illustrated by the tract shown, which lies on Muddy Bayou, 3 miles west of Waterproof in Tensas Parish. Fertile soils, the approximately 230 frost-free days, and the annual precipitation of 50 inches or more are favorable for many crops. Farming is diversified. Livestock and crops produce the farm income, but of the two, crops are more important. Crop acreage per farm, however, is rather small. Cotton leads in both acreage and value, although corn, oats, soybeans, and lespedeza are included in the rotation.

# Coastal Prairie of Louisiana

DN—1402

PLATE 136.—At the time of the Louisiana Purchase in 1803, only a small part of the Mississippi Basin was actually settled by the French. Even the part that comprises the present State of Louisiana was not fully occupied. The Coastal Prairie that extends westward from the Mississippi lowland was still open country, and with the transfer of jurisdiction to the United States, it became part of the national public domain. As in most other parts of the public domain, the land was subdivided into townships and sections, and opened for settlement. Demarcation of holdings in this part of Louisiana is therefore derived from the rectangular land divisions, which also furnish the background from which the land use pattern developed. The prairie land is nearly flat with scattered depressions; much of the land had to be drained before it could be used for crops. With improved drainage, the soils of the Coastal Prairie are very productive; they consist predominantly of dark brown silt loams with heavy subsoils. A frost-free season of around 270 days and an average annual precipitation of approximately 58 inches, well distributed over the seasons, are favorable for a number of crops. The area shown lies just west of the district occupied by the French settlers and about 6 miles southwest of Lafayette in Lafayette Parish. As may be noted, tree growth is confined to the shallow bottoms of the drainage channels. As the farms are mainly small, the land is used intensively. Farming is diversified and most of the farm income is derived from crops. Livestock accounts for a minor part only. Of the cash crops grown in rotation, cotton leads, followed by sweetpotatoes, sugarcane, and rice. Toward the Texas border, cotton and sugarcane decline in relative importance and rice becomes more important.

# Mississippi Lowland with French Settlement, Louisiana

DN-1401

PLATE 137.—When at the turn of the 17th century the French established the Louisiana Colony at the mouth of the Mississippi, they impressed their cultural distinction on the land. French community settlers usually followed the institutionalized long-lot system in dividing the land. The terrain along the lower Mississippi and the bayous in Louisiana provided a particularly favorable natural environment for use of long-lot divisions. The better drained land on the natural levees on the banks of the rivers was used by the settlers. Homesteads were rather closely spaced. They formed line villages along the roads on both sides of the rivers. Their relatively narrow lots extended back from the rivers. In this way, all settlers had access to land and water transportation and communication facilities. The fact that rivers were not straight also affected the alinement of lots. Inside the bends of the rivers, the lots converged toward the apex of the bend, while outside the bends, the lots frequently fanned out from the bend. A situation of

this kind is illustrated in the photograph, which shows a bend in the Bayou Lafourche, Assumption Parish. Bayou Lafourche is in reality a delta branch of the Mississippi. Near the upper end, the natural levees form a ridge some 6 to 8 miles wide and 15 to 20 feet high, with the river flowing at its crest. Drainage of the land, therefore, is away from the river. Toward the gulf, levees are narrower and lots are correspondingly shorter. Soils of the levees are fertile fine sandy or silt loams which, combined with the approximately 270 frost-free days and approximately 60 inches of annual precipitation, are favorable for a variety of crops. Actually, agriculture is largely specialized. Farms in the environs of the same area are frequently large; some are of plantation size. The principal crop is sugarcane, and corn and some rice are grown. The adjacent swamps and marshlands are the breeding ground of muskrats, which are trapped for their pelts, and thus are an economic asset of the region.

241

# Lower Coastal Plain, Mississippi

DN—1400

PLATE 138.—There is a noticeable distinction in the distribution of cropland between the Interior Coastal Plain of Mississippi and the Lower Coastal Plain. In the Lower Coastal Plain, the few scattered farms are on the uplands while the river and creek bottoms are mainly swamps. The distributional order, therefore, is just about reversed from the order farther inland. The alluvial plains of the larger rivers are often miles wide. They support a heavy forest growth composed mainly of water-loving species, among which are oaks, gum, cypress, tupelo, and spruce pine. The soils are fertile, but their reclamation for agricultural production would require flood protection and improved drainage, in addition to clearing. This is more a matter of cost-benefit relationships than an engineering problem. Precipitation near the coast is higher than it is farther inland. The average of 60 and more inches annually frequently occurs in heavy downpours that flood the river bottoms. Heavy rainfall has its drawbacks on the uplands also. Much of the plain is dissected, and because of the danger from erosion it is not suited to arable use. In addition, the frost-free season of more than 240 days makes the area almost subtropical. Farms are located on the smoother areas where the soils are sandy loams. Most of the land is in forest, to which it is well adapted, but timber stands are depleted. Extensive tracts in southern Mississippi have been included in purchase areas of the national forests. Farming is diversified. Either livestock or crops may be the leading farm-income producer. Cotton, sweetpotatoes, and sugarcane for sirup have always been the leading cash-producing crops in these parts of the Coastal Plain. Of late, however, tung nuts have forged ahead. Already the tung nut is the chief crop in some localities of southern Mississippi.

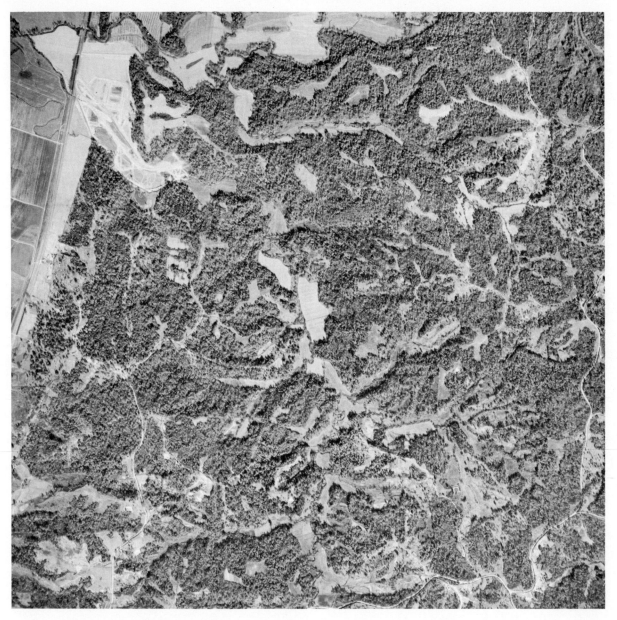

DN-1399

PLATE 139.—Loess is usually considered an eolian deposit of the pleistocene period. It has provided the parent material for soil over extensive areas of the United States. Soils developed from loess usually are productive and fairly easy to till, but because of the uniform silty texture of the material, loess is also highly erosive. Therefore, in strongly rolling to hilly loess country the danger of erosion is always present. When used for cultivated crops, proper care in tilling the land is essential to preserve the soil. Of the loess areas in the United States, the Bluff Hills that flank the Alluvial Valley of the Mississippi to the east are the best known. These hills, on which the loess mantle reaches a thickness of 40 feet in places, rise up to 200 feet from the alluvial plains. Erosion has cut deeply into the loess and the underlying Coastal Plain deposits and has dissected the upland into a maze of ridges, with narrow valley bottoms and crests. The Bluff Hills are predominantly rough and only the smoother valley bottoms and ridge crests are cleared and used for crops. The cleared area comprises about one-fourth of the total land area. The hill section shown lies immediately northeast of Yazoo City. The land is mainly in woods of the oak–hickory type, with some beech trees in places, to prevent erosion. The rainfall averages 52 inches annually and frequently falls in heavy downpours. The long, warm summers would be favorable for many crops; but as most farms are small, with small and irregular fields in valleys and on ridgetops, and are operated by tenants, the main crop is cotton. Livestock, largely cattle, which use the cleared and openly wooded pastures, contribute a minor share to the farm economy of these hills.

# Yazoo Basin, Mississippi River Bottoms, Mississippi

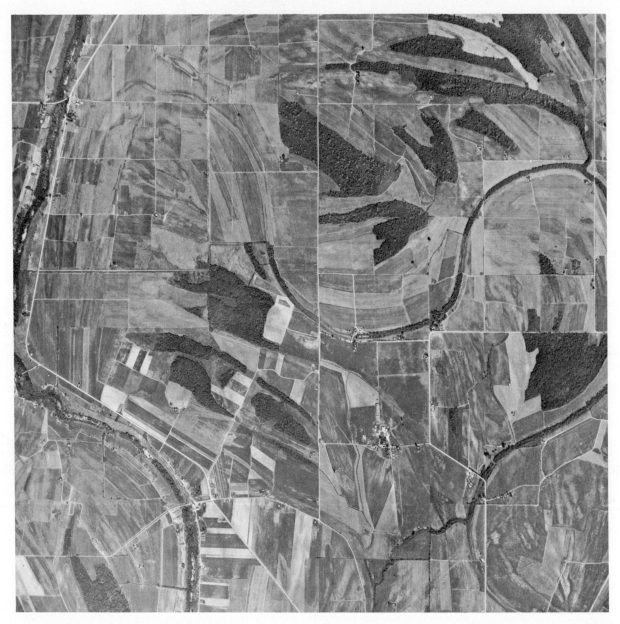

DN-1398

PLATE 140.—Although Mississippi lies entirely within the humid, warm–temperate part of the Coastal Plain, the acreage of cropland is unevenly distributed. Of the 6 million acres of harvested cropland in the State, 2 million are concentrated in the Yazoo Basin, which comprises approximately only one-seventh of the State's total land area. Such a concentration of cropland was made possible only through protection of the land from overflow and installation of improved drainage to lower the groundwater table. The alluvial soils of the delta are fertile, and when the land became available for cultural use, agricultural expansion was brought about not only by the efforts of the local population, but also by people from uplands who were attracted to the lowlands. Aside from the backwater areas that must be left in forest, most of the land is cleared and used for crops, and a smaller acreage is left in forest or is used for pasture. Woodlots are usually confined to the lower, wetter spots, as may be seen on the tract shown, which lies 3 miles southwest of Drew, in Sunflower County. Differences in elevation between swells and depressions are frequently less than 5 feet, but even after the land is cleared and drained these swells and depressions remain distinguishing marks that reveal the alluvial buildup of the soil. The fertile soils combined with the warm long summers would permit production of a diversity of crops. Most of the farms are relatively small. Many are managed as plantation units operated by tenants. As cotton has a relatively high per acre value, these small farms have made cotton the principal cash crop of the Yazoo Basin. Livestock is only a minor part of the farm economy of the area.

# Upper Coastal Plain, Northern Mississippi

DN-1397

PLATE 141.—Arable land use on the Upper Coastal Plain of northern Mississippi has been adjusted to several factors of environment. The outstanding characteristic of the area is the concentration of fields in the creek bottoms, but only a sprinkling of farms and fields is found on the upland. Lay of land and quality of soil are largely responsible for this distributional order. Much of the land is badly dissected, and this has produced its strongly rolling to hilly surface. On the level upland tracts, the soil usually is a heavy silt or clay loam with a compact clay subsoil. This land is poorly drained and difficult to cultivate, and it has a rather low productivity. The broad alluvial creek and river bottoms, however, usually have silt loam soils that are productive when drained. Moreover, draining these bottom lands is not the problem it is farther south where precipitation is considerably higher than the 50 inches normal in this part of the country. Easier tillage and greater productivity account for the preferential use of the alluvial bottoms as illustrated. The tract shown lies approximately 3 miles south of Loyd in Calhoun County, on tributary creeks of the Yalobusha River. In these environs, although three-fourths of the land is in farms, less than a fourth is used for crops. Most of the land is woodland but very little is in commercial stands. Pasturing the woodland is common practice. Livestock and its products, however, provide only a minor part of the farm income. This is Cotton Belt country with long and warm summers; the frost-free period usually lasts around 215 days; and the farm economy is founded on cash crops, of which the chief one is cotton. Many of the farms, however, operate on a subsistence level.

# Northern End Mississippi-Alabama Black Prairie, Mississippi

DN-1396

PLATE 142.—Approximately a third of the Mississippi–Alabama Black Prairie Belt lies in Mississippi, where it forms the northern end of the crescent. Although it is usually included in the prairie belt because the land is underlain by the chalks on which the humid prairies developed, most of the land in the northern end was originally woodland. It was composed largely of post and white oak, and had to be cleared. Within the shallow belt basin, the moderately rolling upland is divided by broad alluvial valleys, which originally were in a semiswampy condition. Land use has changed considerably since the area was settled. The better drained upland, where the soils developed from calcareous chalk formations, was the first to be cleared and used for crops. A frost-free season of more than 210 days and a normal precipitation of 50 inches a year are favorable for production of cotton. Cotton was one of the principal crops of the early settlers. It is still the main crop of the region although the land on which it is produced is not exactly the same. The medium to heavy textured soils were productive in the first years of cultivation, but they lost much of their fertility because of washing and depletion. With the reclamation of the bottom lands through dredging and straightening of the creeks, most of the fields are now on the fertile lowlands while much of the upland is used for pasture. The tract shown lies at the confluence of Conewar and Old Town Creeks, 3 miles southeast of Verona in Lee County. With the shift in land use, the dominance of cotton in the farm economy of the region is declining, and livestock farming, especially dairying, is gaining in importance.

# Jackson Purchase of Tennessee

PLATE 143.—Physiographically, the Jackson Purchase area of western Tennessee belongs to the Coastal Plain. In location, the area is confined to the upland between the Mississippi and Tennessee River Valleys. The valley borders are deeply dissected. On the interior upland, low hills between the larger streams rise gently to 150 feet from the broad, flat valley bottoms. Most of the land is smooth enough for agricultural use. Originally, the wide creek and river bottoms were wet and swampy, but organized drainage districts have dredged and straightened these watercourses, and to-day most of the alluvial flats are used for crops. Brown silt loams underlain by a silty clay loam or clay are the most extensive upland soils. They have all the characteristics of soils developed from loess. The loess deposits are deepest on the Mississippi Bluffs, thinning out toward the east until finally they give way to the sandy Coastal Plain deposits as the parent material of soils. Summers are warm and long, and the frost-free season runs for 200 to 230 days. Of the normal annual precipitation of 50 inches, about half falls in summer. After the land was bought from the Indians, it was divided into townships for settlements. But as the townships were not subdivided according to the public land system, neither roads nor fields are laid out with much regularity. The area shown lies west of Gibson in Gibson County. It is near the northern limit of the Cotton Belt, but cotton is still the main crop. Vegetables and berries are grown. Livestock and its products contribute to the farm income. Although cropland is the dominant use of the land, a good part of it is used for pasture. When Tennessee attained Statehood in 1796, the Jackson Purchase was still unsettled. For settlement purposes, it was divided into rectangular tracts. The difficulties of adjusting field operations on small rectangular tracts to the contour of strongly rolling land are apparent.

247

# Nashville Basin, Tennessee

DN-1394

PLATE 144.—The Nashville Basin, or Central Basin of Tennessee, like the Blue Grass Region of Kentucky, attracted settlers from across the Appalachian Mountains during colonial times. That the Blue Grass Region and Nashville Basin were selected by these early settlers as advanced outposts of homesteading indicates that in their opinion the natural environment of these basins offered greater advantages for settlement than the surrounding country. As development has shown, their confidence in the area was not misplaced. In the Nashville Basin, a propitious combination of land relief, soils, and climate has produced a favorable physical setting for agricultural use of the land. The surface is mainly slightly to moderately rolling. The knobs scattered over the area become more numerous toward the border. Dark-brown loams or silt loams, underlain by a reddish-brown silt-clay developed from solid limestone, are the prevalent soils of the basin. In places, they are shallow and rocky, but for the most part, they are easy to till and are adapted to a variety of crops. As the area is lower than the surrounding country, the climate is slightly warmer. Frost-free days average 200 yearly, a long enough time in which to grow cotton, although it is not the major crop. Precipitation averages around 50 inches annually and is well distributed over the seasons. The area shown lies near the border of the Nashville Basin in Rutherford County, 6 miles northeast of Murfreesboro. Some knobs appear in the photograph. Farming is diversified. Livestock provides the major portion of the farm income, with a good share derived from dairying. Corn, hay, and some small grains are the more important crops. Cotton and tobacco are the principal cash crops grown for market.

# Nashville Basin Border, Tennessee

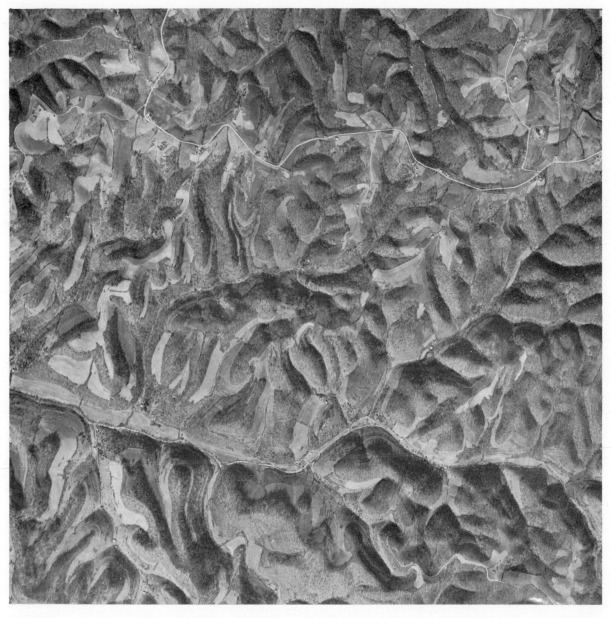

DN-1393

PLATE 145.—A more or less broad belt of hilly country forms a transition zone between the Nashville Basin and the surrounding Highland Rim. Rivers and creeks have cut their channels 400 to 500 feet below the plateau level. Near the headwaters, the valleys are shallow, but they deepen and broaden out with the approach to the basin. Near the basin, the valley floors are wider than the ridges, which finally break up into detached hills. In their middle courses, the short tributary branches of the creeks have cut deeply into the sedimentary rocks of cherty limestone, shale, and massive limestone at the bottom. The short valleys are known locally as "hollows" and most of them have names. Soil distribution follows closely the land-relief forms. On the smoother upland, the soil is a light gray gravelly loam; on the steeper slopes it is a stony loam; and in the valley bottoms and on the lower slopes, it is a reddish loam or clay loam, stony in places. The climate is temperate; the frost-free season runs around 190 days; and the annual precipitation averages 54 inches. Adjustment of land use to these conditions has produced the long, narrow fields along the ridges, their lower slopes, and the floors of the valleys as illustrated. The tract shown lies on the headwaters of Martins Creek, and forms part of the southern boundary of Jackson County. Most of the farms are small to medium-sized, owner-operated, but not fully mechanized. Many operate on a self-sufficing level. Agriculture is diversified. Corn is the chief crop, followed by lespedeza and others; but the principal cash crop is burley tobacco. Much of the land is in pasture. Livestock and its products produce the major part of the farm income.

249

# Southern Appalachian Mountains, Tennessee

DN-1392

PLATE 146.—Settlement in the southern Appalachians differs markedly from settlement in the northern part of this mountain chain. In the northeastern States, the mountain areas were settled in colonial times. Later, with the opening of the West and the industrialization of the country, many mountain people resettled in the plains or moved to towns for work in factories. The western slope of the southern Appalachians was settled near the turn of the 18th century, when the handicaps of mountainous country to mechanized agriculture were not evident. The descendants of these hardy mountaineers occupy the land today. Some shifts in farms have occurred, however, in the last 50 years. For example, in mountainous Cocke County in eastern Tennessee, the number of farms increased, with some minor setbacks, by 30 percent from 1900 to the peak number in 1935, but has since declined and is now back to the 1900 level. The land use pattern in Cocke County is illustrated by a tract that lies 4 miles south of Del Rio on the French Broad River. Elevation of the locality is around 2,500 feet. Because of the elevation, the frost-free season, which normally runs from 170 to 180 days, is somewhat shortened. Precipitation is well distributed over the seasons and averages 42 to 46 inches a year. Much of the land is steeply sloping. The soils, which developed mainly from slates and shales, are of medium texture and are moderately productive. As a rule, farms and fields are small and irregularly distributed. Much of the cleared land is used for pasture. Farming is of the general type, and many farms are in the low-income class. Livestock and crops are almost equally important in the farm economy. Prevailing crops are corn, forage crops, and small grains, with tobacco as a cash crop. Much of the more rugged mountain land is included in national forests and the Great Smoky National Park.

# Valley of East Tennessee

DN-1391

PLATE 147.—The southern division of the Appalachian Valley, which passes through Tennessee and is flanked by the Blue Ridge on the east and the plateaus on the west, is known also as the Valley of East Tennessee. Folding and faulting of sedimentary rock formations—mainly dolomite, shale, sandstone, and limestone—exposed them to weathering, solution, and erosion, and produced the peculiar arrangement of roughly parallel ridges and valleys. Sandstone, which is more resistant to weathering, is usually found on the ridges, and the more soluble limestone is found in the valleys. Soils have a similar distribution. Sandy loams are found frequently on the ridges; stony, sandy, or silt loam on the slopes; and silt loams on the lower slopes and rolling valley floors. Nearly 300 square miles of valley land are submerged, however, by the waters of reservoirs constructed for development of hydroelectric power. In such environs, physiographic features provide the controlling factor in the spatial order of major land uses. Cultivated and pasture lands are confined largely to the valley floors and lower slopes, while the ridges are usually in forest. In parts of the valley, the type of farming carried on shows the influence of climate. Summers are longer and warmer in the southern than in the northern part. The frost-free season runs for 200 days or more, and the average annual precipitation is around 52 inches. This is warm enough for cotton, which is not the principal crop, although some is grown. Farming is more of the general type with local specialties added. Dairy and poultry farms are numerous. Truck and strawberry farms are more localized. Peach and apple orchards are found throughout the valley, but there are also local concentrations. Cash grains and forage crops are grown. The sample area shown lies a mile south of Ooltewah in Hamilton County. It includes a portion of White Oak Mountain, which rises nearly 500 feet from the valley floor. Location of fields and forest shows adjustment to topography.

251

# Highland Rim, Alabama

DN-1389

PLATE 148.—In northern Alabama, the Highland Rim and the Tennessee Limestone Valley merge into a plain. Locally, the distinction between the two is based on the color of the soils. The plateau section is called "gray lands," and the valley section "red lands." The dividing line follows no well-defined surface relief feature, although the surface relief of the two areas differs somewhat. On the whole, the gray lands are more rolling and dissected than the red lands, especially near watercourses. Soils differ in productivity also. The red soils, which developed from a nearly pure massive limestone, range in texture from loam to silty clay loam. The gray soils, which derived from a cherty limestone, are usually silt loams and are frequently cherty and gravelly. Considerably more acreage is left in woods and pasture on the gray than on the red lands. The area is near the northern limit of the Cotton Belt, but summers are warm and long enough to grow cotton. The annual average precipitation is around 53 inches, and the frost-free period lasts normally more than 200 days. Farming on the red lands depends mainly on cotton. Cotton is grown on the gray lands also, but corn, forage crops, and pasture take up considerable acreages of these lands as livestock becomes more important. Erosion is active on the rolling land. The land is divided into rectangular holdings, as may be noted on the gray-land tract shown, which lies on Sugar Creek in the northwest corner of Limestone County. Although property lines are derived from the rectangular system of land division, fields are frequently adjusted to the relief of the land, particularly in the more dissected portions. The rougher and steeper slopes are used as woodland, most of which is pastured. Soil conservation practices have been adopted on some of the fields.

# Sand Mountain, Alabama

DN-1390

PLATE 149.—Contrasts in land use are not uncommon in mountainous country. Ordinarily, they follow an accepted order, although departures occur. One such departure is found on Sand Mountain in northeastern Alabama. As a rule, population is denser and land use more intensified in the valleys than on the mountains. Here, on the central section of Sand Mountain, the reverse is true. In reality, Sand Mountain, which occupies a broad belt in northern Alabama, is the southward extension of the Cumberland Plateau, from which it is separated in the north by the Tennessee Valley. Land use capability on Sand Mountain is not uniform. At its northern end, the mountain shares the physical characteristics of the Cumberland Plateau. Because of the cool climate, comparatively little land is used for crops. With the decrease in elevation southward, the summers become warmer and longer. The frost-free period is 200 days or more, and the mean annual precipitation is around 54 inches, which permits the growing of cotton, the main crop in the central section. Toward the west, the plateau is dissected into narrow ridges; the rough and stony land is suited only to forestry and is included in the national forest. The photograph illustrates land use on the central part of Sand Mountain near Kilpatrick, a village in the southwestern part of DeKalb County, with an elevation of more than 1,100 feet. The land is rolling, and much of it is cleared and cultivated. The sandy loam soil developed from the weathered material of sandstone. The soils are easy to cultivate and respond readily to good management and use of fertilizer, although their productivity is not inherently high. Cotton and corn, the principal crops, are likely to induce erosion if not properly cultivated. Property lines are derived from the rectangular land-division system, but fields are adjusted to the lay of the land. To combat erosion and preserve the soil, contour plowing and terracing are generally practiced.

# Black Prairie, Alabama

DN-1388

PLATE 150.—Bordering the western end of the Piedmont is a crescent-shaped shallow basin known as the Black Prairie of Alabama and Mississippi. The rough border of the Piedmont and the inland sloping cuestas or escarpments of the Red Hills in the Coastal Plain form the basin borders within which the runoff from the Piedmont is collected by the Tombigbee and Alabama Rivers and carried through two gaps in the cuestas to the gulf. Originally, to a large extent, the gently rolling floor of the basin was prairie with a black clay soil developed from a soft limestone, which geologists called "Selma Chalk." It was from the combination of black soil and grass vegetation that the region obtained the name Black Prairie, which is now a misnomer. Because of lack of experience in handling the soil, much of the originally fertile black soil has been washed away and the subsoil exposed. The climate is pleasant, and the rainfall averages 50 inches or more annually. Summers are long and warm, normally with more than 220 frost-free days, and winters are mild. For decades, cotton was the principal crop, but in recent years it has declined in importance. Within the last half-century, the acreage of cotton in the Black Prairie counties has decreased by approximately a million acres. The heavy plastic clays are slow in warming up in the spring, and the plant is late in forming bolls. Because of this, cotton is more exposed to attack by boll weevils. The prairie soils are now used mainly for pasture and forage crops, as may be noted in the tract of former prairie land shown, which lies 5 miles north of Safford in Dallas County. The bottom lands are drained but part of the upland has been invaded by brush. The Black Prairie of Alabama and Mississippi provides an outstanding example of how former highly productive cropland has been reduced to lower uses.

# Coastal Plain, Alabama

DN-1387

**PLATE 151.**—On the Coastal Plain of Alabama, the rougher and more dissected portions, the flatwoods, the swampy creek, and river bottoms, and the light sandy lands are mainly in forests. In some parts of the plains, the physical conditions of surface relief and soils are more favorable for agricultural use of the land, and cropland predominates. An area of this kind is found in southeastern Alabama. The tract shown lies 3 miles northeast of Headland in Henry County. Surface erosion and solution in the underlying shell marl formations produced the gently rolling upland with steeper slopes and more dissected borders near the streams. Short tributary creeks frequently have their sources in springs that issue from steep-walled holes on the side of the upland. The many shallow or steep-walled sinkholes scattered over the upland contain water intermittently and are swampy the rest of the time. The soils are sandy loams, which are easy to cultivate and with proper management are fairly productive. Winters are mild; occasional cold snaps occur but hardly any snow. Summers are warm and long, with an average frost-free season of 240 days or more. Precipitation is normally more than 54 inches per year. According to the climatic index, the area belongs in the Cotton Belt and for a long time, cotton was the principal crop. Cash crops are still the main support of the farm economy, but in recent years, cotton has given way to peanuts as the leading crop. As a source of farm income, cotton is almost on a par with livestock; neither is very important in this locality.

# Gulf Coast Forest Belt, Florida

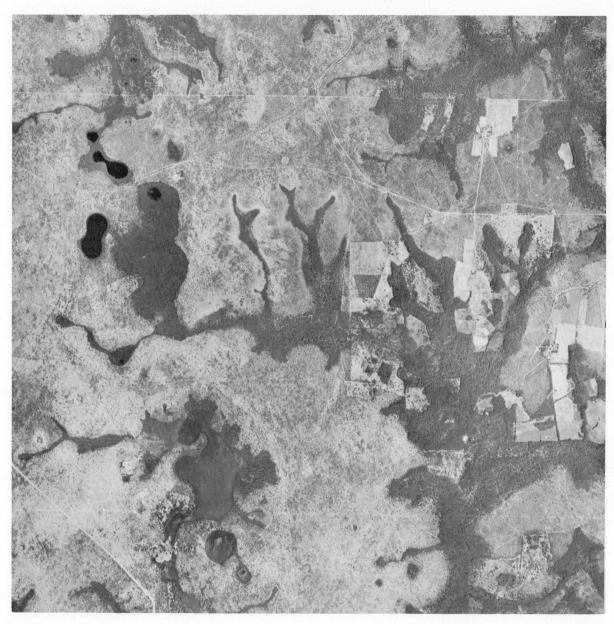

DN-1386

PLATE 152.—Along the Gulf Coast of northwestern Florida lies a broad belt in which use of the land for agricultural production is at a minimum. In a number of counties here, the land in farms is less than 10 percent of all land and the acreage used for crops is considerably less. That agriculture is so little developed in this belt is due largely to the physical conditions that govern land use as an economic enterprise. Although much of the land is rolling within the elevation zone of up to 300 feet above sea level, extensive tracts of level wet lands are also interspersed. Over much of the area, the surface forms show the characteristics of solution in the underlying limestone and marl strata. Many of the sinkholes and irregularly shaped depressions are lakes; others are swamps which frequently border drainage channels.

The soils developed largely from unconsolidated marine deposits; they consist chiefly of sands with a low or moderate productivity rating. In places, precipitation exceeds 60 inches annually. Heavy downpours are frequent. Summers are long and warm and winters are mild. The ground seldom freezes, and soil leaching is a year-long process. Forestry is the principal use of the land, and grazing is a less productive second use. The tract shown lies 4 miles southeast of Wausau in Washington County. The products of the land are mainly lumber and naval stores. Much of the forest consists of longleaf and slash pine on which the bark of the older trees is chipped for several seasons to induce the flow of gum. The gum is collected and processed into turpentine and rosin for market.

# Warm Temperate-Subtropical Transition Zone, Florida

DN-1385

PLATE 153.—In the transition from the warm temperate to the subtropical climate, temperature is a controlling factor in determining how Florida land can be used. Adjoining the citrus fruit belt to the north is a thermal zone in which heavy frosts occur too frequently to permit commercial production of citrus fruits. The winters, however, are too short and mild to provide the needed period of dormancy for deciduous fruits. This 100-mile-wide belt is not confined to Florida; it extends from the Atlantic coast westward into Texas. Within this belt, an exotic from China, the tung oil tree, has been found to fit into the climatic environment. The chilling requirements of these trees during the dormant period are only around 400 hours at 45° or lower. Also, the annual precipitation of 45 inches, which is evenly distributed over the seasons, is sufficient to meet their moisture requirements. Well-drained land with suitable soil is necessary for commercial production. The first tung oil from commercial groves was produced near Gainesville in 1928. Since then, production of tung oil has spread westward and is now an established and growing industry. The tung grove shown is 12 miles north of Gainesville in Alachua County, Florida. This grove is more than 20 years old and is still in production. Indications are that the productive life of tung trees should average at least 30 years. The land is slightly rolling with a light-textured soil. Green manure crops are grown and fertilizers are applied to maintain fertility. Aside from the tung groves, farming of a general type is practiced. Vegetables and tobacco are the crop specialties grown.

# Lake District, Central Florida

DN—1384

PLATE 154.—Physiographically, the peninsula of Florida has been roughly divided into Coastal Lowlands and Central Uplands, a distinction that is significant when land use is considered. Most of the cultivated land is in the higher center part of the State. The upland is not uniform, as there are nearly level tracts in the north. In the center of Florida, however, the upland forms a rolling-to-hilly ridge with elevations up to 300 feet in spots. Here it is dotted with large and small lakes. The area is known as the Lake District, and the citrus fruit industry is centered here. The lakes are distributed irregularly. Most of the smaller lakes and depressions have no surface connections but form closed basins. The area is underlain by limestone, and the surface forms are the result of internal erosion through solution rather than surface erosion. The soils of this rolling upland are usually light in texture. They range from loamy to fine sand, and peaty muck is found frequently in the depressions. The climate is subtropical but summer temperatures are tempered by the waters of the many lakes and the frequent showers. Rainfall averages 50 inches or more annually, but it is heavier in summer and lighter in winter. Night frosts occur occasionally, but as a rule they are not severe enough to damage the groves. Most of the rolling upland is in citrus groves. The lake country 3 miles southeast of Winter Haven in Polk County is shown. Orange and grapefruit groves occupy most of the upland; they produce the main crops of the citrus fruit industry and of the regional agriculture as a whole. Livestock farming is also represented, especially dairy farming, which supplies the needs of the local city markets.

# Everglades on Shore of Lake Okeechobee, Florida

DN-1383

PLATE 155.—Much of the land in the southern tip of Florida consists of an immense sawgrass marsh, known as The Everglades, which comprises more than 4,000 square miles. The Everglades slope slightly southward from Lake Okeechobee at the northern end to Florida Bay on the South. They are separated from the Atlantic by a narrow rocky swell and are bounded inland by swamps or higher ground. All this marshland is less than 20 feet above sea level. The soils of the Everglades are chiefly organic. Peat and muck more than 10 feet thick in places rest on either marl or limestone over the entire area. The climate of the Everglades is subtropical, that is, it is neither extremely hot in summer nor cold in winter. Frosts occur only occasionally. Precipitation is rather heavy; some parts of the Everglades average more than 60 inches annually. Attempts to drain the Everglades started in the 1880's, although the present reclamation program had its inception in the first years of the present century. Since then, hundreds of miles of drainage canals have been dredged through the glades, and a levee has been constructed around the southern end of Lake Okeechobee to prevent reflooding. So far, agricultural development is confined largely to the shores of Lake Okeechobee. A section of the developed area on South Bay is shown. Near the lake the soil is muck, with some mineral content. Farther back in the glades the soil is peat or peaty muck, which must be conditioned for cultivation. Vegetables are grown during the cooler season for the northern winter market. Other important crops are sugarcane and some horticultural specialties. Climate is a primary asset in the economy of this region.

# Okefenokee Swamp, Georgia

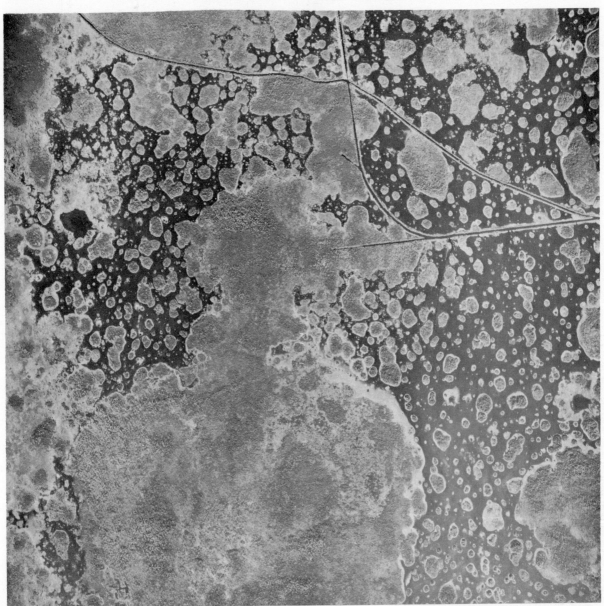

DN-1382

PLATE 156.—A chain of wet lands along the Atlantic seaboard has the Dismal Swamp in Virginia and the Okefenokee Swamp in southeastern Georgia as terminals. The Okefenokee, the largest swamp, comprises nearly 700 square miles. It is separated from the Atlantic coast by Trail Ridge, which reaches an elevation of 150 feet in places and is some 20 to 30 feet higher than the swamp back of it. Drainage of the swamp, therefore, is to the west and south, the direction in which the rivers that originate in the swamp flow. The Suwannee River flows westward into the Gulf, and the St. Mary's River forms the Georgia–Florida boundary from the swamp to the Atlantic. Natural features of the swamp include islands, lakes, prairies, pineland, and cypress thickets. What the natives call prairies are expanses of clear shallow water, occupied by lily pads, clumps of cane, saw-grass, and other aquatic plants, over which are scattered small islands—"houses"—on which cypress and shrubs have become established.

The Okefenokee Swamp has a colorful history that goes back to the Indians, from which the name, which means "trembling earth," is derived. The Seminoles, who occupied the swamp when the white settlers arrived, used it as a hideout until they were dislodged in 1838 and removed to the Florida Everglades. The white settlers used the swamp largely as a hunting and trapping ground. In 1889, the Suwannee Canal Company attempted to drain the swamp across Trail Ridge. Around 22 miles of canals were dug, but the main canal was never completed. The canals were used in lumbering operations, and today they are used by fishermen and those who are attracted to the scenic beauty and wildlife. In 1919, the Georgia Assembly set the swamp aside as a game reserve. In 1937, the Federal Government bought the land and established a wildlife refuge, which contains more than 500 square miles of swampland. A section of the swamp on the canal 3 miles west of Camp Cornelia is shown. The "prairies" with their many small islands stand out clearly from the wooded swamp.

# Dougherty Plains, Southwestern Georgia

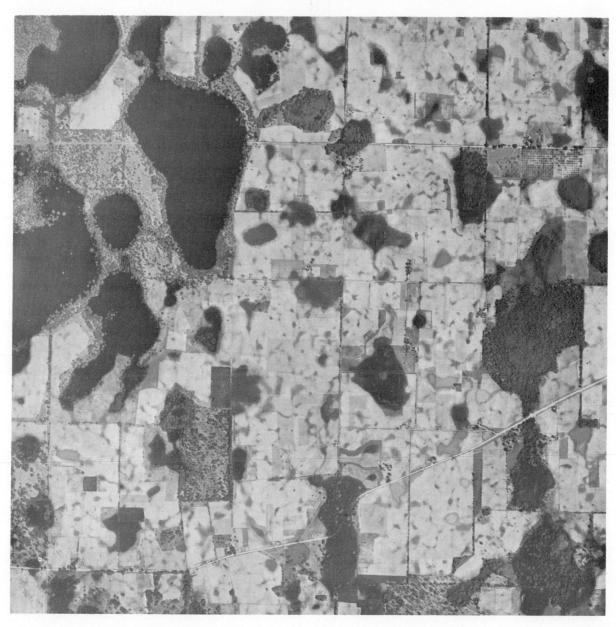

DN-1381

PLATE 157.—The southwestern section of the Coastal Plain in Georgia has developed cultural landscape characteristics of its own, which are partly of historical origin and partly imposed by natural conditions. This part of Georgia was settled in the 1820's and 1830's. In 1819-20, after the Indian claims were extinguished and before the land was deeded to settlers, it was divided into square lots of 250 acres each. These land divisions provided the boundaries of land ownership. Subdivision into fields produced the rectangular land use pattern illustrated. The tract shown lies in the Dougherty Plains 4 miles west of Newton in Baker County. The surface of the plain is nearly level but is pitted with both large and small sinkholes. Most of them are small shallow depressions, which are dry and cultivated during the warm season. Many have no surface drainage connections. Some of the larger depressions are lakes or ponds that hold water the year round. Others are swamps, as are the flood plains of the larger drainage channels that traverse the region. Sandy loams with a red sandy clay subsoil predominate, and because of the red subsoil, the region is sometimes referred to as red land. The land is easy to cultivate and rather productive. A warm climate with long summers and short winters, in which snow seldom falls, permits the growing of a variety of crops. The average annual precipitation is close to 50 inches and is fairly evenly distributed over the seasons. Climatically, the area is part of the Cotton Belt, and some cotton is grown, but peanuts are the chief cash crop. The lower Flint River basin also has production centers of pecans, melons, and vegetables. Although livestock is important in the farm economy, it is not a principal source of farm income.

# Upper Coastal Plain at Fall Line, Georgia

DN—1380

PLATE 158.—Geologically, the Fall Line separates the metamorphic rocks of the Piedmont from the sedimentary formations of the Coastal Plain. Frequently, no such sharp distinction can be detected in use of the land. Where the lower border of the Piedmont and the upper edge of the Coastal Plain merge, a belt of predominantly wooded country is usually found. The reason for the scarcity of cultivated land in this belt must be sought in the surface relief conditions. The swiftly flowing waters of the creeks and rivers that descend from the plateau have cut deeply into the underlying strata and have produced a rugged topography. Compared with the wide flood plains along watercourses in the Coastal Plain, the river bottoms on the Piedmont side are narrow. Because of the steeper slope gradient of the rivers and the narrowness of the valleys, many hydraulic power sites are found along the Fall Line. Dams, reservoirs, and electric power plants are conspicuous landscape features. The section of the transition belt shown lies 9 miles southeast of Knoxville in Crawford County, near the Peach County boundary. Adjacent to the upper rougher portion of the Coastal Plain lies a belt of smoother rolling country pitted with sinkholes, the result of solution in the underlying beds of sandy limestone and calcareous clay. As a rule, soil distinctions between the Piedmont and the Coastal Plain are pronounced. Heavy soils predominate on the Piedmont and light-textured soils on the Coastal Plain. Warm and long summers, with around 240 frost-free days, and a normal annual precipitation of 50 inches, permit the growing of a variety of crops. Cotton is the main cash crop, but fruits, particularly peaches, are also important. Livestock and its products also contribute a good share to the farm income.

# Great Appalachian Valley Abutting Piedmont Hills, Georgia

DN-1379

PLATE 159.—In the Appalachian Mountains and valleys of northwestern Georgia, land use at times shows strong contrasts as a result of adjustment to physiographic conditions. The sharpest contrast of this kind can frequently be identified with changes in the geologic structure. An instance is illustrated in the area shown, which lies at the junction of Bartow, Polk, and Paulding Counties. Most of the farmland shown is in Bartow County; most of the forest land is in Paulding County; and the corner of Polk County shares both. The great Appalachian Valley, in which the farms are located, extends in this area south of the Blue Ridge and borders the hilly Piedmont. Agricultural land use in the valley and forest use in the hills are sharply defined by a fault that separates the limestone and shales of the valley floor from schists and gneisses of the Piedmont. Weathering, erosion, and solution have produced the marked surface distinctions. A smoothly rolling valley floor with some rough spots and hills is on one side of the fault line, and the Piedmont hills are on the other. The Piedmont hills are only 200 to 300 feet higher than the floor of the Appalachian Valley but as they are steeply dissected into a maze of rough and broken ridges, they are left in forest. Farming in the valley shows the influence of climate and soils. The soils are predominantly medium to heavy though gravelly in many places. The valley has an elevation of around 700 feet and a mild climate with a frost-free season that covers usually more than 200 days. More than 50 inches of precipitation is well distributed over the seasons. Cotton is the main cash crop, although corn, hay, some small grains, and vegetables are grown. Livestock and its products provide about a third of the farm income.

263

# Big Dukes Pond on Middle Coastal Plain, Georgia

DN-1378

PLATE 160.—In Georgia, the land use patterns in the eastern part of the Coastal Plain are distinct from those in the western part. These distinctions are due largely to the historical background of settlement and ground conditions. Settlement east of the Oconee River antidates statehood. The acreage deeded to settlers depended on the headright provision of the colonial government. The land was not divided for the settlers; each settler took what he believed himself entitled to. As a result, landlines, fields, and roads do not fit into any systematic arrangement, as may be seen in the tract shown, which lies in Jenkins County. The second object of interest is Big Dukes Pond, the large depression on the low divide between Ogeechee and Buckhead Creek 7 miles northwest of Millen. Many irregular sinkhole depressions indicate that the surface forms are largely the result of solution in the underlying beds of impure limestone encountered at a depth of 35 to 50 feet. These sinks are usually only from 4 to 10 feet deep. A peculiarity of Big Dukes Pond is that it has acquired some of the characteristics of bays. A smooth oval shoreline and sandy rim in the southeast quadrant indicate that the same forces—intermittent pluvial and dry windy periods— that formed the spoilrims of the bays were not confined to the lower levels of the Coastal Plain during the Pleistocene Epoch. The soils of this area are mainly sandy loams and shallow muck deposits are frequently found in the wet areas. A mild climate with warm long summers and abundant precipitation is characteristic of this part of the Cotton Belt. Cotton is the main cash crop, although about a third of the farm income is derived from livestock and its products.

# Old Shore Lines in Coastal Flatwoods, South Carolina

DN-1377

PLATE 161.—On the lower terrace of the Coastal Plain in South Carolina, comparatively little land is used for tilled crops. In a number of counties, the acreage of cropland is less than 10 percent of the total land area. That agriculture is so little developed in this part of the State is largely the result of deficient drainage. Land relief over extensive interstream areas is so flat that rainwater, of which around 50 inches falls as the annual average, moves and drains off very slowly. Consequently, it has little cutting power to extend the heads of the creeks onto the flats. Differences in elevation between the broad swampy river bottoms and the interstream flats usually are less than 50 feet, and the slope is confined mainly to belts that border the river bottoms. It is within these belts of better drained land that settlement and agricultural development are found. The terraces and shorelines, which are better drained, are used for homesteads and farmland. A sample area 9 miles southwest of Moncks Corner is shown. The soil of the better drained land is a light colored sandy loam. On the poorly drained land, the soils are usually darker and heavier. With proper management, the soils are fairly productive, and as the growing season normally covers more than 250 frost-free days, they are adapted to many crops. Farm income is derived mainly from cash crops. Cotton and tobacco lead as cash crops, but corn, hay, and feed crops are also important. Most of the land, even the land in farms, is in forest. The forest consists of more or less open stands of longleaf and loblolly pine with a carpet of grasses that furnish pasture in spring and summer.

# Carolina Bays on Middle Coastal Plain, South Carolina

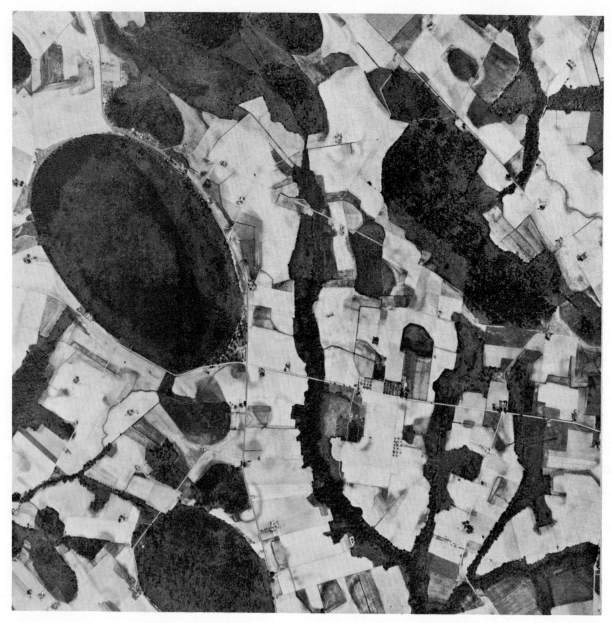

DN-1376

PLATE 162.—The Coastal Plain of the Carolinas can be divided into two belts geologically—the interior belt in which the cretaceous and tertiary formations reach the surface, and the lower belt in which the older formations are covered by quaternary marine deposits. It is within the belt of quaternary deposits that the so-called Carolina Bays are found. In South Carolina, these bays are most numerous on the higher level of this belt. In places, these shallow oval depressions, which range from a few acres to several square miles, comprise the major part of the land. True to their characteristics, they occupy primarily interfluvial land and are frequently without drainage outlets or connections. In these instances they constitute the chief impediment to cultural use of the land. Most of these bays are basins that must be reclaimed through drainage if use as cropland is contemplated. An area of this type, halfway between McColl and Clio in Marlboro County, is illustrated. As may be seen, many of the smaller bays are now used for cultivated crops, but each so used must have artificial drainage installed. The soils of the dry land are light gray sandy loams. In the smaller bays, the soils are medium or dark gray, silt, or clay loams. Those of the larger bays, like Mossey Ocean on the western margin of the photograph, are black or clay loams. The darkness of the soil derives largely from its organic matter content. Long warm summers and an annual mean precipitation of 48 inches would permit the growing of a variety of crops, but the farm economy is based on cotton. Livestock and its products account for a relatively small part of the farm income in this area.

# Thermal Belt of Upper Piedmont, South Carolina

DN-1375

PLATE 163.—The Upper Piedmont bordering the mountains is strongly rolling, and in places even hilly. Land of this kind, especially when used for row crops, washes easily if cultural practices are not adapted to conservation. The soils are erosive. The surface soil usually is a sandy or sandy clay loam with a yellow or red-brown compact subsoil. With proper management, these soils are very productive. A decrease in acreage of cropland during the last few decades indicates that some of the land is better suited to woodland and pasture than to cultivated crops. Terracing and contour plowing are used widely in the Piedmont, as may be observed in the sample area shown. This tract lies on South Pacolet River, 3 miles northeast of Inman in Spartanburg County. Crops are grown on the contour here, and peach orchards are laid out and planted in the same way. Next to cotton, peaches are the chief cash crop. That this fruit can play such an important part in the local economy is largely because of the nearby mountains. Along the Piedmont side of the Blue Ridge, lies a thermal belt in which, as a result of excellent air drainage, late and damaging frosts during blossom-time are rare. In the southern end of the belt, peaches, and farther north, apples, are grown as commercial crops. The climate in the southern part of the belt is warm enough at an elevation of around 1,000 feet to permit production of cotton as the main crop. The frost-free period is normally more than 200 days, and the average annual precipitation is 50 inches or more. Other important crops are corn, small grains, and hay, which are grown mainly for use on the farm. Livestock, the mainstay of the early settlers, still produces a good share of the farm income and is increasing in importance.

# Blue Ridge of North Carolina

DN-1374

PLATE 164.—The Blue Ridge is a broad mountain massif in North Carolina. In its southward extension from Virginia, it is composed partly of the Blue Ridge Plateau in the east, and is flanked by mountain chains on the west. Physiographically, the distinction between the plateau and the mountains is sufficiently pronounced to be reflected in density of settlement and acreage of cleared land. Actually, there is little difference in this respect. Except for the highest peaks, crop and pasture lands are as much in evidence in the mountains as they are in the plateau back of the rim. A section of mountainous land in Watauga County— the western slope of Rich Mountain from the crest down to Cove Creek—is shown. Differences in elevation within this section range from 2,800 to 4,600 feet. Crop and pasture lands are found on all levels, and concentrations occur in the lower valleys. Most of

the fields are small, and ordinarily the steeper slopes are used for pasture. The climate in these elevations is cool, even in summer; the frost-free period runs from around 150 to 170 days. Precipitation, which is well distributed over the seasons, averages more than 50 inches annually. In winter, snow may cover the land for weeks; in some years it may be on the ground for 2 months or more. Soils, which developed from crystalline rocks, are medium to heavy and are fairly productive. Farming is diversified. Most of the farms have less than 10 acres of cropland and operate on the subsistence level. Livestock and its products are the principal items in the farm economy. Burley tobacco is the leading cash crop, although vegetables, particularly cabbage and potatoes, are important also. Corn, some small grains, and forage crops are grown mainly for use on the farm.

# Middle Carolina Piedmont, North Carolina

DN-1373

PLATE 165.—Although the Carolina Piedmont is one physiographic province, use of the land is not uniform. Land use responds to surface relief, climate, soils, and location in respect to markets. These factors have produced a diversity of land use patterns. Near the mountains the land is likely to be strongly rolling to hilly, a situation favorable to the raising of livestock or the growing of orchard fruits. Near the lower border, the land is frequently rough and badly dissected. Much of it is left in woods. In the center, the surface generally is smoothly rolling and most of the land is suitable for cultivation. This is also the part of the Piedmont in which an unusual number of good-sized industrial towns provide farmers with nearby markets. Most of the land is utilized for agricultural production, as shown by a tract 2 miles southeast of Mt. Ulla in Rowan County. The soils are derived mainly from the weathered material of crystalline rocks. In texture, they are chiefly clay loams and clays, red and fairly productive. Climatically, the area lies near the northern limit of the Cotton Belt. The summers are warm and long, with an average of 200 frost-free days. Precipitation averages around 46 inches a year and is well distributed over the seasons. Farming is diversified. The farms usually are medium-sized and well equipped. The major part of the farm income is derived from crops, although livestock and its products, particularly dairy products, are a close second. The leading cash crop is cotton, but corn, wheat, oats, lespedeza, vegetables, and tree fruits also contribute to the farm economy.

# Durham Basin in the Triassic Belt, North Carolina

DN-1372

PLATE 166.—The Piedmont is sometimes subdivided into belts that are identified with geologic formations. As in other places, the petrographic nature of the underlying rocks has influenced surface relief and soil development. To this extent, it has also reacted on land use. Intensity of land use or acreage of land used for crops in proportion to the land area is associated with the geologic background to some extent, although other factors are involved also. The triassic belt lies at the lower border of the Piedmont and in the lower Piedmont erosion is active. Differences in elevation between the creek bottoms and the divides are not much more than 100 feet at the most, but the slopes are badly dissected and only small tracts are smooth enough for cultivation. The tract shown lies in the Durham Basin, 6 miles east of Durham. The soils of this section developed mainly from the weathered material of sandstone and shale. The surface soil is usually a sandy loam. Below it is a red, heavy plastic subsoil. On the slopes along the creeks, the soil is frequently shallow. These soils are not highly productive. The frost-free period approximates 210 days, and the summers are warm. Annual precipitation averages close to 46 inches, of which slightly more than half falls during the warm season. Climatically, the region lies in the Cotton Belt, but very little cotton is grown. Most of the farms are small; their numbers and acreages of cropland have fluctuated considerably during the last decades. Farming depends largely on tobacco as the main cash crop of the area. Woodland is the predominant land use; much of the woodland is pastured, but livestock is of secondary importance in the farm economy.

270

# Little Singletary Lake, North Carolina

DN—1371

PLATE 167.—The major drawbacks to expansion of agriculture in the Coastal Plain of North Carolina are the many depressions and the large areas of poorly drained land interspersed with stretches of light sandy soil. Locally, swampland was formerly called bay, pocosin, or swamp indiscriminately. Since aerial photography has exposed their characteristics, the oval wet or swampy depressions peculiar to the Carolinas are usually referred to as bays. The larger swamps near the coast are pocosins, although there are pocosins with interposed bays. Because of ground conditions, the concentration of bays in North Carolina differs from the concentration in South Carolina. The greatest concentration of bays in North Carolina is on the quaternary portion of the sand apron that extends from the Sand Hills, along Cape Fear and South Rivers, to the coast. Many of these bays are large and well-formed. In the aggregate, they occupy a considerable acreage. Frequently, they occur in a chain pattern, as may be noted from the photograph, which shows the bays on the Bladen-Cumberland County boundary east of Jerome. Most of them are shallow basins with bottoms usually less than 5 feet below the surrounding country. Some are lakes; others may contain water intermittently. The soil of the bays is a black sand that contains much organic matter; that outside the bays and swampy bottoms is a light gray sand. The vegetation of the bays consists mainly of gallberry and huckleberry bushes, and bay trees, from which the bays received their name. Some of the smaller bays farther inland have been drained and are used for crops, but until recently no attempt had been made to drain the larger ones for this purpose. Outside the bays and bottoms, the forest is cutover longleaf pine. Farming in this area depends on cash crops. Although this is Cotton Belt climate, cotton is not a major crop. Tobacco is the leading product.

271

# Lower Coastal Plain Terraces, North Carolina

DN-1370

PLATE 168.—The lower Coastal Plain of North Carolina contains extensive tracts of level land. The tributary creeks of the rivers have not cut their channels back far enough to affect materially the drainage on the flats. As a result, much of the land is inadequately drained. The drainage channels, which usually are not more than 20 to 30 feet below the general level of the country, are flanked by slightly rolling, gently sloping land. Most of the farmsteads and fields are located on the better drained land near the creeks. But even in these locations, drainage is not always adequate to obtain the best yields from crops. Many individual farmers have installed additional drainage, as outlets were available without crossing other properties. To improve drainage farther upstream would mean community drainage enterprises. Land use on the more rolling land is illustrated by a tract that lies 3 miles east of La Grange at the confluence of Mosely and Falling Creeks in Lenoir County. Drainage ditches are noticeable in a number of places. Bottom land has been cleared and drained also. For some time, it was used for corn, but as the soil was heavier than on the upland and was subject to flooding, the attempt was not too successful. Today, these bottomlands are used mainly as pasture and hay lands. The upland soils are light and range from sand to sandy loam. As the land is near the coast, the climate is maritime. Long, warm summers and mild winters are characteristic. The annual average precipitation, which is somewhat heavier in the warm than in the cold season, is close to 50 inches. The type of farming has changed in recent decades. Until the invasion of the boll weevil in the 1920's, cotton was the chief crop. Now corn leads in acreage, but tobacco is the outstanding cash producer. Livestock—mainly hogs and dairy products—contributes to the farm income.

# Literature Cited

(1) ABERNETHY, T. P.
1932. FROM FRONTIER TO PLANTATION IN TENNESSEE; A STUDY IN FRONTIER DEMOCRACY. 392 pp. Chapel Hill, N. C.

(2) ADAMS, J. T., GRAVES, H. S., FILENE, E. A., and others.
1933. NEW ENGLAND'S PROSPECT: 1933. Amer. Geog. Soc. of N. Y. Spec. Pub. 16, 502 pp., illus. New York.

(3) ALBRECHT, W. A.
1942. HEALTH DEPENDS ON SOIL. The Land, 2: 137–142, illus.

(4) ARNOLD, J. R., and LIBBY, W. F.
1951. RADIOCARBON DATES. Science 113: 111–120.

(5) BARBER, E. L.
1951. VARIABILITY OF WHEAT YIELDS. 74 pp., illus. Washington, D. C., U. S. Bur. Agr. Econ. (Mimeographed.)

(6) BARNES, C. P.
1935. ECONOMICS OF THE LONG-LOT FARM. Geog. Rev. 25: 298–301, illus.

(7) BARNES, J. R., ELLIS, W. C., LEGGAT, E. R., and others.
1949. GEOLOGY AND GROUND WATER IN THE IRRIGATED REGION OF THE SOUTHERN HIGH PLAINS OF TEXAS. Tex. Bd. Water Engin. Prog. Rept. 7, 51 pp., illus. (In cooperation with U. S. Geol. Survey.)

(8) BEERS, F. W.
1881. ILLUSTRATED HISTORICAL ATLAS OF THE COUNTY OF CHAUTAUQUA, NEW YORK. 137 pp. New York.

(9) BELCHER, J. C.
1954. THE NONRESIDENT FARMER IN THE NEW RURAL SOCIETY. Rural Sociol. 19: 121–136, illus.

(10) BENNETT, H. H.
1950. OUR AMERICAN LAND. THE STORY OF ITS ABUSE AND ITS CONSERVATION. U. S. Dept. Agr. Misc. Pub. 596, 31 pp., illus.

(11) BLUME, F.
1852. UEBER DIE HANDSCHRIFTEN UND AUSGABEN DER AGRIMENSOREN. *In* die Schriften der Romischen Feldmesser, v. 2, by F. Blume, K. Lachman, and A. Rudorff. 536 pp. Berlin.

(12) BRANDES, E. W.
1936. SUGARCANE: ITS ORIGIN AND IMPROVEMENT. U. S. Dept. Agr. Yearbook 1936: 561–611, illus. (74th Cong., 2d Sess., House Doc. 338.)

(13) BRANNON, H. R., JR., DAUGHTRY, A. C., PERRY, D., and others.
1957. HUMBLE OIL COMPANY RADIOCARBON DATES I. Science 125: 147–149.

(14) BRETZ, J.
1928. THE CHANNELED SCABLAND OF EASTERN WASHINGTON. Geog. Rev. 18: 446–477, illus.

(15) BUELL, M. F.
1946. THE AGE OF JEROME BOG, "A CAROLINA BAY." Science 103: 14–15.

(16) CALIFORNIA DEPARTMENT OF WATER RESOURCES, DIVISION OF RESOURCES PLANNING.
1957. THE CALIFORNIA WATER PLAN. Calif. Dept. Water Resources Bul. 3. 246 pp., illus.

(17) CAMP, A. T., EVANS, R. C., and McDOWELL, L. G.
1954. CITRUS INDUSTRY OF FLORIDA. 249 pp. [Florida] Dept. Agr., Tallahassee.

(18) CARLTON, HARRY.
1941. THE FROZEN-FOOD INDUSTRY. 187 pp., illus. Knoxville, Tenn.

(19) CARTER, G. F.
1951. MAN IN AMERICA: A CRITICISM OF SCIENTIFIC THOUGHT. Sci. Monthly 73: 297–307.

(20) CARTER, R. M.
1947. THE PEOPLE AND THEIR USE OF LAND IN NINE VERMONT TOWNS. Vt. Agr. Expt. Sta. Bul. 536. 72 pp., illus.

(21) CARTER, W. T., BECK, M. W., STRIKE, W. W., and others.
1928. SOIL SURVEY (RECONNAISSANCE) OF WEST CENTRAL TEXAS. U. S. Bur. Soils, Advance Sheets—Field Operations of the Bureau of Soils, 1922, pp. 2,041–2,131, illus. (In cooperation with Texas Agr. Expt. Sta.)

(22) CLAYTON, C. F., and PEET, L. J.
1933. LAND UTILIZATION AS A BASIS OF RURAL ECONOMIC ORGANIZATION. Based on a study of land utilization and related problems in 13 hill towns of Vermont. Vt. Agr. Expt. Sta. Bul. 357, 144 pp., illus.

(23) COCKERILL, P. W., HUNTER, B., and PINGREY, H. B.
1939. TYPE OF FARMING AND RANCHING AREAS IN NEW MEXICO, PART II. N. Mex. Agr. Expt. Sta. Bul. 267, 104 pp., illus.

(24) COLTON (G. W. and G. B.) and COMPANY.
1870. TENNESSEE. (Map.) New York.

(25) COONS, G. H.
1936. IMPROVEMENT OF THE SUGAR BEET. U. S. Dept. Agr. Yearbook 1936: 625–656, illus. (U. S. 74th Cong. 2d Sess., House Doc. 338.)

(26) COOPER, M. R., BARTON, G. T., and BRODELL, A. P.
1947. PROGRESS OF FARM MECHANIZATION. U. S. Dept. Agr. Misc. Pub. 630, 101 pp., illus.

(27) CRANE, H. R.
1956. UNIVERSITY OF MICHIGAN RADIOCARBON DATES I. Science 124: 664–672.

(28) DANIEL, W. J.
1942. PENNSYLVANIA PAID ITS SOLDIERS WITH LAND. Pa. Dept. Int. Aff. Monthly Bul. 10 (10): 21–26.

(29) DAVIDSON, R. D.
1952. FEDERAL AND STATE RURAL LANDS, 1950, WITH SPECIAL REFERENCE TO GRAZING. U. S. Dept. Agr. Cir. 909, 100 pp., illus.

(30) DAVIS, E. M., and SCHULTZ, C. B.
1952. THE ARCHAEOLOGICAL AND PALEONTOLOGICAL SALVAGE PROGRAM AT THE MEDICINE CREEK RESERVOIR, FRONTIER COUNTY, NEBRASKA. Science 115: 288–290.

(31) DAY, C. A.
1954. A HISTORY OF MAINE AGRICULTURE, 1604–1860. Maine Univ. Bul. v. 56, No. 11, 318 pp. (Univ. of Maine studies, 2d ser. No. 68.)

(32) DILLMAN, A. C.
1947. PAPER FROM FLAX. U. S. Dept. Agr. Yearbook 1943–47: 750–752, illus.

(33) DILLON, L. S.
1956. WISCONSIN CLIMATE AND LIFE ZONES IN NORTH AMERICA. Science 123: 167–176, illus.

(34) DONALDSON, T.
1884. THE PUBLIC DOMAIN. Ed. 3, 1,343 pp., illus. Washington, U. S. Govt. Print. Off.

(35) DOUGLAS, E. M.
1930. BOUNDARIES, AREAS, GEOGRAPHIC CENTERS AND ALTITUDES OF THE UNITED STATES AND THE SEVERAL STATES . . . . Ed. 2, U. S. Geol. Survey Bul. 817, 265 pp., illus.

(36) DYER, C. D.
1950. WORKING TREES FOR NAVAL STORES. Ga.
Agr. Ext. Serv. Bul. 532, (rev.) 47 pp.,
illus.

(37) EGLESTON, M.
1866. THE LAND SYSTEM OF THE NEW ENGLAND
COLONIES. *In* Johns Hopkins University
Studies in Historical and Political Sci-
ence, v. 4, [Nos.] 11 and 12, 56 pp.
Baltimore.

(38) ELLIOTT, F. F.
1933. TYPES OF FARMING IN THE UNITED STATES.
Fifteenth Census of the United States,
Census of Agriculture. 225 pp., illus.

(39) ELTING, I.
1886. DUTCH VILLAGE COMMUNITIES ON THE
HUDSON RIVER. *In* Johns Hopkins University Studies in Historical and Political
Science, v. 4, [No.] 1, 68 pp.

(40) EMMONS, E.
1858. AGRICULTURE OF THE EASTERN COUNTIES;
TOGETHER WITH DESCRIPTIONS OF THE
FOSSILS OF THE MARL BEDS. N. C. Geol.
Survey Rpt., 314 pp., illus.

(41) ENGELN, O. D. VON.
1942. GEOMORPHOLOGY, SYSTEMATIC AND RE-
GIONAL. 655 pp., illus. New York.

(42) EVANS, G. L., and MEADE, G. E.
1945. QUATERNARY OF THE TEXAS HIGH PLAINS.
*In* Contributions to Geology, 1944, Tex.
Univ. Pub. 4401. Pp. 485–507, illus.

(43) EVERTS, ENSIGN and EVERTS [publishing com-
pany].
1876. NEW HISTORICAL ATLAS OF CORTLAND
COUNTY, NEW YORK. 100 pp.

(44) FENNEMAN, N. M.
1931. PHYSIOGRAPHY OF WESTERN UNITED
STATES. 534 pp., illus. New York.

(45) FENNEMAN, N. M.
1938. PHYSIOGRAPHY OF EASTERN UNITED
STATES. 714 pp., illus. New York.

(46) FISK, H. N.
1944. GEOLOGICAL INVESTIGATION OF THE ALLU-
VIAL VALLEY OF THE LOWER MISSISSIPPI
RIVER. 78 pp., illus. Vicksburg, Miss.,
Miss. River Comn.

(47) FLETCHER, S. W.
1950. PENNSYLVANIA AGRICULTURE AND COUN-
TRY LIFE, 1640–1840. 605 pp., illus.
Harrisburg, Pa. Hist. and Mus. Comn.

(48) FLINT, R. F.
1947. GLACIAL GEOLOGY AND THE PLEISTOCENE
EPOCH, NEW YORK. 589 pp., illus. New
York.

(49) FLINT, R. F.
1940. PLEISTOCENE FEATURES OF THE ATLANTIC
COASTAL PLAIN. Amer. Jour. Sci. 238:
757–787, illus.

(50) FOWLER, E. D., and SNYDER, J. M.
1926. SOIL SURVEY OF JENKINS COUNTY, GEORGIA.
122 pp., illus. Washington, D. C. (U. S.
Dept. Agr. Bur. Soils in coop. with Ga.
State Col. Agr.)

(51) FREY, D. G.
1951. POLLEN SUCCESSION IN THE SEDIMENTS
OF SINGLETARY LAKE, NORTH CAROLINA.
Ecology 32: 518–533, illus.

(52) FRIIS, H. R.
1940. A SERIES OF POPULATION MAPS OF THE
COLONIES AND THE UNITED STATES, 1625–
1790. Geog. Rev. 30: 463–470, illus.

(53) GLENDENING, G. E.
1952. SOME QUANTITATIVE DATA ON THE IN-
CREASE OF MESQUITE AND CACTUS ON A
DESERT GRASSLAND RANGE IN SOUTHERN
ARIZONA. Ecology 33: 319–328, illus.

(54) GREELEY, W. B., CLAPP, E. H., SMITH, H. A.,
and others.
1923. TIMBER, MINE OR CROP? U. S. Dept. Agr.
Yearbook 1922: 83–180, illus.

(55) GREGORY, H. E.
1916. THE NAVAJO COUNTRY, A GEOGRAPHIC AND
HYDROGRAPHIC RECONNAISSANCE OF PARTS
OF ARIZONA, NEW MEXICO, AND UTAH.
U. S. Geol. Survey Water-Supply Paper
380, 219 pp., illus.

(56) HALL BROTHERS, CIVIL and MINING ENGINEERS.
1895. HALL'S ORIGINAL COUNTY MAP OF GEORGIA,
SHOWING PRESENT AND ORIGINAL COUN-
TIES AND LAND DISTRICTS. Compiled from
State records. Atlanta, Ga.

(57) HANSEN, P. L., and MIGHELL, R. L.
1956. ECONOMIC CHOICES IN BROILER PRODUC-
TION. U. S. Dept. Agr. Tech. Bul. 1154.
27 pp., illus.

(58) HARBECK, G. E., JR.
1948. RESERVOIRS IN THE UNITED STATES. U. S.
Geol. Surv. Cir. 23, 72 pp., illus.

(59) HAREN, C. C.
1952. THE LAND RESOURCES OF FLUVANNA COUN-
TY, VIRGINIA. U. S. Agr. Res. Serv. ARS
43–31, 98 pp., illus.

(60) HARRIS, M.
1953. ORIGIN OF THE LAND TENURE SYSTEM IN
THE UNITED STATES. 445 pp., illus. Ames,
Iowa.

(61) HARRISON, R. W.
1951. LEVEE DISTRICTS AND LEVEE BUILDING IN
MISSISSIPPI; A STUDY OF STATE AND LOCAL
EFFORTS TO CONTROL MISSISSIPPI RIVER
FLOODS. 254 pp., illus. [Stoneville,
Miss.], Delta Council, Board of Missis-
sippi Levee Commissioners, Board of
Levee Commissioners for the Yazoo-
Mississippi Delta, and Mississippi Agri-
cultural Experiment Station. (U. S.
Bur. Agr. Econ. cooperating.)

(62) HECHT, R. W., and VICE, K. R.
1954. LABOR USED FOR FIELD CROPS, U. S. Dept.
Agr. Statis. Bul. 144. 45 pp.

(63) HOCHMUTH, H. R., FRANKLIN, E. R., and
CLAWSON, M.
1942. SHEEP MIGRATION IN THE INTERMOUNTAIN
REGION. U. S. Dept. Agr. Cir. 624, 70
pp., illus.

(64) HORBERG, L.
1950. BEDROCK TOPOGRAPHY OF ILLINOIS. Ill.
State Geol. Surv. Bul. 73, 111 pp., illus.

(65) HORNADAY, W. T.
1889. THE EXTERMINATION OF THE AMERICAN
BISON, WITH A SKETCH OF ITS DISCOVERY
AND LIFE HISTORY. *In* U. S. Natl. Mus.
Annual Rpt., 1887, pt. II, pp. 367–548,
illus.

(66) HUFFINGTON, R. M., and ALBRITTON, C. C., JR.
1941. QUATERNARY SANDS ON THE SOUTHERN
HIGH PLAINS OF WESTERN TEXAS. Amer.
Jour. Sci. 239: 325–338, illus.

(67) HUNTER, B., COCKERILL, P. W., and PINGREY,
H. B.
1939. TYPE OF FARMING AND RANCHING AREAS
IN NEW MEXICO, PART I. N. Mex. Agr.
Expt. Sta. Bul. 261, 68 pp., illus.

(68) INMAN, B. T., and JENKINS, W. B.
1948. GRAPHIC SUMMARY OF FARM TENURE IN
THE UNITED STATES. Cooperative report.
40 pp., illus. Washington, D. C., U. S.
Dept. Commerce and U. S. Dept. Agr.

(69) JOHNSON, V. W., and BARLOWE, R.
1954. LAND PROBLEMS AND POLICIES. 422 pp.,
illus. New York.

(70) JONES, H. A., and EMSWELLER, S. L.
1931. THE VEGETABLE INDUSTRY. 431 pp., illus.
New York.

(71) JOURNAL of AGRICULTURE and FOOD CHEMISTRY.
1954. AIRBORNE CUSTOM APPLICATION. Jour.
Agr. and Food Chem. 2: 550–552, illus.

(72) KARPOFF, E.
1957. RECORD POULTRY OUTPUT, LOW EGG PRICES
IN 1956. U. S. Agr. Market. Serv. Agr.
Situation 41(5): 7.

(73) KELLOGG, C. E.
1936. DEVELOPMENT AND SIGNIFICANCE OF THE
GREAT SOIL GROUPS OF THE UNITED STATES.
U. S. Dept. Agr. Misc. Pub. 229, 40 pp.,
illus.

(74) KINCER, J. B.
1936. TEMPERATURE, SUNSHINE, AND WIND. 34
pp., illus. In Atlas of American Agriculture . . . (Climate). Washington,
U. S. Govt. Print. Off. (This section of
Atlas issued as separate in 1928.)

(75) KOLLMORGEN, W. M., and JENKS, G. F.
1951–52. A GEOGRAPHIC STUDY OF POPULATION
AND SETTLEMENT CHANGES IN SHER-
MAN COUNTY, KANSAS. Part I: Rural;
part II: Goodland; and part III,
Inventory and Prospects. Kans. Acad.
Sci. Trans. 54: 449–494, illus.; 55:
1–37, illus.

(76) KRIESEL, H. C.
1956. DAIRYMEN MAY GET HIGHER PRICES EVEN
WITH MILK PRODUCTION UP. U. S. Agr.
Market. Serv. Agr. Situation 40(6):
4–5, illus.

(77) LACKEY, E. E.
1939. ANNUAL RAINFALL VARIABILITY MAPS OF
THE UNITED STATES. U. S. Monthly
Weather Rev. 67: 7.

(78) LEGNAZZI, E. N.
1887. DEL CATASTO ROMANO E DI ALCUNI STRU-
MENTI ANTICHI DI GEODESIA. 311 pp.,
illus. Padova (Padua).

(79) LIBBY, W. F.
1951. RADIOCARBON DATES, II. Science 114:
291–296.

(80) LOBECK, R. K.
1939. GEOMORPHOLOGY, AN INTRODUCTION TO
THE STUDY OF LANDSCAPES. 731 pp., illus.
New York.

(81) LUGN, A. L.
1935. THE PLEISTOCENE GEOLOGY OF NEBRASKA.
Nebr. Geol. Survey Bul. 10, 2d ser., 223
pp., illus.

(82) McKITTRICK, R.
1918. THE PUBLIC LAND SYSTEM OF TEXAS, 1823–
1910. Univ. Wis. Bul. 905, 172 pp., illus.
(Univ. Wis. Econ. and Polit. Sci. ser.,
v. 9, No. 1.)

(83) McLENDON, S. G.
1924. HISTORY OF THE PUBLIC DOMAIN OF GEOR-
GIA. 200 pp., illus. Atlanta.

(84) MAGEE, A. C., McARTHUR, W. C., BONNEN, C. A.,
and HUGHES, W. 'F.
1952. COST OF WATER FOR IRRIGATION ON THE
HIGH PLAINS. Texas Agr. Expt. Sta.
Bul. 745, 32 pp., illus. (U. S. Dept. Agr.
cooperating.)

(85) MANGELSDORF, P. C., and SMITH, C. E., JR.
1949. A DISCOVERY OF REMAINS OF PRIMITIVE
MAIZE IN NEW MEXICO. Jour. Hered. 40:
39–43, illus.

(86) MARBUT, C. F.
1936. SOILS OF THE UNITED STATES. Atlas of
American Agriculture, Pt. III, 98 pp.,
illus. Washington, U. S. Govt. Print.
Off.

(87) MARR, J. C.
1940. SNOW SURVEYING. U. S. Dept. Agr.
Misc. Pub. 380, 46 pp., illus.

(88) MARSCHNER, F. J.
1940. RURAL POPULATION DENSITY IN THE
SOUTHERN APPALACHIANS. U. S. Dept.
Agr. Misc. Pub. 367, 18 pp., illus.

(89) MASON, J. E., and GRUEHN, E. L. K.
1937. PRESENT RANGE PASTURE PRACTICES AND
LAND USE RECOMMENDATIONS FOR THE
CUMBERLAND PLATEAU. A summary of
opinion. 16 pp., illus. Washington,
D. C., U. S. Dept. Agr. (Mimeographed.)

(90) MILEY, D. G., and ROBERTS, A. L.
1945. THE ECONOMICS OF COTTON GIN OPERATION.
Miss. Agr. Expt. Sta. Bul. 421, 33 pp.,
illus.

(91) MILLER, E. W.
1949. STRIP MINING AND LAND UTILIZATION IN
WESTERN PENNSYLVANIA. Sci. Monthly
69: 94–103, illus.

(92) MORSE, W. J., and CARTER, J. L.
1937. IMPROVEMENT IN SOYBEANS. U. S. Dept.
Agr. Yearbook 1937: 1154–1189, illus.

(93) MORTENSON, W. P.
1956. POULTRY PRODUCERS AND POULTRY PRODUC-
TION. U. S. Bur. Census of Agr.
1954, v. 3, Spec. Rpts., ch. 4, pt. 9,
Farmers and Farm Production in the
United States. 34 pp., illus.

(94) NATIONAL SOIL and FERTILIZER RESEARCH COM-
MITTEE, the FERTILIZER WORK GROUP.
1954. FERTILIZER USE AND CROP YIELDS IN THE
UNITED STATES. U. S. Dept. Agr. Agr.
Handbook 68, 75 pp., illus. (Soil and
Water Conservation and Production Eco-
nomics Research Branches, Agr. Res.
Serv., U. S. Dept. Agr., cooperating.)

(95) NEW JERSEY AGRICULTURAL EXPERIMENT STA-
TION
n. d. SCIENCE AND THE LAND: THE 1946–47
ANNUAL REPORT OF THE NEW JERSEY AGRI-
CULTURAL EXPERIMENT STATION, RUTGERS
UNIVERSITY, NEW BRUNSWICK, NEW JER-
SEY. 111 pp., illus.

(96) NORTON, L. M.
1935. READINGS IN SOCIAL SCIENCE, LOUISIANA,
1699–1876. 200 pp., illus. La. State
Univ. [Baton Rouge.]

(97) PATTISON, W. D.
1957. BEGINNINGS OF THE AMERICAN RECTAN-
GULAR LAND SURVEY SYSTEM, 1784–1800.
248 pp. Chicago.

(98) PAULIN, C. O.
1932. ATLAS OF THE HISTORICAL GEOGRAPHY OF
THE UNITED STATES. Part 1, text, 162
pp.; part 2, 166 plates. New York, Car-
negie Institution of Washington and the
American Geographical Society of New
York.

(99) POTTER, G. F., and CRANE, H. L.
1951. TUNG PRODUCTION. U. S. Dept. Agr.
Farmers' Bul. 2031, 41 pp., illus.

(100) RASMUSSEN, W. C., and SLAUGHTER, T. H.
1955. THE GROUND-WATER RESOURCES. In The
Water Resources of Somerset, Wicomico
and Worcester Counties. Md. Bd. Nat.
Resources Bul. 16, pp. 1–170, illus.

(101) RAY, L. L.
1949. PLEISTOCENE RESEARCH 9. PROBLEMS OF
PLEISTOCENE STRATIGRAPHY. Geol. Soc.
Amer. Bul. 160: 1463–1474.

(102) ROE, F. G.
1951. THE NORTH AMERICAN BUFFALO; A CRITI-
CAL STUDY OF THE SPECIES IN ITS WILD
STATE. 957 pp., illus. Toronto.

(103) RUBIN, M., and SUESS, H. E.
1955. RADIOCARBON DATES II. Science 121:
481–488.

(104) SCIENCE.
1954. SCIENCE NEWS. Science 120: 17.

(105) SCIENCE.
1956. ARCHEOLOGY IN ALABAMA. Science 124: 577.

(106) SCIENCE.
1956. OLDEST TRACES OF EARLY MAN IN THE AMERICAS. Science 124: 396.

(107) SENZEL, I.
n. d. BRIEF NOTES ON THE PUBLIC DOMAIN. 20 pp., illus. U. S. Bur. Land Mangt. [Washington, D. C.]

(108) SENZEL, I.
1950. GRAPHIC NOTES ON THE PUBLIC DOMAIN. Ed. 4, 5 pp., illus. [Washington, D. C.] U. S. Bur. Land Mangt. (Mimeographed.)

(109) SHANTZ, H. L., and ZON, R.
1936. NATURAL VEGETATION. 29 pp., illus. In Atlas of American Agriculture . . . Washington, U. S. Govt. Print. Off. (This section of Atlas issued as separate in 1924.)

(110) SHERMAN, C. E.
1925. ORIGINAL OHIO LAND SUBDIVISIONS. V. 3 of The Final Report of the Ohio Cooperative Topographic Survey. 233 pp., illus. [Columbus.]

(111) SMILEY, T. L.
1951. A SUMMARY OF TREE-RING DATES FROM SOME SOUTHWESTERN ARCHAEOLOGICAL SITES. Univ. of Ariz. Lab. Bul. of Tree-Ring Res. 5, 32 pp., illus.

(112) SOLBERG, E. D.
1952. RURAL ZONING IN THE UNITED STATES. U. S. Dept. Agr. Agr. Inform. Bul. 59, 85 pp., illus.

(113) STALLINGS, J. H.
1951. MECHANICS OF WIND EROSION. U. S. Dept. Agr. Soil Conserv. Serv. SCS–TP–108, 12 pp. Washington, D. C.

(114) STINE, O. C., and BAKER, O. E.
1918. ATLAS OF AMERICAN AGRICULTURE, PART V, THE CROPS, SECTION A, COTTON. Advance sheets, 4, originally intended to be included in the Atlas of American Agriculture. 28 pp., illus. Washington, U. S. Govt. Print. Off.

(115) SUTHERLAND, J. G., and BROOKS, J. H.
1950. MECHANICAL HARVESTING OF COTTON IN NORTH CAROLINA. N. C. Agr. Expt. Sta. Inform. Ser. 22, 36 pp., illus. (U. S. Bur. Agr. Econ. cooperating.)

(116) TAYLOR, F. G.
1944. A SAGA OF SUGAR, BEING A STORY OF THE ROMANCE AND DEVELOPMENT OF BEET SUGAR IN THE ROCKY MOUNTAIN WEST. 234 pp., illus. Salt Lake City.

(117) THORNTHWAITE, C. W.
1934. INTERNAL MIGRATION IN THE UNITED STATES. 52 pp., illus. Philadelphia.

(118) THORNTHWAITE, C. W.
1941. ATLAS OF CLIMATIC TYPES IN THE UNITED STATES, 1900–1939. U. S. Dept. Agr. Misc. Pub. 421, 7 pp., illus.

(119) TOBIN (EDGAR) AERIAL SURVEYS.
194–. [REGIONAL SURVEY MAPS AND TOWNSHIP SECTIONAL MAPS—SOUTHERN STATES.] San Antonio.

(120) TURNER, F. J.
1921. THE FRONTIER IN AMERICAN HISTORY. 375 pp. New York.

(121) U. S. AGRICULTURAL MARKETING SERVICE.
1955. FARM POPULATION ESTIMATES FOR 1955. U. S. Agr. Market. Serv. AMS–80, 9 pp. (Mimeographed.)

(122) U. S. BUREAU of AGRICULTURAL CHEMISTRY and ENGINEERING.
1942. PRODUCTION OF NAVAL STORES. U. S. Dept. Agr. Misc. Pub. 476, 10 pp., illus.

(123) U. S. BUREAU of AGRICULTURAL ECONOMICS.
1950. GENERALIZED TYPES OF FARMING IN THE UNITED STATES. U. S. Dept. Agr. Agr. Inform. Bul. 3, 35 pp., illus.

(124) U. S. BUREAU of AGRICULTURAL ECONOMICS.
1951. REVIEW AND OUTLOOK, NAVAL STORES. 27 pp., illus. Washington, D. C. (Mimeographed.)

(125) U. S. BUREAU of AGRICULTURAL ECONOMICS.
1952–53. CROP PRODUCTION PRACTICES. Labor, Power, and Material, by Operation. sec. 1, Northeast. sec. 2, Corn Belt and Lake States. sec. 3, Appalachian, Southeast, and Mississippi Delta. sec. 4, Great Plains. sec. 5, Mountain and Pacific States. U. S. Bur. Agr. Econ. F. M. 92, Sects. 1–5.

(126) U. S. BUREAUS OF AGRICULTURAL ECONOMICS and HOME ECONOMICS, and U. S. FOREST SERVICE.
1935. ECONOMIC AND SOCIAL PROBLEMS AND CONDITIONS OF THE SOUTHERN APPALACHIANS. U. S. Dept. Agr. Misc. Pub. 205, 184 pp., illus.

(127) U. S. BUREAU of LAND MANAGEMENT.
n. d. REPORT OF THE DIRECTOR OF THE BUREAU OF LAND MANAGEMENT, 1955, STATISTICAL APPENDIX. 153 pp.

(128) U. S. BUREAU of PLANT INDUSTRY, SOILS, and AGRICULTURAL ENGINEERING.
1951. SOIL SURVEY MANUAL. U. S. Dept. Agr. Agr. Handb. 18, 503 pp., illus.

(129) U. S. BUREAU of RECLAMATION.
1945. COMPREHENSIVE PLAN FOR WATER RESOURCES DEVELOPMENT, CENTRAL VALLEY BASIN, CALIFORNIA. U. S. Bur. Reclam. Proj. Rpt. 2–4.0–3, 281 pp., illus. [Washington, D. C.] (Mimeographed.)

(130) U. S. BUREAU of RECLAMATION.
1949. THE STORY OF HOOVER DAM. U. S. Bur. Reclam. Conserv. Bul. 9, 71 pp., illus.

(131) U. S. BUREAU of the CENSUS.
1953–56. STATISTICAL ABSTRACT OF THE UNITED STATES: 1953, 1956. Washington, U. S. Govt. Print. Off.

(132) U. S. BUREAU of the CENSUS.
1955. CURRENT POPULATION REPORTS, POPULATION CHARACTERISTICS. Ser. P–20, No. 63, 4 pp.

(133) U. S. CONGRESS.
1834. [ANNALS, 1ST. CONG., 2D SESS.] THE DEBATES AND PROCEEDINGS IN THE CONGRESS OF THE UNITED STATES . . . . VOLUME II, COMPRISING (WITH VOLUME I) THE PERIOD FROM MARCH 3, 1789, TO MARCH 3, 1791, INCLUSIVE. Compiled . . . by Joseph Gales, Sr. Washington, [D. C.]

(134) U. S. DEPARTMENT of AGRICULTURE.
1940–56. AGRICULTURAL STATISTICS, 1940, 1952, AND 1955. Washington, U. S. Govt. Print. Off.

(135) U. S. DEPARTMENT of AGRICULTURE.
1938–49. YEARBOOK OF AGRICULTURE, 1938, 1941, 1948, 1949. Washington, D. C., U. S. Govt. Print. Off.

(136) U. S. FOREST SERVICE.
1936. THE WESTERN RANGE. U. S. 74th Cong., 2d Sess., Senate Doc. 199, 620 pp., illus.

(137) U. S. FOREST SERVICE.
1940. CHEROKEE NATIONAL FOREST (CHEROKEE DIVISION). (Map.) Washington, D. C.

(138) U. S. GEOLOGICAL SURVEY.
1946. OKLAHOMA (COMANCHE COUNTY) LAWTON QUADRANGLE. Lawton, Okla.

(139) U. S. GREAT PLAINS COMMITTEE.
1936. THE FUTURE OF THE GREAT PLAINS. Report of the Great Plains Committee. 194 pp., illus. Washington, D. C.

(140) U. S. PRODUCTION and MARKETING ADMINISTRATION, AGRICULTURAL CONSERVATION PROGRAMS BRANCH.
1951. AGRICULTURAL CONSERVATION PROGRAM: MAPS 1949. 57 pp. Washington, D. C.

(141) U. S. WORK PROJECTS ADMINISTRATION, [FLORIDA], DIVISION of PROFESSIONAL and SERVICE PROJECTS.
1940. SPANISH LAND GRANTS IN FLORIDA. vol. 1. Unconfirmed Claims. 374 pp. State Library Board, Tallahassee, Fla. (Mimeographed.)

(142) U. S. WORK PROJECTS ADMINISTRATION, FEDERAL WRITERS' PROJECT.
1939. TENNESSEE; A GUIDE TO THE STATE. Compiled and written by the Federal Writers' Project of the Work Projects Administration for the State of Tennessee. 558 pp., illus. New York.

(143) VAN DERSAL, W. R.
1938. NATIVE WOODY PLANTS OF THE UNITED STATES. Their Erosion-control and Wildlife Values. U. S. Dept. Agr. Misc. Pub. 303, 362 pp., illus.

(144) VISHER, S. S.
1941. DISTRIBUTION OF TORRENTIAL RAINFALLS IN THE UNITED STATES. Sci. Monthly 53: 410–416.

(145) VISHER, S. S.
1941. TORRENTIAL RAINS AS A SERIOUS HANDICAP IN THE SOUTH. Geog. Review 31: 644–652, illus.

(146) VISHER, S. S.
1954. CLIMATIC ATLAS OF THE UNITED STATES. 403 pp. Cambridge, Mass.

(147) VOELKER, S. W.
1952. LAND-USE ORDINANCES OF SOIL CONSERVATION DISTRICTS IN COLORADO. Colo. Agr. Expt. Sta. Tech. Bul. 45, 55 pp. (Great Plains Council Pub. 5.)

(148) WAHLENBERG, W. G., and GEMMER, E. W.
1936. SOUTHERN FOREST RANGES. In Appendix to The Western Range, U. S. 74th Cong., 2d Sess., Senate Doc. 199, pp. 567-580, illus.

(149) WALTER, G. H.
1949. AGRICULTURE AND STRIP COAL MINING. U. S. Agr. Market. Serv. Agr. Econ Res. 1: 24–29, illus.

(150) WEAVER, J. C.
1954. CHANGING PATTERNS OF CROPLAND USE IN THE MIDDLE WEST. Econ. Geog. 30: 1–47, illus.

(151) WEAVER, J. C.
1954. CROP-COMBINATION REGIONS FOR 1919 AND 1929 IN THE MIDDLE WEST. Geog. Review 44: 560–572, illus.

(152) WEAVER, J. C.
1954. CROP-COMBINATION REGIONS IN THE MIDDLE WEST. Geog. Review 44: 175–200, illus.

(153) WEBBER, H. J.
1934. WHAT RESEARCH HAS DONE FOR SUBTROPICAL AGRICULTURE. Achievements of the Citrus Experiment Station. 28 pp., illus. Berkeley, Calif. Agr. Expt. Sta.

(154) WEBBER, H. J., and BATCHELOR, L. D.
1943. THE CITRUS INDUSTRY, VOL. I. HISTORY, BOTANY, AND BREEDING. 1,028 pp., illus. Berkeley, Calif.

(155) WEICK, F. E.
1954. AIRCRAFT SPRAYING AND DUSTING. Jour. Agr. and Food Chem. 2: 546–549, illus.

(156) WILKINS, A. H.
1932. THE FORESTS OF MAINE. Maine Forest Serv. Bul. 8, 110 pp., illus.

(157) WILLIAMSON, M. T.
1888. MAP OF SHELBY COUNTY, TENNESSEE. Cincinnati.

(158) WILSON, C. M.
1951. THE BOX BUTTE TABLELAND. Ohio Jour. Sci. 51: 227–248, illus.

(159) WILSON, S. M.
1923. THE FIRST LAND COURT OF KENTUCKY, 1779-1780. An address before the Kentucky State Bar Association at Covington, Kentucky. Reprinted from the Proceedings of the twenty-second annual meeting of the association, 1923. 164 pp., illus. Lexington, Ky.

(160) WISE, E. N.
1955. THE C-14 AGE DETERMINATIVE METHOD. In Geochronology, Univ. Ariz. Phys. Sci. Bul. 2, pp. 170–176.

(161) WOLFE, P. E.
1953. PERIGLACIAL FROST-THAW BASINS IN NEW JERSEY. Jour. Geol. 61: 133–141, illus.

(162) WOOD, R. G.
1935. A HISTORY OF LUMBERING IN MAINE, 1820–1861. Maine Bul., v. 37, No. 7, 267 pp., illus.

(163) WOOFTER, T. J.
1930 BLACK YEOMANRY; LIFE ON ST. HELENA ISLAND. 291 pp., illus. New York.

(164) WOOTEN, E. O.
1932. THE PUBLIC DOMAIN OF NEVADA AND FACTORS AFFECTING ITS USE. U. S. Dept. Agr. Tech. Bul. 301, 52 pp., illus.

(165) WOOTEN, H. H.
1953. MAJOR USES OF LAND IN THE UNITED STATES. U. S. Dept. Agr. Tech. Bul. 1082, 100 pp., illus. supplement—basic land use statistics, 1950. 78 pp.

(166) YARNELL, D. L.
1935. RAINFALL INTENSITY-FREQUENCY DATA. U. S. Dept. Agr. Misc. Pub. 204, 68 pp., illus.

(167) YOUNG, V. A., ANDERWALD, F. R., and McCULLY, W. G.
1948. BRUSH PROBLEMS ON TEXAS RANGES. Tex. Agr. Expt. Sta. Misc. Pub. 21, 19 pp., illus.

U.S. GOVERNMENT PRINTING OFFICE: 1958—471954